Meteorology for Glider Pilots

Meteorology for Glider Pilots

INTERNATIONAL EDITION

C. E. WALLINGTON

JOHN MURRAY

Printed in Great Britain by
J. W. Arrowsmith Ltd., Bristol BS3 2NT
0 7195 3303 1

Contents

Preface   ix

GENERAL METEOROLOGY

1 Pressure   3
2 Wind   15
3 Temperature   26
4 Moisture   36
5 Clouds   42
6 Visibility   55
7 Fronts   60
8 Depressions   78
9 Anticyclones   89
10 Tropical Weather   95

GLIDING METEOROLOGY

11 Airflow over Hills   111
12 Dry Thermals   123
13 Cumulus Convection   143
14 Convective Storms   156
15 Thermal Soaring Prospects   177
16 Sea-Breezes   185
17 Lee Waves   206
18 Wave Soaring   232

WEATHER FORECASTS

19 Charting the Weather   239
20 Temperature-Height Diagrams   252
21 Gliding Forecasts   263
22 Weatherwise   286

TECHNICAL NOTES

23 Altimeter Setting   295
24 Geostrophic Winds   300
25 Thermal Depth Prediction   304
26 Using Aerological Diagrams   317

    Units and Abbreviations   322
    Conversion Factors   324
    Bibliography   325
    Index   326

Plates

1	Small cumulus	44
2	Hooked cirrus	45
3	Cirrocumulus	46
4	Cirrostratus	50
5	Altocumulus	51
6	Altostratus	52
7	Large cumulus	53
8	Valley fog	55
9	Satellite cloud pictures	83
10	Small cumulus over Waikerie	144
11	Cloud streets	146
12	Satellite view of cloud streets	151
13	Radar view of swifts in dry thermal streets	154
14	Large cumulus	157
15	Cumulonimbus development	159
16	Large cumulus with distant cumulonimbus	161
17	Mammatus cloud	162
18	Radar echoes from swifts in a line squall	163
19	Downdraught from convective storm	165
20	Funnel cloud	172
21	Fragments of sea-breeze frontal cloud	188
22	Cumulonimbus at sea-breeze front	205
23	Thin wave cloud	212
24	Lee waves and cumulus	215
25	Rotor cloud	216
26	Wave cloud near Mount Cook	233
27	Radar echoes from rainclouds	241

viii   **Plates**

28 Satellite view of cumulus over UK   242
29 Distant satellite view of cloud patterns   249
30 Altocumulus castellanus   265
31 Jet stream cirrus   268

For the plates listed above, acknowledgements are due to R. K. Pilsbury (2, 3, 4, 5, 15, 17, 30, 31), R. S. Scorer (6), NASA (9, 12, 28, 29), W. G. Harper (13, 18, 27), C. S. Lowndes (20), J. S. Williamson (21), P. M. Saunders (22), P. A. Wills (26). All the others are by the author.

Preface

No other sport is so interwoven with the ways of the weather as gliding. Very early in his career the glider pilot finds meteorology infused into his initial instruction. Often his early lessons materialise from irritating delays in his training programme; the wind is either too light or too strong, or it rains on the wrong day, or convection is too weak and sporadic. But natural curiosity whetted by minor frustrations prompts him to learn more about the elements in which he flies. So, from conversations with his instructors and gliding colleagues, and from his sharpened interest in weather forecasts disseminated by the press, radio and television, he gleans something of the practical significance of depressions, anticyclones, fronts and cool changes.

As his flying ability progresses the pilot's meteorological interest tends to be directed from the broad-scale weather features towards local phenomena, which can present both hazards and opportunities for soaring. He experiences the effects of rugged terrain on hill lift and local eddies. He climbs in convection currents and, if lucky, he finds himself soaring in lee waves. At this stage, his task is not so much to understand or forecast the phenomena in which he soars as to visualise the pattern of lift and to fly correctly within it. At first, he is not sure how much of any failure to stay in lift is due to his handling of the aircraft and how much is due to the natural capriciousness of the atmosphere. Flying ability normally improves with experience, but the rate of progress made in understanding the atmosphere varies considerably among the individuals who comprise the gliding fraternity. For some pilots meteorology is a science akin to their own professions, while for others the weather was no more than a topic for casual conversation before their introduction to gliding. Whatever their scientific standards, however, most pilots are perpetually seeking to expand their meteorological knowledge.

To any meteorologist like myself, involved in gliding, the glider pilot's thirst for meteorological knowledge is usually made obvious by his keen perception of weather patterns in flight and the numerous questions he asks at opportune moments. The substance and level of the first edition of this book was based mainly on such questions put to me by glider pilots in the 1950s. And, because that decade also saw both a surge in flying techniques and research into atmospheric phenomena particularly relevant to gliding, the time was right to produce a book especially for glider pilots. The book was written with four main needs in mind. First and foremost, most glider pilots needed a textbook for self-tuition. Secondly, the glider pilot needed to acquire a mature appreciation of the actual weather he would encounter; he could not turn a blind eye to observations which do not fit oversimplified concepts. Thirdly, there was a need to arm the glider pilot with new, but not readily available, knowledge arising from research into atmospheric phenomena of particular relevance in gliding. Fourthly, there was a growing need for a textbook suitable for lectures and short courses on meteorology for gliding which were gaining popularity at the time.

These needs are still with us. A new generation of glider pilots has swelled the growing membership of the sport. Modern gliders give the pilot more aerodynamic efficiency, but, at the same time, they enable him to explore a wider range of meteorological conditions. This efficiency is not fully used unless the pilot adapts his flying techniques to the performance of his aircraft, and such adaptation calls for specialised knowledge of gliding meteorology. Furthermore, a growing number of globe-trotting glider pilots are anxious to extend their meteorological repertoires to cover foreign climes.

This third edition still aims at satisfying the glider pilot's thirst for meteorological knowledge. But, since the first edition was written, I have travelled and flown in many lands and have become even more deeply involved in gliding. Continuing exploration and accumulated experience of glider pilots throughout the world have elaborated and refined our knowledge of gliding weather phenomena. The existence of 'thermal shifts' in marked wind shears was not suspected until the early 1960s. Modern high-speed cross-country soaring has called for and yielded more knowledge of narrow bands of lift, that exist more often than is generally suspected. New phenomena have been discovered. Discovery of the power and fascination of convergence lines in some regions must surely spur pilots to note the structures observed and search their own regions for similar phenomena. And, what is probably the most exciting of recent discoveries is the 'thermal wave', that can sometimes lift pilots out of the confines of thermal soaring into a widespread wave pattern aloft.

So, this third edition is international. It consolidates some established concepts; it introduces new knowledge, and it is reshaped to fit the way that pilots have appeared to work through the earlier texts. In the first ten chapters the aim is to cover the necessary meteorological groundwork. Then once the broad meteorological scene is set, Chapters 11 to 18 elaborate on those aspects of the subject particularly relevant to soaring flight. Chapters 19 to 22 talk about meteorological services and gliding forecasts, leaving the technical notes at the end of the book for those who wish to delve deeper into altimetry, geostrophic winds, thermal depth prediction and aerological diagrams.

There is no universal set of units used in gliding meteorology. So the units and abbreviations used in this book are those which appear to be a reasonably coherent set for a typical international pilot. They are listed on page 322.

Much of a meteorologist's work entails collecting observations, data and theories from various sources and passing them on to others in a suitable form. Therefore, I am indebted to many of my friends in the gliding world for recounting to me their various flying experiences, and to many of my meteorological colleagues whose expertise and scientific papers have contributed so much to gliding meteorology. Those friends are now so numerous that I am hesitant to single out names, but I cannot let the occasion pass without thanking Professor R. S. Scorer for introducing me to gliding meteorology, Ann Welch for sharing her wide experience and infectious enthusiasm, and my family for its considerable contribution to gliding affairs from behind the scenes.

January 1977   C.E.W.

General Meteorology

1

Pressure

We live at the bottom of an ocean—a great ocean of air encasing the earth and effectively about 400 km deep. We call this ocean the atmosphere. We feel its undercurrents as winds, sometimes as gales sweeping across the countryside, sometimes as light breezes gently filtering through the trees—but always driven by an illimitable supply of energy—energy from the sun. The linkage between this energy and wind can be summarised briefly, though rather loosely, as follows. Heat rays from the sun produce an uneven distribution of temperature changes over the globe; the tropics receive more radiant heat than the Poles; temperature is quick to rise over desert sands whereas much of the heat received by a marshland is used for evaporation; snow surfaces and thick cloud layers reflect, rather than absorb, much of their incident heat rays; and, of course, night follows day and winter follows summer as the Earth spins on its elliptic path around the sun.

This uneven distribution of temperature leads to variations in atmospheric pressure, and it is these variations which are directly linked with winds over the Earth. But the winds themselves affect the temperature distribution by transporting warmth, or cold, or layers of cloud from place to place, and the whole process is geared to the spinning motion of the Earth and modulated by the evaporation and condensation of water in the atmosphere. So the weather we experience is the by-product of interwoven cycles of events into which the sun injects a daily supply of energy. A convenient starting point for dissecting and understanding the weather machine is an appreciation of atmospheric pressure.

The air in the atmosphere is fairly light, but its weight is by no means negligible. At low levels, the air is compressed by the weight of the air above it, and the total weight of a column of air extending from the ground to the top of the atmosphere amounts to almost one kilogram for every square centimetre of ground it covers—or about one ton per square foot. This weight of air per unit area is

3

called the *atmospheric pressure*, or sometimes *barometric pressure*, *baros* being the Greek word for 'weight'.

A vital duty of most meteorological services is to measure the atmospheric pressure at frequent intervals at a large number of observing posts scattered throughout the territories they serve. The most commonly used measuring instrument is the mercury barometer. It is a simple device consisting in principle of mercury in a U-shaped glass tube which is open at one end and closed at the other, as shown in Figure 1.1. The atmospheric pressure is measured in terms of the length of a column of mercury. In most weather

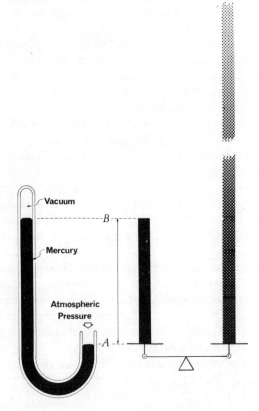

Fig. 1.1 The mercury barometer is a form of balance; the weight of air resting on the mercury's surface at A exactly balances the weight of mercury in the column between the levels A and B.

conditions this length lies somewhere between 700 and 800 mm (between about 28 and 31 in.) at places at or near mean sea-level (MSL). Meteorologists and aviators find it more convenient to talk of pressure in terms of millibars (mb) rather than lengths of mercury. By definition a millibar is a pressure of 1000 dynes per square centimetre, but we need only remember that the atmospheric pressure at MSL in most weather systems lies between about 950 and 1050 mb.

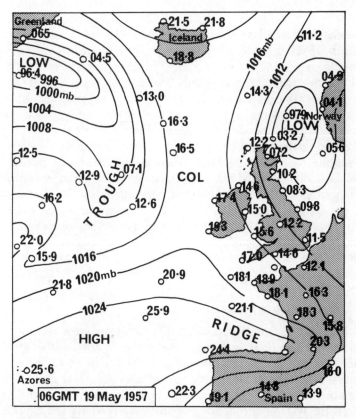

Fig. 1.2 The atmospheric pressure map for 06 GMT 19 May 1957. To the right of each 'station circle' are the last three figures of the pressure in millibars and tenths, e.g. 25.6 at Azores denotes a pressure of 1025.6 mb, while 96.4 reported by the ship south of Greenland means 996.4 mb.

The pressure map

As soon as pressure measurements from a number of observing stations are available, a pressure map can be plotted. Figure 1.2 shows a map for Europe and part of the Atlantic. The observing stations, some of which are ships at sea, are indicated by small circles. To the right of each *station circle* are the measured pressures in millibars and tenths of millibars.

The first step in diagnosing the pressure pattern is to draw *isobars* on the map, isobars being lines joining places having equal pressure. Drawing these lines for the values 996 mb, 1000 mb, 1004 mb, and so on, yields the pressure map for the particular time the measurements were made. The pattern reveals two areas of low pressure which we label *LOW*. They may be referred to as *depressions*, or simply *lows*, while the suitably labelled *high* pressure area has the alternative name of *anticyclone*. The pressure map also shows a *trough* (of low pressure), a *ridge* (of high pressure) and a *col*—that is a region of fairly uniform pressure between two highs and two lows. It is difficult to measure the precise dimensions of these features labelled on the pressure map but, roughly speaking, the depression over the North Sea is about 1000 km (approximately 500 naut. miles) in diameter and the anticyclone west of Spain covers an area of approximately 2000 × 1000 km. Meteorologists would consider these dimensions as quite normal. Depressions or anticyclones of less than about 500 km in diameter would be described as small, but the figures quoted in this chapter should not be taken to define rigid limits; they merely serve to acquaint the reader new to meteorology with the magnitude and character of pressure systems in general.

Global pressure patterns

Figures 1.3 (a) and (b) show typical pressure patterns over most of the world for a day in January and a day in July. Although the patterns may, at first sight, appear to be a chaotic collection of pressure systems of motley shapes and sizes, certain characteristics can be discerned. There appears to be a chain or belt of small low pressure systems meandering approximately along the Equator. The shift of this belt from just south of the Equator in January to the northern side in July indicates the seasonal migration of the world's weather systems north and south with the sun.

(a)

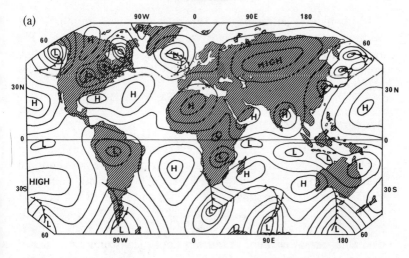

(b)

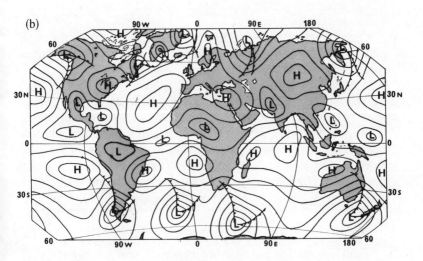

Fig. 1.3 Typical MSL pressure maps for (a) a day in January, and (b) a day in July. Notice that the approximately east–west belts of anticyclones in the subtropics and low pressure centres near the Equator shift north and south during the year with the sun.

In temperate latitudes low pressure patterns dominate the oceanic scene and the seaboards of the continents, but notice the anticyclones over Canada and Siberia on the January day; such high pressure systems as these are common over the cold interior of continents in winter.

Movement of pressure systems

At most meteorological offices pressure maps are prepared at regular intervals throughout the day and night, the conventional chart times being midnight, 6.00 a.m., 12.00 noon and 6.00 p.m. GMT (or, more professionally, 00, 06, 12 and 18 GMT). A number of stations supplement these main charts with intermediate 3-hourly or even hourly maps, and, once a sequence of charts is available, the movement of current depressions and anticyclones can be measured. Figures 1.4(a) and (b) show examples of MSL pressure patterns in the northern and southern hemispheres together with trajectories of the low and high pressure centres, traced over the previous 24 hours by noting their positions on successive charts.

Notice that in both hemispheres of the earth the depressions and anticyclones moved in a broad sense from west to east. This is typical of pressure systems in temperate and high latitudes.

Unlike low pressure systems, anticyclones are seldom resolute travellers. Now and again a high may appear to move very fast, but most of the anticyclones are sluggish and occasionally erratic in their movements. In some regions of the world, the tendency for high pressure systems to stagnate is so prevalent that any anticyclone in such a locality is given the appropriate geographical name. The *Azores High*, for instance, is a name given to any anticyclone

---

Fig. 1.4(a) Movement and development of depressions and anticyclones over the North Atlantic on 19 and 20 May 1957. The last chart shows the tracks of the principal lows and highs with dots indicating their position every six hours. The intermediate charts for 18 GMT 19 May and 06 GMT 20 May are not shown in this sequence. The low pressure centre at the centre of the chart for 12 GMT 20 May is a secondary depression that formed, at some time between 12 and 18 GMT on 19 May, in the trough of low pressure extending southwards from between Greenland and Newfoundland on the 12 GMT 19 May chart.

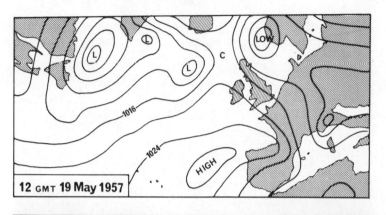

12 GMT 19 May 1957

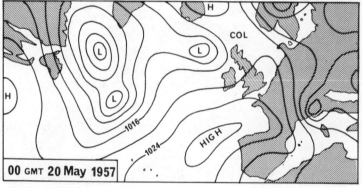

00 GMT 20 May 1957

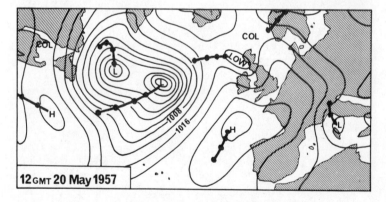

12 GMT 20 May 1957

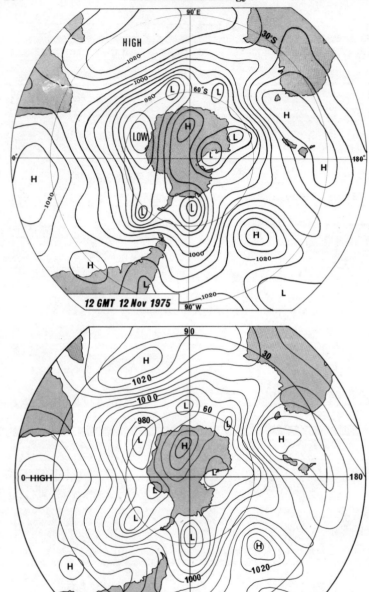

12 GMT 12 Nov 1975

12 GMT 13 NOV 1975

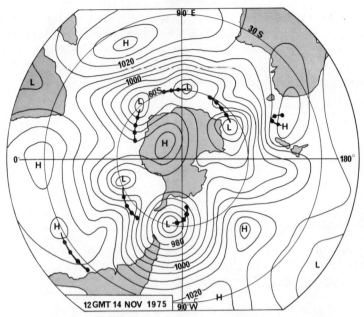

Fig. 1.4(b)   This set of three charts shows the movement and development of pressure systems over much of the southern hemisphere in a 48
hour period in November 1975. The third figure of the series also shows
tracks of several of the high and low pressure systems over the previous 48
hours. Dots on the tracks denote previous positions at 12 hourly intervals.
Notice how the pressure systems tend to move from west to east.

which happens to be stagnating in the neighbourhood of the
Azores; the fact that it has a special name indicates the observed
predominance, particularly during the summer, of high pressure
systems in this region. There is an Azores anticyclone centred to the
south-west of the Azores in Figure 1.3(b). The *Siberian Anticyclone*
is the commonly used name signifying the persistence of anticyclones, such as that shown in Figure 1.3(a), over Siberia during the
winter.

Decrease of pressure with height

Because the air at any level in the atmosphere has to support the
weight of the air above it, the lower layers are compressed much

more than those above. Thus, atmospheric pressure decreases with height. The precise relationship between altitude and pressure depends on the prevailing pressure system and on the temperature, warm air taking up more space than cold and dense air. The approximate relationship between pressure and altitude is:

MSL	1000 mb
3000 ft (1000 m)	900 mb
10 000 ft (3000 m)	700 mb
20 000 ft (6000 m)	500 mb
30 000 ft (10 000 m)	300 mb
40 000 ft (13 000 m)	200 mb

Pressure measurements

Another instrument used for measuring atmospheric pressure is the *aneroid barometer*, which is essentially a sealed can shaped like a bellows and almost exhausted of air. High atmospheric pressure compresses the can; low pressure allows it to expand. This slight compression or expansion in response to high or low atmospheric pressure is amplified by a system of levers and indicated by a pointer on a dial. Figure 1.5 illustrates the principle. The pointer can take

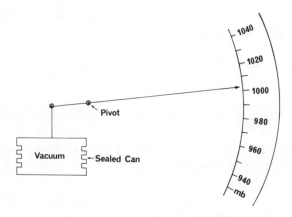

Fig. 1.5   Principle of the aneroid barometer. Atmospheric pressure is measured by noting how much it compresses a sealed can. The pointer can take the form of a pen tracing the pressure changes on a slowly moving chart; such an instrument is then called a barograph.

the form of a pen tracing the pressure changes on a slowly moving chart. Such an instrument is then called a *barograph*.

In order to map pressure systems and deduce winds from pressure patterns, it is necessary to have a set of pressure measurements at one level. But it is not feasible for all observing stations to be at the same level. Therefore, it is a common practice for a meteorological observer to read his barometer, then calculate what the pressure would be, if the barometer were at some standard level. In most areas this standard level is taken to be MSL, but in some high-level regions, such as much of South Africa, it is convenient to take a higher altitude as the standard level or to map the contours of a pressure surface that is likely to be close to the height of the high-level terrain, as illustrated in Figure 1.6.

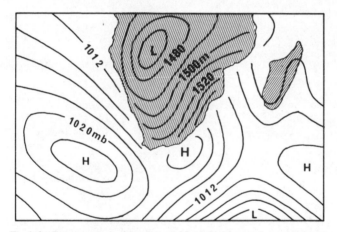

Fig. 1.6 Because much of Southern Africa is high ground, overland maps are drawn for a standard level close to that of the general terrain. The isobaric pattern shown here over the land area corresponds approximately to the pressure pattern at an altitude of 1500 m (5000 ft). For practical purposes, however, it is more convenient to draw lines indicating the altitude where the pressure of 850 mb is calculated to be. Thus, the lines shown are labelled as altitudes in metres. Over the adjacent sea the usual MSL isobars are drawn.

One of the best indications of the movement and behaviour of a pressure system is the change of pressure at observing points in or around the system. Pressure will fall as a depression approaches or deepens, and rise during the advent or intensification of a high pressure system. So the *pressure tendency*, which is the conventional meteorological way of describing pressure change, figures prominently in meteorological reports.

Pressure changes are usually slow—often less than half a millibar per hour. Some phenomena, such as tornadoes, hurricanes and some thunderstorms can produce very sudden localised pressure changes, but, in most meteorological contexts, a pressure fall of about 3 mb/h is considered to be rapid—such a fall would normally be indicative of the speedy approach of a vigorous depression.

2

Wind

We have spoken of the movement of depressions and anticyclones but such movement may not be real in the sense that a definite object moves from place to place. The movement of pressure systems is akin to that of ripples on water; a particular set of ripples may have an observed movement but a cork floating on the surface does not move horizontally with them; it merely bobs up and down as the ripples pass by. So we cannot argue that because a depression moves east the air within it also flows to the east. To determine the actual air movement we must look to the *pressure gradient*, that is the rate at which the atmospheric pressure changes with distance across the isobars. Figure 2.1 illustrates what is meant by pressure gradient in actual figures, but numbers are not always needed; the gradient is often adequately described as weak or slack when the

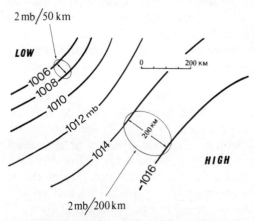

Fig. 2.1 The pressure gradient is a measure of the closeness of the isobars. It can be stated as the difference in pressure between two isobars divided by the distance between them, but can often be adequately described as weak or slack when the space between the isobars is wide, and strong or tight when the isobars are close together.

spacing between the isobars is wide, and strong or tight when the isobars are close together.

Geostrophic Wind

The pressure gradient just measured is an indication that any vertical column in the high pressure region contains more air by weight than a column covering an equal area under low pressure. This pressure difference produces a force directed towards restoring the balance—from the heavy column to the lighter, like the force that drives water through a sluice gate from the high water side to the low. But in the atmosphere this pressure force does not produce a simple flow of air from high to low pressure. The earth is rotating, and because of this rotation any air moving over the earth's surface is subjected to a force tending to pull it off its course. Explanation of this terrestrial trick is not easy, so let us leave it for a technical note later in this book. At this stage all we need to know is that the earth's spinning motion exerts a force that causes the bulk of the air at low levels in temperate and high latitudes to flow practically parallel to the MSL isobars instead of across them. The wind does not blow directly into depressions or out of anticyclones; it blows around such pressure systems, the sense of direction being remembered by a rule known as *Buys–Ballot's Law*, which states that:

If you stand with your back to the wind in the northern/southern hemisphere   atmospheric   pressure   decreases   towards   your left/right.

Figure 2.2 illustrates the flow associated with high and low pressure systems. This *geostrophic wind*, as it is called, is also controlled by the pressure gradient; the stronger or tighter the gradient the stronger the wind. Thus the pressure map gives us an instantaneous view of the broad-scale airflow. We can visualise the isobars as streamlines or channels along which the wind blows— slowly where the pressure gradient is weak and quickly through the narrow channels formed by closely packed isobars.

Observations and simplified theoretical reasoning have led to the practice of assuming that, in latitudes higher than about 20 degrees, wind at about 1500 ft (500 m) above MSL is approximately equal to the geostrophic wind indicated by the MSL pressure pattern. This

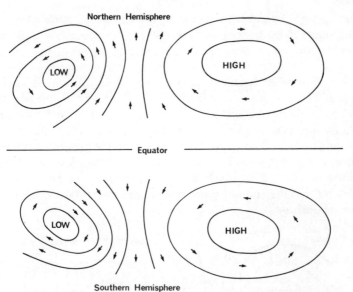

Fig. 2.2 Geostrophic wind blows anticlockwise around low pressure systems and clockwise around anticyclones in the northern hemisphere—and in the reverse directions in the southern hemisphere. The closer the isobars the stronger the winds. In latitudes higher than about 20°, wind at about 1500 ft (500 m) above MSL is approximately equal to the geostrophic wind indicated by the MSL pressure pattern.

assumption is not precisely correct, but it is part of common practice and is adequate for many aviation requirements.

The geostrophic assumption does not apply generally in the tropics. With the exception of tropical cyclones, pressure systems at low latitudes are weak with slack pressure gradients and winds do not blow along the isobars. Winds associated with tropical cyclones are described in Chapter 10.

Surface wind

At low levels air flowing over land or sea usually has some turbulence, which may range from a gentle stirring motion through a depth of 100 m or 200 m in light winds to vigorous eddying up to 3000–6000 ft (1000–2000 m) in strong winds. This turbulence is tantamount to a frictional force retarding the airstream; it prevents the low-level wind from attaining the full geostrophic speed. A secondary consequence is that the low-level wind is deflected slightly away from the geostrophic direction towards low pressure. Figure 2.3 illustrates the result. Very close to ground-level, where the friction effect is usually most marked, the surface wind is often about 20–30 degrees from the isobars and about two-thirds of the speed of the geostrophic wind. In routine meteorological messages the *surface wind* is taken to be that blowing at 33 ft (10 m) above an open site such as an airfield. The reason for not choosing a lower level is that winds within a few metres of ground-level are sometimes so affected by small local obstacles and the nature of the ground that they do not represent the general surface wind in the neighbourhood.

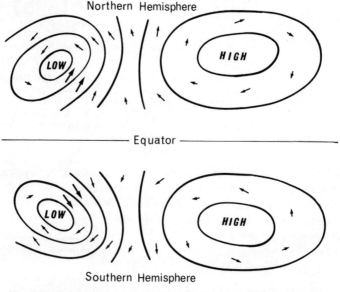

Fig. 2.3 Close to sea- or ground-level, winds flow slightly across the isobars, from high pressure towards low pressure at about two-thirds of the geostrophic wind speeds.

Variation of wind with height

The geostrophic wind concept is applicable to the flow of air not only at or near the 1500 ft (500 m) level but also at higher levels—

right up through the atmospheric layers in which our cloud and weather systems evolve. A chart of the atmospheric pressure pattern, at say 30 000 ft (10 000 m) above MSL represents the instantaneous wind flow at this level; the wind blows approximately along these high-level isobars with a speed proportional to the pressure gradient—just as it does at lower levels.

The pressure patterns at any two levels are rarely identical, but they are linked by the temperature distribution between the two levels; the pressure difference between the top and bottom of a warm column of air is less than that between the top and bottom of a cold (denser) column of equal height. Where temperature gradients exist, between neighbouring warm and cold airstreams, the pressure pattern at high levels will be different from the MSL pattern and the resultant wind speeds and directions will also change with height.

Figures 2.4(a) and (b) show typical high-level flow patterns associated with MSL depressions in the northern and southern hemispheres.

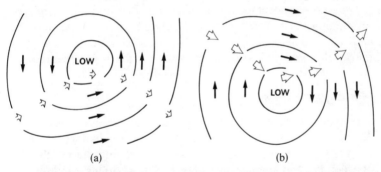

(a)   (b)

Fig. 2.4(a) and (b)   The shapes of pressure patterns are not the same at all heights. In this illustration a depression is depicted as a set of isobars enclosing the low pressure around which there is a geostrophic wind flow (black arrows). At a height of 30 000–40 000 ft (10 000–13 000 m) wind flow over such depressions is more likely to be like that depicted by the broad arrows in this illustration.

Jet streams

Atmospheric situations that produce particularly strong winds aloft often channel these winds into an imaginary but distinctive tube like that sketched in Figure 2.5. Such a concentration of strong

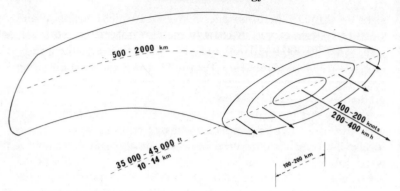

Fig. 2.5   A jet stream is best visualised as a tube of strong winds, although there is not, of course, a rigid boundary to the tube.

winds along an axis is called a *jet stream*. Jet streams come and go in a variety of shapes and sizes; over Europe jet streams of 100–200 knots (200-400 km/h) along a length of between 500 and 2000 km (250 and 1000 naut. miles) at an altitude of about 40 000 ft (12 000 m) are not uncommon; over the USA longer, meandering jet streams often stretch from the Rockies to the Atlantic seaboard, and high over Japan and New Zealand conditions are favourable for the development of 300 knot (600 km/h) winds in jet stream cores.

Wind observations

In modern meteorological practice wind direction, that is the direction *from* which the wind blows, is reported in degrees true or in points of the compass. In Figure 2.6 showing the relationship between the two angular measures, the apostrophes stand for 'by'; for example, NE'N is pronounced 'north-east by north'. To complete our vocabulary relating to wind direction we must note that the wind *backs* when its direction changes in an anticlockwise sense in Figure 2.6 and *veers* when the direction turns clockwise.

Wind speeds are usually reported in knots or kilometres per hour, but as a result of pioneer work by Admiral Beaufort, who classified wind forces according to their effect on a 'well-conditioned man-of-war', the Beaufort wind scale is more familiar to some users of meteorological information. The descriptions and Beaufort equivalents of wind speeds up to 71 knots are tabled opposite.

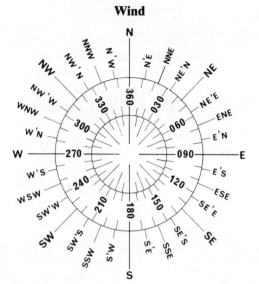

Fig. 2.6   Relationship between degrees true and points of the compass.

Table 2.1   WIND SPEED CLASSIFICATION

Meteoro-logical classi-fication	Speed		Approximate Mean Speed		Beaufort Force	Terms used in general weather forecasts
	km/h	knots	km/h	knots		
Calm	Less than 2	Less than 1	0	0	0	Calm
Light air	2–6	1–3	4	2	1 ⎫	
Light breeze	7–12	4–6	10	5	2 ⎬	Light winds
Gentle breeze	13–19	7–10	16	9	3 ⎭	
Moderate breeze	20–30	11–16	25	13	4	Moderate wind
Fresh breeze	31–39	17–21	35	19	5	Fresh wind
Strong breeze	40–52	22–27	46	24	6 ⎫	Strong wind
Moderate gale	53–61	28–33	57	30	7 ⎭	
Fresh gale	62–74	34–40	68	37	8	Gale
Strong gale	75–87	41–47	81	44	9 ⎫	
Whole gale	88–102	48–55	95	52	10 ⎪	Severe
Storm	103–117	56–63	110	60	11 ⎬	gale or
Hurricane	118–142	64–71	125	58	12 ⎭	storm

Wind measurements

Instruments used to measure wind speed are called *anemometers*. The *pressure tube anemometer* depicted in Figure 2.7 basically measures the pressure force exerted by the wind blowing on to the open end of a pivoted tube kept pointing into wind by a wind vane. It is similar in principle to a pitot head and an airspeed indicator.

A more commonly used wind-speed measuring instrument is the *cup anemometer* which comprises three or more cups at the end of

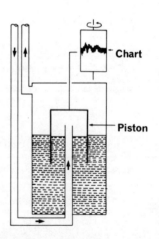

Fig. 2.7   Principle of the pressure tube anemometer. An open-ended tube at the top of a mast is free to rotate about a vertical axis and kept pointed into wind by a wind vane, while the wind blows past small holes in an otherwise closed adjacent or coaxial tube. As in the pitot head principle, pressure in the open-ended tube is increased by the wind pressure, while pressure in the closed but perforated tube is kept static (or reduced if the tube and its perforations are designed to produce suction). These two tubes are connected to air spaces inside and outside a piston in a water tank. Variations in the pressure difference cause the piston to move up and down. This up and down movement is traced by a pen on to a slowly moving chart.

horizontal arms radiating from a vertical shaft. As the cups catch the wind the assembly spins about the vertical shaft whose rate of rotation is measured by a form of speedometer indicating the wind speed. A somewhat similar type of anemometer more familiar on the American scene has, in place of the cup assembly, a propeller centred on a pivoted horizontal shaft kept into wind by a vane.

Another type of anemometer employs the principle illustrated in Figure 2.8. Anemometers of this type are not normally so precise or

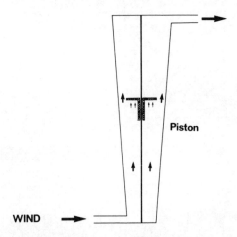

Fig. 2.8   In this type of anemometer wind blows in at the base of a vertical perspex cone, and out at the top. This flow of air pushes a lightweight piston in the cone upwards along a thin central rod. The stronger the wind the greater the pressure on the piston, but the higher the piston goes the greater the leakage of air around it. Thus the height to which the piston moves is a measure of wind speed. This principle is used for an inexpensive hand-held anemometer. Usually the cone is about 15 cm (6 in.) high and about 3 cm (1¼ in.) in diameter. In some versions of this instrument a much thinner cone containing a light pith ball instead of a piston is used.

robust as the pressure tube or cup types, but they are inexpensive, compact and accurate enough for many practical purposes.

By comparing wind-speed estimations with anemometer readings it is not difficult for an observer to learn to estimate wind speed with reasonable accuracy by the feel of the wind on his face or the sound in his ears, but without adequate training and occasional checking many observers and most amateurs tend to overestimate the speed of moderate to strong breezes.

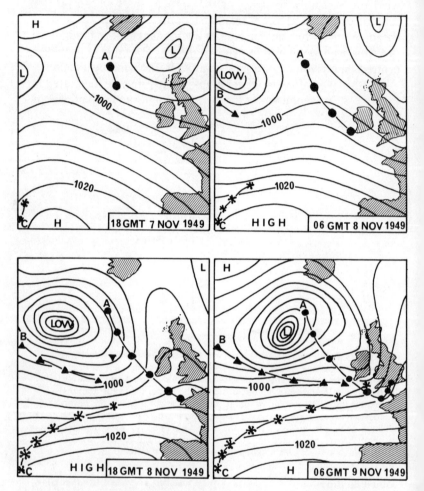

Fig. 2.9 A sequence of charts is used to trace trajectories of the air. Black dots, triangles and asterisks denote positions of the air parcels whose trajectories are labelled A, B, and C in this illustration. These positions are shown at 6 hourly intervals, although the charts shown here are for 12 hourly intervals. Notice how the warm air, from C, becomes sandwiched between the cold air from A and cold air from B.

Air trajectories

Although a pressure map gives us an instantaneous view of the broad-scale airflow, it is not always easy to see at a glance where the air flowing over any particular spot has come from. In the middle and high latitudes of the northern hemisphere warm air usually comes from the south, but not all southerly winds are warm. Occasionally southerly winds bring cold air that has flowed from a cold northern source but has followed a curved trajectory, flowing some considerable distance southwards then turning up towards the north. Figure 2.9 illustrates how this can happen.

This figure illustrates a sequence of pressure charts and the trajectories of three parcels of air propelled by the winds associated with the moving pressure patterns. Air that moved along trajectory A first moved towards the south-south-west in the flow around the depression north of the British Isles. But, as this depression moved away towards the east, this air was left behind and then caught up in the circulation of the next depression moving in from the west. Thus this cold air moved south to the English Channel then up into southern England as a cold south-south-west wind. The other two trajectories are more straightforward. Trajectory B also represents the path of cold air that flowed with the winds around the southern half of the deep depression before approaching the British Isles as a cold westerly wind. Trajectory C is the path of warm air that flowed from the Azores to become sandwiched between the two colder masses that moved along trajectories A and B.

Fortunately, it will not normally be necessary for us as glider pilots to work out trajectories of air masses from sequences of pressure maps. But it will help our understanding of meteorological phenomena if we realise that the paths along which air masses flow are not necessarily the same as the impressions we may get from looking at a single instantaneous pressure map.

3

Temperature

Heat and light are propagated through air and through space in the form of pulses or vibrations known as electromagnetic waves. Every object, whatever its temperature, emits heat by radiation and also receives heat radiating from its surroundings. The intensity of the outgoing radiation depends on the temperature of the object; the hotter the object the more intense the radiation. The temperature affects not only the intensity but also the wavelengths on which the radiation takes place. A red-hot object emits electromagnetic waves which are particularly intense for wavelengths of just under one-thousandth of a millimetre and our eyes interpret such electromagnetic waves as red light.

Radiation heat from the sun (*insolation*) arrives at the top of the atmospheric layer in which our clouds and weather occur mostly on wavelengths between 0.0003 and 0.003 mm. This waveband includes short waves that are particularly prone to scattering by molecules of dry air and water vapour, and since our eyes recognise such electromagnetic waves as blue light we see the sky as a blue canopy above. When larger dust and smoke particles accrue in the atmosphere the blue light from the sun may be almost entirely cut off, while the longer waves penetrate the haze and make the sun visible as a fiery red ball. Although these interactions between solar radiation and the air produce visible effects, their nature is such as to produce only a small direct effect on the temperature of the air. On a cloudless day the bulk of the incoming solar radiation passes through the air almost without heating it. It is the Earth's surface that receives this heat and this surface warms the air with which it is in contact. The practically incessant stirring motion of the air then spreads the heat upwards into the atmosphere. By comparison with the sun's rays radiation of heat from the Earth's surface *terrestrial radiation*) takes place on long wavelengths of about 0.004–0.04 mm. Some of the radiation happens to have a direct heating effect on water vapour and carbon dioxide in the air. This direct absorption of terrestrial radiation adds to the fundamental fact that air in the weather systems we experience is heated by the earth from below rather than by the sun from above.

The fate of insolation received at the earth's surface depends on the slope and nature of the surface itself; sun-facing slopes receive more radiant heat than surfaces more obliquely inclined to the sun's rays; some surfaces reflect rather than absorb radiant heat. Grass and foliage use the blue and red radiation in the solar spectrum for photosynthesis but reflect the intermediate green waveband. Snow- or ice-covered ground reflects between 40–90% of the incident radiation, whereas a dark mould surface will reflect only 10–15% of the incoming radiant heat. The reflective power varies with the state of the ground; dry sand reflects about 20% while for wet sand the reflection drops to 10%. The reflective power of a water surface varies according to the sun's zenith angle; it is about 2% when the sun is directly overhead and 35% when the sun is only 10 degrees above the horizon. Cloud layers also reflect radiation; thin layers not more than 500 ft (150 m) thick can reflect between 5 and 65% of the incident radiation, while for thicknesses of about 3000 ft (1000 m) or more reflection from an extensive layer of cloud is between 45 and 85%.

The meteorological word for this reflective power is *albedo*. It is expressed as a fraction instead of a percentage; a reflective power of 65%, for example, is more professionally described as an albedo of 0.65.

The troposphere

Because the air is heated from the earth below it is not surprising to find that air temperature usually decreases with height. The higher we go the colder it is, until we get to heights that are out of range of the broad scale and long-term effects of the heating and stirring from below.

The vertical extent of the broad-scale and long-term effects of heating and stirring from below is usually evident from measurements of the air temperature aloft. To obtain such measurements, meteorologists use an apparatus called a *radio-sonde*; this is a lightweight radio transmitter coupled with devices for measuring pressure, temperature and humidity. The apparatus is carried up into the air by a gas-filled balloon, and while ascending it emits radio signals which can be monitored and translated into pressure, temperature and humidity readings by operators or data-processing apparatus on the ground. The balloon normally ascends to between 60 000 ft (20 000 m) and 90 000 ft (30 000 m) before bursting and leaving the radio-sonde with a small parachute to check its rate of fall if it is expected to descend over populated districts. When plotted against height the temperature readings usually yield graphs like those shown in Figure 3.1. The characteristics common to all of

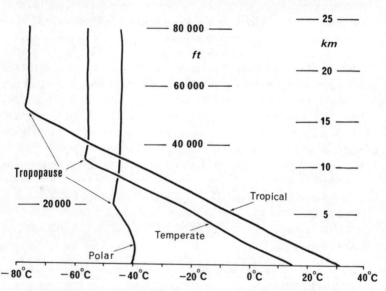

Fig. 3.1 Characteristic variations of temperature with height in tropical, temperate and polar latitudes. The level where the temperature ceases to decrease with height and becomes almost constant with height is called the tropopause. The tropopause is the base of the stratosphere. Notice that the temperature of the stratosphere over the tropics is colder than that of the stratosphere over the poles.

these graphs are the expected decrease of temperature in the lower part of the atmosphere and a fairly constant temperature with height at higher levels. The level at which the temperature stops decreasing with height is distinctive enough to merit a special name: it is called the *tropopause*. Below the tropopause is the *troposphere*; immediately above is the *stratosphere*.

The tropopause acts as a sort of lid on cloud formation through-out the world. Clouds are rarely found in the stratosphere, so when discussing clouds and weather systems we can keep our ideas of height and depth in perspective by remembering that almost all cloud is confined to the troposphere. At the same time the tropopause must not be regarded as a level in the sense of being rigid, flat or horizontal. Arching from a high level over the tropics to low altitudes over the Poles, as shown in Figure 3.2, it has transient

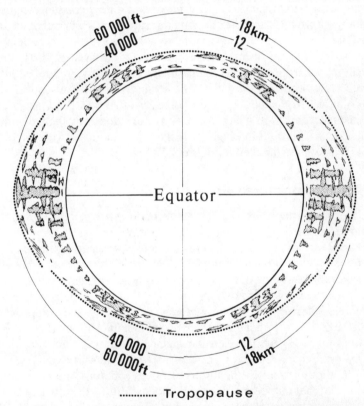

Fig. 3.2   The dotted line denotes the approximate mean height of the tropopause. It is high over the Equator and low over the Poles. Apart from transient humps, hollows, breaks, and a seasonal tendency to rise in the summer and lower in the winter, the tropopause is generally at a high level over the tropics and relatively low over the poles. Almost all the clouds we see in the atmosphere are in the troposphere, between the Earth's surface and the tropopause.

humps, hollows and faults superimposed on a seasonal tendency to
rise in the summer and lower in the winter. The axes of jet streams
are usually near the top of the troposphere and often not far from
steps or faults in the tropopause.

Lapse rate

In many meteorological processes the rate of change of temperature with height plays a more important role than that of the
temperature itself, and, for brevity, this rate of change is referred to
as the *lapse rate*. The lapse rate is not a universal unchanging
constant; it varies in time, place and height. On average the lapse
rate in the troposphere is approximately 2°C (3.6°F) per 1000 ft
(6.5°C per km) but the finer scale structure often has significant
variations from the average. Some weather systems produce
isothermal layers in which the temperature does not change with
height, or *inversions* in which the temperature increases with height.
Such layers are labelled in Figure 3.3.

Dry adiabatic lapse rate

Because atmospheric pressure decreases with height, air that
moves upward in the atmosphere expands, and as it expands it
cools. Descending air is compressed, and is warmed by this compression. The physical properties of air are such that if a parcel of
dry air moves up or down in the atmosphere, without exchanging
any heat with its surroundings, the temperature of the parcel will
decrease during ascent and increase during descent by approximately 3°C (5.4°F) per 1000 ft change of height (1°C per 100 m), as
indicated in Figure 3.4. This particular lapse rate is known as the
Dry Adiabatic Lapse Rate (DALR). 'Dry' because it refers to dry
air (although it also applies to air that contains water vapour
provided that this vapour does not condense during the process) and
'Adiabatic' because it does not exchange any heat with its surroundings.

In the real, restless atmosphere parcels of air are persistently
stirred up and down by turbulence and eddies that often extend up
to a few thousand feet in most wind conditions, but these parcels
mix with and exchange heat with the surrounding air. Thus, as the

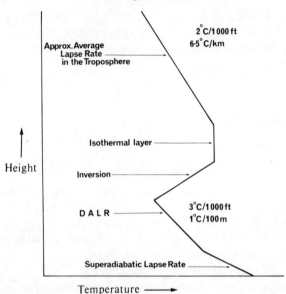

Fig. 3.3   The approximate average lapse rate in the troposphere is 6.5°C per km but local variations are frequent. Any layer in which the temperature remains constant with height is called an isothermal layer. A temperature increase with height is called an inversion. The Dry Adiabatic Lapse Rate (DALR) has a special significance in convection, as discussed in later chapters in this book.

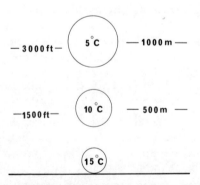

Fig. 3.4   When a bubble of air rises in the atmosphere it encounters lower pressure (because the pressure decreases with height) and expands. As it expands it cools at the dry adiabatic lapse rate of 1°C per 100 m.

vertical stirring goes on, the temperature lapse rate of the surrounding air will be brought closer and closer to the DALR. In fact, the
lapse rate of well-stirred air from ground- or sea-level up to a height
of a few hundred or a few thousand feet is often very close to the
DALR.

Superadiabatic lapse rates

Over ground being heated by sunshine, bubbles of warm air
heated close to the ground rise and mix with the surrounding air.
But, when the rate of ground heating by strong sunshine is rapid the
mixing is often too slow to form a well-mixed layer with a dry
adiabatic lapse rate. So the decrease of temperature with height is
greater than the DALR. Such a decrease with height is called a
superadiabatic lapse rate. It is not a fixed lapse rate with a constant
value; it is any lapse rate with a greater decrease of temperature
with height than the DALR, as illustrated in Figure 3.3. It is often
found over sun-heated ground up to a few hundred feet in temperate climates and a few thousand feet in hotter regions.

Stability

If a parcel or bubble of dry air were to rise without mixing in a
layer of air in which the general lapse rate is less than the DALR,
the rising air would become cooler and denser than the air around it,
as depicted in Figure 3.5(a). Being denser than its surroundings the
bubble would sink down again towards its original level. The fact
that the bubble would mix with the surrounding air does not alter
this conclusion; until the bubble becomes completely eroded by
mixing it will still be slightly cooler than the surrounding air. Thus
the general lapse rate will tend to suppress random vertical currents
within the layer.

If, however, the general lapse rate is greater than the DALR the
rising bubble would become warmer than its surroundings and
would therefore be propelled further upwards because of its
buoyancy, as shown in Figure 3.5(b).

The layer in which the general temperature lapse rate inhibits
random vertical air currents is called '*stable*', while the layer whose
lapse rate boosts vertical motion is called '*unstable*'. These two

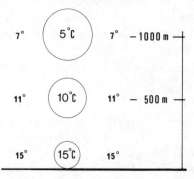

Fig. 3.5(a)   An atmospheric layer is said to be stable when it suppresses vertical motion. In this illustration let us suppose that the actual temperature of an airstream is 15°C at ground-level, 11°C at 500 m, and 7°C at 1000 m. If a bubble of air from ground-level were to ascend in this airsteam to, say, 1000 m, it would expand and cool at the DALR to 10°C at 500 m and 5°C at 1000 m, as indicated already in Fig. 3.4. Thus it would be colder than the surrounding air at these levels. Therefore, it would be denser; so negative buoyancy would force it back towards the ground. Thus, the airstream in this illustration would tend to suppress vertical motion.

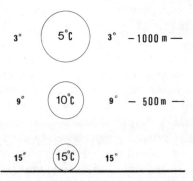

Fig. 3.5(b)   Suppose the temperature in an airstream is 15°C at ground-level, 9°C at 500 m and 3°C at 1000 m. If a bubble of air from ground-level ascends in this airstream—and expands and cools as in Figs. 3.4 and 3.5(a)—it will become warmer than the surrounding air. Therefore, it will be buoyant and will continue to ascend. The airstream layer in which vertical motion is given such a boost is called unstable.

terms are entrenched in meteorological and gliding jargon. They
are often used loosely and imprecisely by both amateur and professional meteorologists to indicate the probable development of
convection phenomena which are discussed later in this book.

Nocturnal radiation

At night the fate of ground without a cloud cover is like that of a
teapot without a cosy – it gets cold, or more precisely, it loses heat
by radiation. As a consequence the air close to the ground is cooled
and its temperature decreases. The effect of this cooling is usually
spread upwards into the atmosphere by turbulence. In light winds
the vertical extent of this turbulence is often about 200 m or less,
and a marked fall of temperature occurs in the low-level layer to
which the cooling is confined. Thus, on cloudless nights with light
winds, *nocturnal radiation* of heat can produce a low-level temperature inversion. The inversion is, of course, a very stable layer. It
damps down whatever vertical stirring motion exists, and so the
cooling is confined to a progressively shallower layer of air. At the
end of a calm clear night it is not unusual for the temperature at 1 m
above the ground to be about 5°C more than at ground-level itself
and about 5–8°C less than the temperature at about 1000 ft
(300 m).

Because cold and dense air tends to sink, valleys and hollows
become particularly cold on calm clear nights.

At ground-level the loss of heat by radiation is partly compen-
sated by the conduction of heat upwards through the ground from
depths down to about 1 m where the earth temperature is very slow
to change and is usually higher than the soil surface on a cold clear
night. This upward conduction of heat is not nearly sufficient to
compensate for the cooling by radiation at the surface, but can cause
local variations of ground temperature. In clear calm conditions
night temperatures at the surface of light sandy soils, which are poor
conductors of heat, are often 2–6°C lower than those at the surface
of clay soils.

Temperature measurements

To obtain air temperatures indicative of weather patterns on a
scale larger than that of local influences, meteorologists have

adopted special standards for temperature measurements. Unless otherwise stated, the *surface air temperature* is taken to be the temperature shown by a thermometer shielded from direct radiation (yet well ventilated) situated at between 1.25 and 2 m above a short grass surface well away from buildings, trees or other large objects.

To achieve such exposure the meteorologist usually houses the thermometer in a carefully sited double-louvred white box called a *Stevenson screen*.

A large Stevenson screen can also house other thermometers, including those which move indicators to record maximum and minimum temperatures, and a *thermograph* that uses the temperature-controlled distortion of a bimetallic strip to record temperature on a slowly moving chart.

4

Moisture

Every year just over 300 000 cubic kilometres of water evaporates into the atmosphere from the sea, which forms a global reservoir of more than 1000 million cubic kilometres of water. Another 60 000 cubic kilometres evaporates annually from lakes, rivers, moist soil, plants and trees.

In the atmosphere this water is mostly in its guise of an invisible gas, *water vapour*. The amount of water vapour in a sample of air depends largely on the path the sample has been following. During a sea crossing or a traverse of relatively moist ground the sample is likely to acquire water that evaporates into the air from the underlying wet or moist surface. This evaporation does not continue indefinitely. A limit can be reached when the air becomes saturated with water vapour. The limit depends mainly on the air temperature; warm air can virtually absorb more water vapour than cold air. A kilogram of hot, tropical air with a temperature of 35°C can hold nearly 40g of water vapour, but only 1g of water vapour is needed to saturate a kilogram of cold continental winter air at − 15°C.

Condensation

If air that is already saturated with water vapour is cooled it becomes *supersaturated*—it contains more water than is required for saturation at the lower temperature. The excess of water vapour normally condenses on to abundant microscopic particles of dust and salt in the atmosphere and forms minute droplets in such vast numbers that they are collectively visible as fog or cloud. Fog is the likely outcome if the moist air is cooled by lingering over a relatively cold land or sea surface. Cloud is the consequence when the cooling is caused by the moist air rising and expanding.

Freezing

The freezing-point of water is 0°C (32°F), but, unless the air temperature is well below freezing-point, a water droplet needs a suitable particle or nucleus on which to freeze. There are not enough suitable freezing nuclei for more than a small fraction of the water droplets that form in most clouds, so it is not at all strange for clouds of *supercooled* water droplets to remain in their unfrozen liquid form above the *freezing-level*, which is the altitude at which the air temperature, decreasing with height, reaches 0°C.

Precipitation

Drizzle, rain, showers, snow and hail are types of *precipitation* that occur when water in the form of drops, interlocking ice crystals, or pellets of ice and water fall out of cloud. Water droplets and ice crystals, however, do not fall out of cloud as soon as they are formed. The diameter of a cloud droplet is typically about 20 microns or less, a micron being one-thousandth of a millimetre. Such a droplet will naturally fall through the air, but its falling speed is so slow that it does not normally reach the ground—it is kept airborne by vertical currents likely to be associated with the cloud-forming process, and, on reaching the base, top or sides of a cloud, soon evaporates into the relatively drier surrounding air. A rain-drop large enough to fall at sufficient speed to reach the ground as a water drop is likely to have a diameter of between 1–4 mm. A 2 mm diameter raindrop is equivalent in size to about a million or so cloud droplets which, as part of a cloud, would be dispersed through a volume of about 1 litre (the size of a small melon). The spacing between the cloud droplets is often about fifty times their diameter. Figure 4.1 illustrates the spaciousness involved.

The physical make-up of the cloud droplets is such that there is little or no chance of them growing into raindrops by direct conden-sation of water vapour on to their surfaces. Therefore, rainfall production involves more complicated processes for gathering billions of tiny, widely scattered cloud droplets into millions of relatively huge raindrops.

There are two basic rainfall production mechanisms. Cloud drop-lets within a cloud are not all the same size, so, although their falling speeds are all very slow, they are not all the same; a relatively large droplet falls faster than small droplets in its path. Thus the large droplet grows by catching up and coalescing with the smaller droplets. This *coalescence process* is sometimes self-exciting.

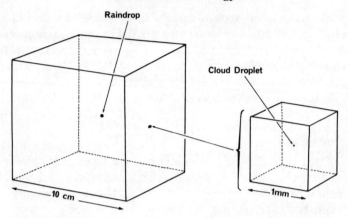

Fig. 4.1   The relative sizes of cloud droplets and rain droplets, together with the spacing between them, are illustrated in this figure. If we picture a 1-litre volume ($10 \times 10 \times 10$ cu cm) to be composed of one million cubes each with a volume of 1 cu mm, the cloud would comprise an average of about one tiny cloud droplet in each millimetre cube. An aggregate of these million cloud droplets would be needed to form one raindrop with a diameter of between about 1 and 4 mm. The enlargement of a millimetre cube on the right gives an indication of the relatively large distances between cloud droplets compared to their diameters.

Raindrops in the atmosphere are liable to disintegrate on reaching critical sizes; the maximum diameter to which a drop can grow before disintegrating into several smaller drops (each of which may grow by the coalescence process) is about 7 mm in calm air and 4 mm in turbulent air. The whole process can produce raindrops within about one hour after cloud formation.

   The other basic rainfall production mechanism is called the *Bergeron–Findeisen* process, after the two meteorologists who expounded the theory. This process occurs in supercooled regions of cloud just above the freezing-level. Most of the cloud droplets do not freeze because of the customary shortage of freezing nuclei. However, the physical make-up of the relatively few ice crystals that do form on the sparse freezing nuclei is such that cloud droplets in the neighbourhood of a crystal evaporate and the resultant vapour condenses on to the crystal, which thereby grows in size. As the crystal falls through the cloud it grows not only by condensation but also by the coalescence process. Like the coalescence mechanism, the Bergeron–Findeisen process can be self-exciting.

When a tiny water drop freezes in the atmosphere its surface usually freezes first. When the interior subsequently freezes it expands and is liable to shatter the outer shell and eject tiny ice particles which form suitable nuclei on which more supercooled droplets can freeze. Thus once the production of ice crystals (*glaciation*) has started in the freezing-region of a cloud it is likely to proceed rapidly. The whole process can produce ice crystals several millimetres across within about one hour.

Hail and snow

When a pellet of ice collides with a water drop the water coats the pellet with either a partly frozen mixture of air bubbles and water or a glossy shell of ice. It is common for clouds in which this process occurs to be deep and to contain updraughts strong enough to support such pellets until they grow to at least several millimetres across. When updraughts in a hail-producing cloud are particularly strong, hailstones are liable to acquire several coatings of opaque or glazed ice before falling out of cloud as formidable missiles. Hailstones of golf ball size are by no means rare, and hailstone diameters of 120 mm (5 in.) have been recorded.

When a cloud is entirely above the freezing-level products of the precipitation processes comprise myriads of interlocking ice crystals, better known as snowflakes.

Latent heat

If you were to take the temperature of water being heated in an electric kettle you would observe this temperature to rise steadily to the boiling-point of water (100°C or 212°F at average MSL pressure) then stay at this temperature until all the water had boiled away. The interpretation of these observations is that during the first stage of this simple, but domestically inconvenient, kitchen experiment heat is being used to raise the temperature of water, but during the boiling stage heat is used to convert the water into vapour. The heat is carried away with the vapour and is called the *latent heat* of evaporation of water.

Water does not need to be heated to 100°C before it evaporates; it will evaporate from any moist surface or damp region into relatively dry airstreams, and the vapour acquires latent heat usually at the expense of the air into which the evaporation takes place.

One of the least impressive but most valuable of the meteorologist's instruments is the *wet and dry bulb hygrometer*. One of two shaded thermometers placed side by side has its bulb covered with muslin kept permanently damp by moisture creeping up through a wick dipped in water. Unless the surrounding air is saturated, water evaporates from the damp muslin and extracts latent heat from the immediate surroundings. Thus the *wet bulb thermometer* is cooled. The drier the airstream flowing past the thermometers the greater the evaporation and the bigger will be the difference betweeen the dry and wet bulb temperatures. A special slide rule or appropriate table is used to calculate the moisture content of the air from the two thermometer readings.

When water vapour condenses back into liquid form it gives up its latent heat to its surroundings. This release of latent heat has a particularly significant effect on the rate of decrease of temperature of a rising bubble of saturated air. When such a saturated bubble ascends it expands, cools and thus becomes supersaturated. Its excess water vapour condenses and gives up latent heat to the air. So the decrease of temperature is less than the dry adiabatic lapse rate described in Chapter 3. In fact the physical properties of air and water are such that the temperature of a rising bubble of saturated air decreases at about half the DALR at low levels in the atmosphere. This lapse rate, of about 0.5°C per 100 m, applicable to rising saturated air is known as the *Saturated Adiabatic Lapse Rate* (*SALR*).

The concept of stability, also introduced in Chapter 3, can be extended to cover layers of saturated air by substituting 'SALR' for 'DALR'.

Moisture measurements

There are several ways of expressing the dampness of the air. The most straightforward method is to state the *water vapour content* in grams per kilogram of dry air, but other modes of expression are sometimes more convenient. The familiar name, *relative humidity*, denotes the actual water vapour content of the air as a percentage of the amount required for saturation. Another method of expressing the moisture content of the air is to state its *dew point*; this is the temperature to which the air must be cooled (without changing its pressure) to bring it to the point of saturation.

These and other forms of expressing the dampness of the air all have their particular uses. In everyday meteorological practice the term dew point is commonly used in conjunction with temperature. But to acquire an understanding of the physical processes of weather it is often more instructive to talk and think in terms of water vapour content; this method of expression more effectively conveys the idea that air can contain and carry with it a certain amount of invisible water vapour.

5

Clouds

Ascending air expands, cools and, if the air is sufficiently moist, some of its accompanying vapour may condense into a cloud of minute water drops. Almost all clouds are born in ascending air. So the pertinent question is: what causes the air to rise? High ground? Yes, that is an obvious answer which many a mountaineer can confirm. If air blowing up a mountainside reaches its *condensation level*—the level at which cooling by ascent produces saturation—then cloud will form. Such cloud does not always hug the hill tops: sometimes it appears high in the sky, the air at low levels being relatively dry. On the other hand, it is not uncommon for the low-level air to be so moist and condensation to be so prolific that many of the tiny cloud particles coalesce into larger drops which then fall out of the cloud as rain, or if the temperature is low enough as snow. Whatever the precise effect may be, this cloud which is produced by air flowing over high ground, as illustrated in Figure 5.1, is called *orographic cloud* and any resultant rainfall is called *orographic rain*.

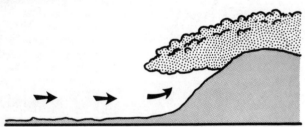

Fig. 5.1   Air flowing up a mountainside cools, and if this cooling leads to condensation then orographic cloud will form.

Convection cloud

When an airstream flows over a relatively warm land or sea surface the air at low levels is heated from below. As it is heated this air becomes lighter and buoyant—and bubbles of it begin to float up into the air aloft. When these upward convection currents are sufficient to support soaring flight in a glider they are called *thermals*. If the air aloft is relatively cold the bubbles may penetrate to heights of several thousand metres in the atmosphere, and here again the ascent will produce cooling, condensation and clouds.

As sketched in Figure 5.2, these clouds have distinctive shapes that outline the formative process. With fairly flat bases, the clouds look like puffs of cotton wool floating in the sky.

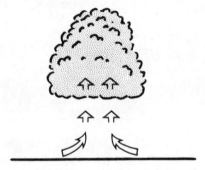

Fig. 5.2   Cloud formed by cooling and condensation in rising convection currents is of the cumulus variety.

Cumulus, as this type of cloud is called, is commonly found in sufficiently moist and relatively cool airstreams that are heated from below. Sometimes clouds are scattered and shallow, say only about 1000 ft (300 m) from base to top; sometimes they grow into *cumulonimbus* clouds that tower upwards to 30 000 ft (10 000 m) or more before spreading out into an anvil-shaped top. Dark and ominous when viewed from below, these thick convection clouds usually produce heavy showers of rain,' hail, sleet or snow and processes within the cloud sometimes generate thunder and lightning.

Cumulus and cumulonimbus are two types of *convection cloud*. Not all convection clouds are born by air rising from ground- or sea-level. Sometimes the temperature lapse rate conditions conducive to convection are created by diverse airflow patterns well above ground- or sea-level.

Plate 1   SMALL CUMULUS
Small fair-weather cumulus floating in the sky as an Olympia 419 takes off
during the 1960 World Gliding Championships at Butzweiler, Germany.

Layer clouds

In weather systems such as fronts, which are described in Chapter
6, air rises very slowly (between about 30 and 300 ft/h) over broad
areas. Again the ascent produces cooling if the air is moist enough,
but, in contrast to the convection type, this cloud forms a relatively

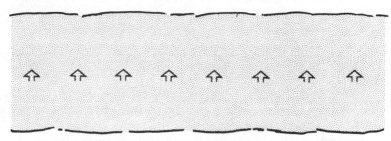

Fig. 5.3   Extensive layer cloud is produced when air is cooled and
condensed as it rises very slowly over a wide area.

Plate 2 HOOKED CIRRUS
Wisps of cirrus cloud often presage the approach of a warm front, especially when the amount of cirrus tends to increase. The cirrus clouds illustrated acquired hooked shapes as the ice crystals forming the clouds fell slowly from a strong wind stream at high levels into a weaker flow several thousand feet below.

smooth broad layer and is known as a variety of the *stratus* types of cloud.

Turbulence cloud

A third cause of air being lifted up to its condensation level is turbulence. As mentioned in Chapter 2, the friction encountered by an airstream flowing over the ground creates a layer of turbulent air from the ground up to 100 m or 200 m in light winds, and to about 3000–6000 ft (1000–2000 m) in strong winds. A sea surface produces a similar but slightly shallower effect. Unless the wind is very strong this turbulence is seldom violent, but even in a light wind, when the turbulence is little more than a gentle stirring motion, some of the air at low levels is lifted up through the turbulent layer,

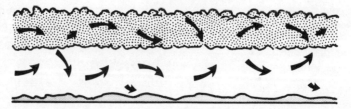

Fig. 5.4 A general stirring up of the air at low levels produces the stratocumulus type of cloud above the condensation level.

and if this lifting extends above the condensation level cloud will form in the patterns indicated in Figure 5.4.

Being somewhat a mixture between stratus and cumulus types, this cloud is called stratocumulus, but if it forms at a very low level it usually looks so grey and formless that it is called stratus.

Plate 3   CIRROCUMULUS
Patches of cirrus cloud occasionally break up into small convective elements. These elements do not normally develop into big convection clouds.

Classification of clouds

From the discussion of cloud formation we see that there are two main classes: cumiliform and stratiform. We can think of these classes as simply heap clouds and layer clouds, but we shall need to acquire some familiarity with the more formal descriptions of cloud types and structure. By international convection, based on world-wide observations, clouds are classified into ten main types. Latin names are used—cirrus (hair), cumulus (heap), stratus (layer), nimbus (shower). The principal features of the classification are described in Table 5.1 and illustrated in Figure 5.5.

Table 5.1 CLOUD CLASSIFICATION

Name	Abbrevia-tions	Description	Examples of cloud symbols used on weather charts
Cirrus	Ci	Detached white or mostly white clouds in the form of delicate filaments, or patches, or narrow bands.	
Cirrocumulus	Cc Ci–Cu	Thin white patch, sheet or layer of cloud composed of very small elements in the form of grains or ripples more or less regularly arranged; most of the elements have an apparent width of less than one degree.	
Cirrostratus	Cs Ci–St	Translucent, whitish veil of cloud generally producing halo phenomena. (Produced by refraction and reflection of light through the prismatic ice crystals of which the cirrus is formed, the most common of the halo phenomena is a white or slightly coloured ring around the sun or moon; the angle between the arc of this halo and the sun or moon is 22 degrees.)	

Table 5.1 (continued)

Name	Abbrevia-tions	Description	Examples of cloud symbols used on weather charts
Altocumulus	Ac Alto–Cu	White or grey patch, sheet or layer of cloud composed of rounded masses or rolls; most of the more or less regularly arranged small elements usually have an apparent width of between one and five degrees.	⌣⌣
Altostratus	As Alto–St	Greyish cloud sheet without halo phenomena and through which the sun is barely visible.	∠
Nimbostratus	Ns Nb–St	Grey cloud layer thick enough to blot out the sun.	⫽
Stratocumulus	Sc St–Cu	Grey or whitish patch, sheet or layer of cloud composed of rounded masses or rolls; most of the more or less regularly arranged small elements have an apparent width of more than five degrees.	⌣
Stratus	St	Generally grey cloud layer with fairly uniform base.	—
Cumulus	Cu	Detached clouds developing vertically in the form of rising mounds with cauliflower-shaped tops.	◠
Cumulonimbus	Cb Cu–Nb CuNim Cu–Nimb	Dense cloud with considerable vertical extent, in the form of a mountain or huge towers. At least part of its upper portion is usually smooth or striated, and nearly always flattened; this part spreads out in the shape of an anvil or vast plume.	△

Observations have shown that clouds are encountered over a range of altitudes varying from sea-level to the tropopause and, by convention, this range is divided into three broad levels; high, medium and low. Each broad level is defined according to the types of cloud it mostly frequently contains. We have:

Cirrus, cirrocumulus and cirrostratus at *high* levels
Altocumulus   at *medium* levels
Stratocumulus and stratus   at *low* levels

The two uppermost ranges overlap and their depths vary with latitude, the approximate limits being:

	Polar regions	*Temperate regions*	*Tropical regions*
High	10 000–25 000 ft (3–8 km)	16 500–45 000 ft (5–13 km)	20 000–60 000 ft (6–18 km)
Medium	6500–13 000 ft (2–4 km)	6500–23 000 ft (2–7 km)	6500–25 000 ft (2–8 km)
Low	0–6500 ft (0–2 km)	0–6500 ft (0-2 km)	0–6500 ft (0–2 km)

Cloud types which are not always confined to one of these three broad levels are:

Altostratus which is usually found at medium levels but often extends higher.

Nimbostratus which is almost invariably found at medium levels, but usually extends to both low and high levels.

Cumulus and cumulonimbus which usually have their bases at low levels but whose tops may reach medium or high levels.

Observed peculiarities in the shape of clouds and differences in their internal structure have led to the subdivision of most of the cloud types into various species. Three of these species are:

Altocumulus castellanus (Ac cas or Alto–Cu Cast)
Altocumulus with marked turrets, groups of which seem to be arranged in lines and connected by a common base. The term castellanus may also be applied to Ci, Cc and Sc.

Altocumulus lenticularis (Ac len or Alto–Cu Lent)
Altocumulus having the shape of lenses or almonds, often very elongated and usually with well-defined outlines.

Plate 4 CIRROSTRATUS
A halo can usually be seen around the sun when the sky is covered with
cirrostratus. On most occasions the halo is faint and may not be noticed
unless the eyes are shaded from the sun itself by a patch of cloud or the
observer's hand. The halo is very faintly coloured. Often there is a
somewhat more colourful, tangential arc at the top of the main halo, and
occasionally other rings and arcs appear.

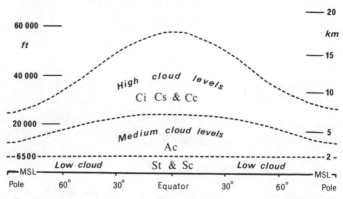

Fig. 5.5   Ranges of altitudes usually associated with the main cloud types.
Boundaries of these layers are not rigid or clear-cut. They are more in the
nature of guidelines.

Stratus fractus (St fra)
Better known as Fracto-stratus (Fr-St). Ragged stratus in irregular shreds. The prefix Fracto may also be applied to ragged Cu.

Cloud observations

At most meteorological observing stations cloud observations comprise three items: the type of cloud, the amount of cloud of this type and the height of the cloud base above the level of the observing station.

The classification of cloud types has already been described and we should note here that each type refers to the shape and not the method of formation of the cloud. This limitation may, at first, appear to be rather unscientific, but the observer seldom has sufficient information to speculate on why the cloud is there or how it attained its shape; it is wiser for him to report what he actually sees and let others interpret his observations according to their special

Plate 5 ALTOCUMULUS
The more or less regularly arranged elements of cloud are associated with gentle convection and wind shear in the cloud layer.

interests. Frequently more than one type is within view and the observer, with procedural rules and codes to guide him, makes a compromise between brevity and thoroughness in describing the state of the sky.

Cloud amount is usually reported in eighths of the sky covered; 4/8 means half covered; 8/8, completely covered. Sometimes the internationally convened word '*oktas*' is substituted for 'eighths'.

The measurement or estimation of the height of cloud base, or *ceiling*, is a task whose difficulty varies considerably with general weather conditions and local facilities. The majority of observers are obliged to make estimations, and however conscientious and experienced an observer may be, he can seldom estimate cloud height with a smaller margin of error than 20% of the actual height. Sometimes the accuracy is worse. To appreciate the difficulty of the task we must realise that our eyes are very poor range-finders; we judge distances by noting the apparent sizes of familiar objects. The

Plate 6 ALTOSTRATUS
Patches of fractostratus are seen in this picture below the grey sheet of altostratus through which the sun is barely visible. Such a sky as this often heralds the onset of rain ahead of a warm front.

method of estimating the distance away of a two-storey house or the altitude of a glider is virtually to compare the apparent sizes of these objects with the standard sizes we know them to be. But clouds are not confined to a small range of standard sizes; they range from small cloudlets to layers covering the whole sky, and so their apparent size is a fickle guide to their height or their distance away. Their apparent speed of movement is often helpful; the lower the clouds the faster they appear to move, but some idea of the wind speed at the level of cloud base is required in order to decide whether such apparent movement is due to the nearness of the cloud or whether the cloud really is moving quickly in a strong wind.

When 8/8 stratiform cloud is present estimation of its height may occasionally be little more than a plausible guess based on experience. Fortunately, the height of such cloud as this can often be found by instrumental techniques. One method involves measuring the time taken for a hydrogen-filled balloon of predetermined buoyancy to rise from the ground to cloud base. At some

Plate 7 LARGE CUMULUS
A large convection cloud towering to about 20 000 ft (6000 m) over Greece. When such clouds penetrate into a strong wind shear aloft their tops are stretched out many miles in the direction of the shear. The long bands of high cloud in this picture have emanated from cumulonimbus clouds some way to the left of this picture.

meteorological stations simple trigonometry is used to derive cloud height at night from the measured angular elevation of the patch of cloud illuminated in the vertical beam of a distance *cloud search-light*, but an increasing number of stations are equipped with various cloud height measuring devices embodying radar, pulsed light, or laser techniques. Such devices are expensive and some need judicious operators, especially on occasions when the merging of low cloud with haze or smoke makes cloud base difficult to discern or define.

Earth-orbiting satellites provide most meteorological services with daily photographs of clouds viewed from distances ranging from about 400 naut. miles (800 km) to 20 000 naut. miles (40 000 km) above the earth's surface. Satellites at about the 1000 km altitude orbit the earth once every 90 minutes, while those put into an Equatorial orbit at about 20 000 naut. miles virtually hover and keep continuous watch over a whole hemisphere.

The photographs reveal cloud patterns that are not readily detectable from networks of earthbound observation stations. However, some skill and experience are needed to interpret fine details in the photographs.

6

Visibility

Fog

On cool clear nights with little or no wind the ground loses heat by nocturnal radiation and the temperature of the ground and the air close to the ground decreases. If the cooling goes on long enough the air will become saturated with the water vapour it contains. The excess water vapour will condense and some of it will be deposited as dew on the ground, but in many cold clear night-time situations deposition of dew does not keep pace with condensation which forms a cloud of water droplets. Usually dense enough to restrict visibility to less than 1000 m, such cloud is better described as *radiation fog.*

Plate 8   VALLEY FOG
After a cold clear night, air in this Austrian valley cooled sufficiently for its water vapour to condense and form fog or low stratus. A temperature inversion exists immediately above the top of this cloud.

The initial depth of radiation fog is critically dependent on the degree of turbulence in the air. In calm conditions the condensation may be confined to a very shallow layer on the ground and the resultant *ground fog* may be less than a few feet deep. But only a slight increase in the stirring motion in the air is enough to spread the cooling up through a hundred feet or more. Not infrequently a sharp increase of turbulence occurs just after dawn when heat from the sun is just strong enough to stir up the air at low levels but not sufficient to warm the air appreciably. It is, therefore, not at all unusual for radiation fog to form suddenly just after dawn.

The clearance of radiation fog is usually effected by one of three mechanisms:

1 Heat from the sun raising the temperature of the air to above its dew point.
2 The arrival of a drier airstream.
3 An increase of wind and low-level turbulence lifting the fog which then becomes a layer of low stratus cloud.

In the absence or failure of such mechanisms the fog will persist throughout the day, and if the subsequent night is also calm and cloudless the fog will tend to deepen as a result of further nocturnal radiation from above the top of the fog out through the usually crystal clear air above.

Night cooling is not the only generator of fog. Hills and mountains may be high enough to reach into or right through a layer of cloud and the cloud on the hillside is naturally known as *hill fog*. The same description can also apply to fog formed more locally as a result of the ascent of air up the mountainsides, but the alternative name, *upslope fog*, is more specific.

Another type of fog forms when a moist airstream flows over a relatively cold land or sea surface; a moist, initially warm, south-westerly airstream flowing from the Azores toward England, for example, is cooled as it passes over the progressively colder sea surface and is liable to form fog by the time it reaches Brittany, the Channel Islands and south-west England. Naturally, such fog can be called *sea fog*, but if we wish to indicate that, unlike radiation fog which forms *in situ*, a fog arrives from somewhere we can call it *advection fog*.

Sailors of polar oceans occasionally encounter *sea smoke*, or *steam fog*, as the sea surface steams into relatively cold air above it. Steaming from lakes and rivers in cold weather or from roads in sunshine after rain gives us a glimpse of this type of phenomenon, but, since such steam can persist or thicken only in rare conditions, steam fog is mainly of academic interest.

Pollution

In densely populated industrial areas coal is burnt at the rate of about 3000 tonnes per square kilometre per year, while for even small provincial towns the annual coal consumption is often as much as 150 tonnes per square kilometre. Millions of tonnes of soot from incompletely burnt coal and particulate matter from other combustion processes together with approximately equal amounts of dust from roads and fields are deposited every year on towns and countrysides throughout the populated world. Many a large city gets over 50 tonnes per square kilometre per year and even the open country in industrialised nations receives several tonnes per square kilometre. In the interval between rising from and returning to ground-level this particulate matter restricts the visibility. Poor visibility may be expected when the pollution is dense, and this density is related not only to the proximity of the pollution source but also to the depth through which the pollution is distributed; a given amount of smoke spread throughout a depth of, say several thousand feet will restrict visibility far less than the same amount confined to a shallower layer of the atmosphere. It follows that smoke or dust haze is particularly likely under low-level temperature inversions; the conditions usually associated with such inversions inhibit the stirring up of the low-level air to above the inversion top. Thus an inversion acts as a sort of lid on whatever smoke or pollution is being injected into the air from below. If this lid is less than about 1000 ft (300 m) the concentration of pollution in very large towns can sometimes limit visibility to less than 1000 m—the conventional visibility criterion for defining fog.

The density of pollution from a source is also related to wind speed. The stronger the wind the farther will the smoke be carried from its source in a given time; thus the pollution will be dispersed throughout a greater volume of air. Light winds tend to inflict dense pollution and poor visibility close to the source of the pollution, whereas fresh winds carry and diffuse the pollution to form a relatively slight haze over a large downwind zone.

Many authorities have taken action to alleviate the dense pollution problem in cities, but sources of pollution have become more numerous and widespread during the past few decades. The net result is that in large regions, such as Europe, atmospheric pollution now has fewer pockets of dense concentrations, but has become generally more widespread.

Visibility in a polluted atmosphere is reduced not merely because of the particulate matter; chemical constituents of pollution often enhance the condensation processes that produce water droplets, and the action of sunlight on motor vehicle exhausts produces the *photochemical smog* for which Los Angeles is renowned. The word 'smog' is a colloquial condensation of 'smoke' and 'fog'. Use of motor vehicles and other oil-burning facilities is now so great that many cities and their environs throughout the world are now afflicted with the problems of smog.

In countries with large regions of low population densities, excellent visibility is often the normal, but pollution can spread hundreds of kilometres from its source. On the last day of the 1976 World Gliding Championships in Finland pollution from European sources about 1200 km away reduced horizontal visibility to 3–5 km. Smoke from bush fires and activities such as sugar cane burning can also spread over vast distances while dust or sand storms produce more local, transient and sharper deteriorations in visibility.

Visibility observations

Pilots and meteorologists are interested in both horizontal visibility and vertical, or air-to-ground, visibility. Adequate techniques are not yet generally available for measuring or forecasting the vertical visibility, and unless stated otherwise, visibility reports or forecasts normally refer only to the horizontal visibility as seen by an observer on the ground. This visibility is usually defined as the greatest distance at which objects are recognisable by an average observer, the objects being such as would be easily identified in a clear atmosphere. At some stations photo-electric methods are used to attain consistency in observation but the more common and reasonably adequate method is for the observer to use a carefully mapped set of objects or lights on which to base his estimations.

The relationship between horizontal visibility at ground-level and air-to-ground visibility is by no means simple; it depends intricately on details of the wind and temperature distributions, the nature of the pollution and the directional effect of reflection and refraction. However, experience suggests that in situations when soaring is possible within a haze layer, it is not uncommon for the air-to-ground visibility to be less than the horizontal visibility at ground-level—especially near the top of the haze layer. When horizontal visibility in smog is less than 4 km it is often difficult to see the ground from 2000 ft.

People's notions of fog usually vary according to their habitats; a countryman or small-town dweller is likely to talk of fog when the visibility is less than about 200 m and dense fog when he cannot see more than about 50 m. He is also likely to describe a situation with visibility between about 200 and 1000 m as 'misty'. The big-city dweller is likely to associate visibilities much less than 50 m with dense fog, but, being surrounded by buildings he will scarcely notice what a countryman would clearly observe as mist.

In meteorological practice the terms used to describe visibility are rigidly defined. Here is the appropriate table for aviation procedures:

Table 6.1 VISIBILITY CLASSIFICATION

Description	Visibility	Basic symbols used in weather charts
Dense Fog	Less than 50 m	
Fog	50–200 m	≡
Slight Fog	200–1000 m	
Mist (due mainly to water drops)		≡
Haze (due mainly to smoke or dust)	1–2 km	∿
		or
Poor visibility*	2–4 km ($1\frac{1}{4}$–$2\frac{1}{2}$ miles)	
Moderate visibility*	4–10 km ($2\frac{1}{2}$–$6\frac{1}{4}$ miles)	∞
Good visibility	10–40 km ($6\frac{1}{4}$–25 miles)	

* Either may be described as Slight Mist or Slight Haze.

NOTE: Several variations of the fog symbol illustrated above are used to map fog characteristics. For example, the symbol ≡ means that the fog has become thinner during the preceding hour and the sky is discernible through the top, while ≡ denotes fog in patches.

7

Fronts

If we were to use a series of successive pressure maps and plot air trajectories (like those illustrated in Figures 1.4 (a) and (b) of Chapter 1) we would find that low pressure systems in temperate and high latitudes often appear to be the meeting places for cold air from high latitudes and warmer air from the subtropics. Sometimes a cold airstream appears to impinge on a relatively warm flow—as depicted in the sequence sketched in Figures 7.1(a) and (b). The transition zone between the warm and cold air is often noticeable enough to justify a specially marked boundary on the weather map. In this example the cold air is replacing the warm air and the boundary is called a *cold front*. On weather charts drawn in colour cold fronts are shown as blue lines. On black and white charts the internationally agreed symbol is that illustrated in Figures 7.1(a) and (b). The spikes are on the warm side of the cold front—which is also the side towards which the front is moving.

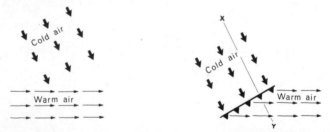

Fig. 7.1(a) The simplest way of picturing the formation of a cold front is to imagine a stream of cold air impinging on a warm air stream—as shown in the left of this diagram. The transition zone or boundary between the warm and cold air is often noticeable enough to justify a specially marked boundary on the weather map. Such a boundary is called a cold front and is indicated on black and white charts by a line with spikes on it, as indicated on the right. This figure refers to the northern hemisphere. The line XY indicates the position of cold frontal cross-sections illustrated later in this chapter. This figure together with Figs. 7.2, 7.3 and 7.4 should be viewed as a sequence to illustrate the formation of cold fronts, warm fronts and occlusions.

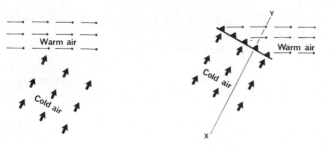

Fig. 7.1(b)   The southern hemisphere version of Fig. 7.1(a).

In such a situation as this it is usual for the speed of the cold airflow to weaken towards the west. The cold air does not continue to penetrate into the warm air; it begins to return to higher latitudes. Such a development is depicted in Figures 7.2(a) and (b). The trajectories do not always turn the same way as is sketched in this figure, but the net result is the same—the cold air retreats before the warm mass and the transition zone between these two masses is often noticeable enough to mark as a *warm front*. On weather charts in colour a warm front is drawn as a red line. On black and white

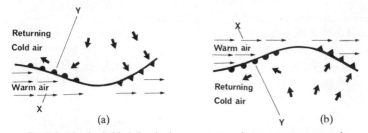

Fig. 7.2   As the cold air impinging on a warm airstream moves towards lower latitudes it sometimes tends to spread out and slow down especially in the west. It is then likely to flow back towards lower latitudes—and be followed obliquely by warm air. The boundary between warm air following cold air is called a warm front. It is indicated on black and white charts by a line with roundels as shown in this figure. (a) refers to the northern hemisphere while (b) is the corresponding pattern for the southern hemisphere. The lines XY are the lines along which cross-sections illustrate warm frontal structure later in this chapter. It should be noted that returning cold air does not necessarily move towards the west. Usually the whole system moves towards the east. Therefore the actual movement of the air is made up of this relative movement towards the west and the movement of the whole system towards the east. The net result is that the returning cold air may in fact be either a westerly or an easterly wind.

charts the internationally agreed symbol is that shown in Figures 7.2(a) and (b).

Still farther to the west a further surge of cold air is likely to make another incursion into the warm air mass, thereby producing another cold front. Thus the warm and cold front will form a *warm sector*—as illustrated in Figures 7.3(a) and (b).

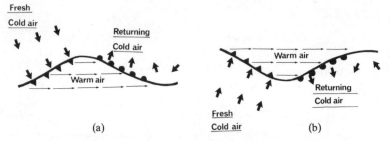

(a)   (b)

Fig. 7.3   A fresh surge of cold air following the formation of a warm front produces a sector of warm air sandwiched between the returning cold air from a previous cold outburst and the fresh cold air. (a) illustrates a northern hemisphere warm sector, while (b) illustrates the southern hemisphere pattern.

In this warm sector the warm air usually overtakes the cold air ahead of it by rising up and over this cold air, while at the following cold front the cold air tends to undercut the warmer air ahead. Thus, after its initial development the warm sector becomes narrower and the cold front catches up the preceding warm front. This is illustrated in Figures 7.4(a) and (b). When the fronts merge they are

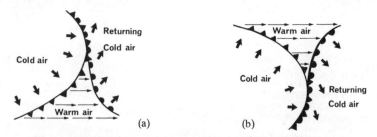

(a)   (b)

Fig. 7.4   Usually the sandwich of warm air in the warm sector becomes squeezed upwards and outwards by the cold air on either side. A cold front usually travels faster than its preceding warm front. When it catches up with the warm front the combination of the two is called an occlusion. (a) illustrates the northern hemisphere occlusion process, while (b) illustrates the southern hemisphere version.

called an *occlusion,* and are drawn as a purple line on coloured weather charts or a combination of the warm and cold front symbols as indicated in Figures 7.4(a) and (b).

Frontal cross-sections

Fronts are usually accompanied not only by temperature changes but also by characteristic three-dimensional weather and cloud structures. These structures are best visualised by taking vertical cross-sections or slices through fronts. Let us view some vertical frontal cross-sections along the dotted lines drawn from X to Y in Figures 7.1 and 7.2. Cold frontal structures can vary considerably in detail from one front to another, but cold fronts are best considered as three distinctive types:

1 *Anabatic cold fronts* (or *anacold fronts*).
2 *Subsiding,* or *katabatic, cold fronts* (or *katacold fronts*).
3 *Unstable katabatic cold fronts* (or *unstable katacold fronts*).

This terminology is not universal in the meteorological world; but if we think of anabatic as a description of rising air and subsiding as sinking air we may anticipate that these names imply active and weak cold fronts respectively in terms of cloud and rain. Katabatic also indicates sinking air, but we shall see that one type of katabatic cold front may also produce convection which means rising air.

Figure 7.5 illustrates the structure of an anacold front. In this structure the cold air is acting something like a wedge prising up the warmer air ahead. The slope of the wedge is only about 1 in 60, so that warm air ahead rises very slowly usually at less than 200 m/h on average over a broad region—but the cooling caused by ascent and expansion is enough to produce condensation and cloud. The cloud is thickest near the leading edge of the cold front and this is where some of the condensed moisture may fall out of the cloud as rain—or snow in particularly cold situations. In this particular illustration, and the other frontal cross-sections to follow, the freezing-level (where the temperature is 0°C) is included to show typical changes in level between the warm and cold air, but the general level can be higher or much lower; in very cold climates the air temperature is often below the freezing-point from ground-level upwards. Precipitation from the main cloud mass is liable to moisten

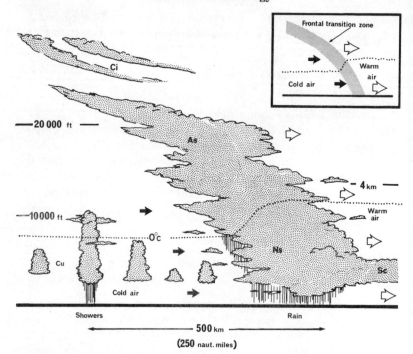

Fig. 7.5   Cross-section of an anacold front along the line XY in Fig. 7.1.
Notice that the frontal transition zone is not vertical; it slopes backwards
with height.

the air below sufficiently to produce ragged stratus cloud. As the
cold air approaches and deepens so the general cloud base rises and
the precipitation eases off.

A subsiding cold front is illustrated in Figure 7.6. Where a cold
front trails towards a region of high pressure, or when the low-
pressure system associated with the cold front begins to fill up, the
air aloft subsides and warms. Thus, it tends to dry out, and the upper
cloud disappears. The front becomes weak, and in some warm
climates it may become almost cloudless. This type of front is
sometimes called a katabatic cold front because katabatic also
means sinking air.

The structure of an unstable katacold front is sketched in Figure
7.7. In this type of cold front the simple wedge shape is transformed
into a more complicated structure. The transformation begins with

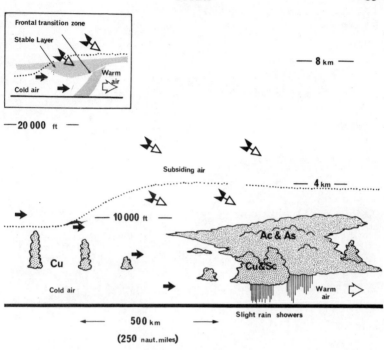

Fig. 7.6 Cross-section of a subsiding cold front. Such a front is sometimes called a katacold front.

a slow general sinking motion, or *subsidence*, in the cold air behind the frontal surface. As this subsiding air is compressed during its slow descent it becomes warmer and its relative humidity decreases. This warming also changes the wind pattern aloft in such a way that the frontal surface between the warm air and the originally cold air bulges well forward of the surface front. Thus the wedge effect that appears to lift the warm air occurs ahead of the surface position of the cold front. Often this lifting is augmented by instability and the result is a belt of cloud with rain, showers and sometimes thunderstorms. The main belt of rain or showers associated with this type of front is sometimes heralded by a line squall (described later in this chapter) and it is not always easy for an observer on the ground to be certain that the front has completely passed. However, the final clearance is often very sharp.

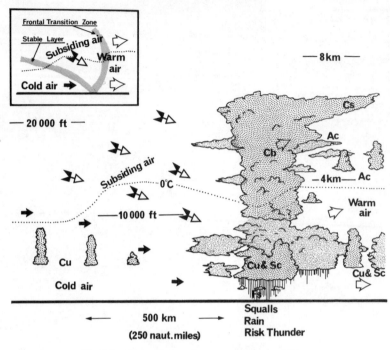

Fig. 7.7   Cross-section of an unstable katacold front.

Cold fronts tend to be of the anabatic types in cold moist climates and close to the centres of depression in lower latitudes. Katabatic types occur more in warm dry regions and not so close to low pressure centres. A cold front does not necessarily remain of one type throughout its entire length or its lifetime. In the very early stages of its development it is more likely to be an anacold front but as it matures a gradual transformation to the katacold type is not uncommon. This transformation tends to be accelerated when the front moves inland from the sea. About half of the cold fronts from the North Atlantic are katacold fronts by the time they reach central England, but almost all of them are of the katabatic form by the time they reach central Europe where they are likely to be of the unstable katabatic type, especially in summer. Anacold fronts tend to move somewhat slowly compared with the unstable katabatic type.

A typical warm frontal cross-section is sketched in Figure 7.8. One of the most significant features of a warm front is the tendency

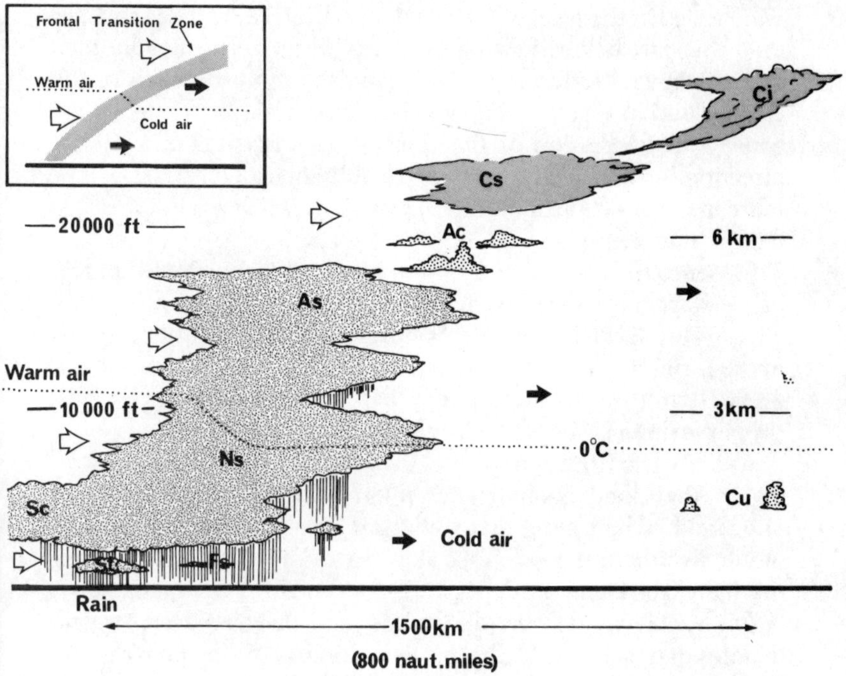

Fig. 7.8 Cross-section of an active warm front.

for the warm air to literally overtake the cold; the warm air appears to climb up and over the preceding cold air. The imaginary frontal surface, separating the warm and cold air masses, has a very gentle slope of about 1 in 180.

As the air ascends this frontal surface it is cooled by expansion and, if this air has sufficient moisture, cloud is readily produced by condensation. About 800 km (400 naut. miles) ahead of the surface front the frontal cloud is high and cold—freezing in fact. The excess moisture here produces ice crystals rather than liquid water drops, and the white wispy clouds visible in this region are easily identifiable as cirrus. These wisps owe their elongated comma shape to the sharp increase of wind with height that is usually associated with such a front. After forming in the warm moist air, the ice crystals fall—often as much as 3000–6000 ft (1000–2000 m)—slowly into the drier air below, where they eventually evaporate. But with the wind speed at the level of the cloud formation being much stronger than that just below, tails of the cirrus wisps lag far behind their quickly moving tufted tops. The schematic representation of this cirrus cloud in Figure 7.8 is not strictly accurate; it is intended to convey an impression of the cloud shape rather than a precise direction for the cloud streaks. In reality, the cloud streaks will be more in the direction of the high-level winds which will be described later in this chapter.

Closer to the front the upward motion and the moisture content of the warm air is often sufficient to produce a milky white veil of cirrostratus. Evidence that this is still ice crystal cloud often appears in the form of a halo; it is the crystals of ice formed delicately and precisely in the high atmosphere that bend the sun's (or moon's) rays to form this characteristic pattern.

As the warm front approaches, the gradual thickening and lowering of the cloud is sometimes interrupted by the presence of altocumulus, indicating that some sort of convective or irregular motion is superimposed on the slow rise of the warm air. But after this hiatus the cloud continues to thicken and lower. Soon the sun is barely visible though the altostratus, and the absence of a halo denotes that, despite its sub-zero temperature, the medium cloud is composed mostly of supercooled water drops.

Within a 150-mile (300-km) belt ahead of the front, condensation is often enough to produce not only a thick layer of nimbostratus but also a downpour of rain which begins to moisten the air at low levels. This moistening, coupled with low-level turbulence in a gradually strengthening wind, favours the formation of low fractostratus just ahead of the front. Behind most, but not all, warm fronts there is little or no general upward motion in the air at medium and high levels. Cloud in the warm sector between the warm and cold front is mostly of the low cloud types. In cool maritime climates this low cloud often forms a cover of stratocumulus, but in warmer inland climates warm sectors tend to be characterised by cumulus clouds—mostly of the small fair-weather variety, but occasionally of deeper convective types.

Just as cold fronts can be weakened by subsidence, upper cloud in warm fronts can be dried out in the subsiding air associated with rising pressure. A subsiding warm front is illustrated in Figure 7.9. This type of warm front is sometimes known as a katabatic warm

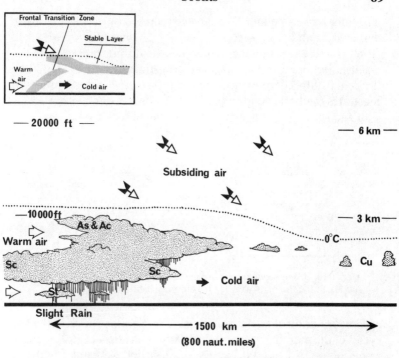

Fig. 7.9   Cross-section of a subsiding warm front.

front, but the word 'subsiding' or simply 'weak' is a better description.

Between the latitudes of about 25 and 50 degrees the warmth and moisture available introduce bigger convective elements into frontal cloud structure. In some regions, such as North Africa, Argentina, and the south and south-eastern states of the USA, instability at medium cloud levels often produce towering convection clouds and thunderstorms. The unstable katacold frontal structure is not radically changed, it already has convection clouds in its basic structure—but they are likely to be more vigorous in regions of warm climates. Many of the cold fronts that cross the southern half of Australia are sharp and vigorous, but warm fronts in this region are often weak with little or no rain.

Because an occlusion is basically the fusion of a warm front and a cold front, there is no need to illustrate its structure with an

additional cross-section. This can be visualised by putting the warm
and cold frontal cross-sections together. However, warm and cold
frontal features are not necessarily present in equal proportions. An
occlusion whose warm frontal characteristics are more evident than
the cold frontal components is called a *warm occlusion*. Figure 7.10
illustrates the basic temperature distributions across a warm occlusion and across the converse structure called a *cold occlusion*.

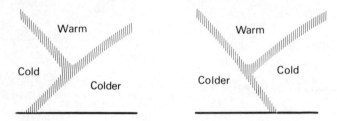

Fig. 7.10   Cross-sections of a warm occlusion (on the left) and a cold
occlusion (on the right) showing the air mass distribution only.

   The formation of an occlusion marks an ageing process in the life
cycles of the merging warm and cold fronts. As the occlusion settles
into a phase of frontal decay the once distinctive frontal features
become blurred with age and the occlusion becomes slow moving.
This is not to say that occlusions are unimportant; the decaying
process is slow, and some of the most prolonged periods of rain or
snow in temperate latitudes are produced by stagnating occlusions.
Furthermore, the warm or cold frontal features of an occlusion are
sometimes rejuvenated by temperature changes on one or both
sides of the front. Thus occlusions may be associated with weather
ranging from a broad belt of cloud with diffuse indistinct frontal
changes to patterns which resemble either warm or cold frontal
systems.

Frontal troughs

   If we recall that, except at very low latitudes, broad-scale airflow
is approximately along lines of barometric pressure, it should be no
surprise to learn that well-defined fronts usually lie along troughs of
low pressure. Figures 7.11(a) and (b) and 7.12(a) and (b) illustrate

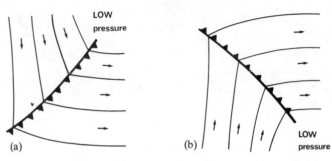

Fig. 7.11 Typical isobaric pattern across a cold front. The front is usually in a trough of low pressure. Arrows indicate the general wind flow. (a) shows the northern hemisphere pattern, while (b) shows a southern hemisphere frontal trough.

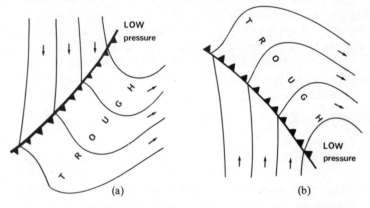

Fig. 7.12 Pressure pattern associated with an unstable katacold front. A trough of low pressure develops ahead of the original front. Sometimes this trough of low pressure becomes more pronounced than the original cold frontal trough. The arrows indicate the general wind flow. (a) shows a northern hemisphere trough while (b) sketches the southern hemisphere version.

typical northern and southern hemisphere pressure patterns associated with anacold and unstable katacold front patterns. In practice the unstable katacold frontal trough is not easy to discern in detail on a weather chart unless the front is traversing a region with a dense network of weather stations. Figures 7.13(a) and (b) illustrate the warm frontal trough.

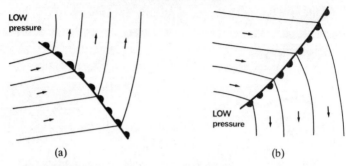

Fig. 7.13   Pressure pattern across a warm front. Such a front is normally in a trough at low pressure. (a) denotes a northern hemisphere warm front while (b) denotes the southern hemisphere pattern.

A front and its associated trough of low pressure normally move together as an entity. Therefore, barometric pressure usually falls ahead of an approaching front and steadies or rises immediately after the front has passed. The pressure fall ahead of a warm front tends to be greater than that ahead of a cold front, but the post-frontal pressure rise is sharper behind a cold front.

Upper winds

As mentioned in Chapter 2, where a temperature gradient exists between neighbouring warm and cold airstreams, the pressure pattern at high levels will be different from the MSL pattern and the resultant wind speeds and directions will also change with height. Therefore, we must expect winds to change with height near fronts. The change is usually such that winds at high levels, near the tropopause, tend to blow almost parallel to active fronts. Figures 7.14(a) and (b) and 7.15(a) and (b) show the high-level wind patterns likely to be associated with warm and cold fronts. These strong winds are often in the form of a jet—the stronger the temperature contrast across a front, the stronger is the jet.

Line squalls

The passage of some fronts, especially cold fronts, is marked by a sharp squally wind change occurring along the line of the front. During the squall the wind speed may reach gale force, at least in

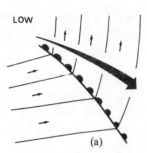 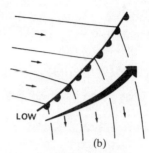

Fig. 7.14 The temperature contrast across a warm front is usually associated with a change of pressure pattern and winds with height. At low levels the wind flow in the region of a warm front is like that indicated by the small arrows in this diagram, but at high levels there is a tendency for a jet stream to form and blow in the direction indicated by the long and broadening arrows. Note the high-level wind is sometimes indicated by the movement of cirrus cloud, while low-level clouds indicate the low-level wind flow. Therefore, local observation of the relative movement of high- and low-level clouds can be used to guess whether or not warmer air is approaching. (a) and (b) indicate northern and southern hemisphere patterns respectively.

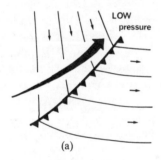 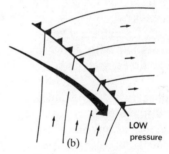

Fig. 7.15 Jet streams at high levels associated with cold fronts are likely to be in the position and direction indicated by the long broadening arrows in this figure. (a) and (b) show the northern and southern hemisphere patterns respectively.

gusts. When such a wind change and increase occur along a line it is called a *line squall*. Often the line is visible in the form of an accompanying sharp onset of rain, or a long roll of dark ominous looking cloud, or the leading edge of a dust storm. The pre-frontal trough of a katacold front is a favourable location for a line squall, especially in warm climates. But every line squall does not necessarily indicate the passage of the front. Local convective storms can

produce line squalls which are short in length, but extensive enough
to appear as a front to an observer on the ground.

Frontal terminology

One of the practical difficulties for discussing fronts is that, for
convenience, we try to use a few definite words and symbols to
represent systems which are not well defined. The word 'occlusion'
is often inadequate to convey more than a rough idea of the frontal
systems to which it is applied; in fact, Canadian meteorologists have
supplemented the frontal nomenclature with the '*trowal*' (trough of
warm air aloft) which they find useful in describing some of the
North American weather systems.

Fronts drawn on weather charts can be considered as convenient
markers with which to track the frontal type of temperature and
weather patterns we have been discussing in this chapter, and it is
often a matter of opinion and usage whether or not a particular
temperature gradient is worth calling a front. Doubt is occasionally
expressed by using such terms as *pseudo-fronts* or *trough*; the first
name is nebulously applied to weather patterns resembling but not
easily traceable as frontal evolutions, and because a front is usually
associated with a trough of low pressure the word 'trough' is
sometimes used as a coarse description of frontal phenomena.
Upper front is a term intended to refer to frontal changes above but
not at ground-level. Such upper-level changes are mostly associated
with the effects of massive mountain barriers, such as the Rocky
Mountains and the Andes, but in practice the description 'upper
front' is occasionally applied to fronts whose structure is not clear.

In some situations a front is followed closely by another front of
the same type, a cold front between warm and cold air, for example,
may be closely followed by another cold front marking the advent of
an even colder air mass. Such a pattern is sometimes described as a
double front. But this term is also applied loosely to a single
transition zone between two air masses whenever noticeable frontal
changes occur along two lines distinct enough to mark and track on
the weather maps; the two lines usually mark the leading and the
trailing edges of the 100–200 km wide frontal transition zone.
However, this ambiguity of terminology is tolerable; it is of little
practical consequence whether a double front comprises two fronts

of the same type close together or a single frontal transition zone marked by two lines on a weather map.

These frontal ramifications may appear confusing, but it is of no use pretending that they do not exist. However, we need not despair of nature's variations on the frontal theme; even the elementary concepts of fronts as simple sloping surfaces is very useful— provided that we do not let it acquire status of an unquestionable doctrine to which the weather ought to conform.

The frontal structures we have been discussing are those found in temperate and high latitudes. From latitudes of 30°N and 30°S towards the Equator convection plays an increasingly dominant role in weather and cloud formation; the warm and cold frontal structures that have been described in this chapter are not representative of frontal phenomena in the tropics.

SUMMARY OF FRONTAL CHARACTERISTICS

WARM FRONTS

WELL AHEAD OF THE WARM FRONT

1 Small amounts of cirrus at first.
2 Streaks of cirrus or the movement of cirrus may reveal that the wind veers (backs) with height in the northern (southern) hemisphere.
3 The cirrus increases to become cirrostratus likely to produce a wide halo around the sun or moon.
4 Pressure begins to fall.
5 The surface wind begins to back (veer) in the northern (southern) hemisphere.

CLOSER TO THE FRONT

1 Medium cloud appears.
2 In cool climates this medium cloud thickens and lowers. In warmer regimes the medium cloud is more likely to be of convective form.
3 The rainbelt arrives.
4 Patches of ragged low cloud may form.
5 Wind gradually increases in speed.

6 The dew point begins to rise in the rain.
7 Pressure fall becomes apparent.

AT THE PASSAGE OF THE FRONT

1 Surface wind veers (backs) in the northern (southern) hemisphere.
2 Pressure ceases to fall and becomes steady.
3 Temperature and dew point increase.
4 Rain eases off, but may be replaced by drizzle in cool maritime climates.
5 Low cloud may persist in cool maritime climates but is likely to break up and lift in warmer drier regimes.

COLD FRONTS

ANACOLD FRONT

Ahead of the front
1 Warm sector cloud:
  (a) in cold moist regimes—stratocumulus or low stratus, possibly drizzle;
  (b) in warm dry regimes—fair weather cumulus.
2 Some medium and high cloud close to the front.
3 Precipitation close to the front.
4 Pressure falling slowly.

At the passage of the front
1 Surface wind veers (backs) in the northern (southern) hemisphere.
2 Precipitation.
3 Pressure rises after falling.

Behind the front
1 Pressure continues to rise.
2 Precipitation gradually eases off.
3 Cloud base gradually rises.
4 Cloud begins to break up after precipitation ceases.
5 Visibility improves after precipitation ceases.

UNSTABLE KATACOLD FRONT

Ahead of the pre-frontal trough
1 Broken stratocumulus or fair weather cumulus.
2 Pressure falling.
3 Wind strengthens close to the front.
4 Altocumulus close to the front—castellanus type denotes vigorous convection at medium levels.

At the pre-frontal trough
1 Surface wind veers (backs) in the northern (southern) hemisphere and may be accompanied by a sharp squall with strong and gusty winds.
2 Cloudy or overcast sky.
3 Precipitation, showers, possibly thunder.
4 A drop in temperature in the rain.
5 Pressure rises sharply after falling.

Between the pre-frontal trough and the original front
1 Precipitation eases off.
2 Cloud breaks up.
3 Pressure rise eases off and may become a slight fall.

At the passage of the original front
1 Cloud breaks up almost completely.
2 Pressure rises.
3 Visibility improves.
4 Fair weather cumulus may form but not immediately.

Superimposed on the cloud and weather characteristics is a general tendency for clouds to be more stratiform in polar and temperate regions, and more convective towards lower latitudes.

8

Depressions

In Chapter 7 we noted that a well-marked front is usually associated with a trough of low pressure. In fact, the development of recognisable front (*frontogenesis*) and the development of depressions (*cyclogenesis*) usually goes hand in hand. Like many other natural phenomena, a depression with fronts is a highly complex product of a few elementary processes, each of which is not difficult to understand; the real difficulty is to unravel the pattern in which these processes are knitted into a complete depression with warm and cold fronts. The process is essentially a three-dimensional occurrence. The temperature difference across a transition zone between warm and cold air causes changes in the high-level wind flow, which reduces the atmospheric pressure, which accentuates the temperature contrast by narrowing the transition zone. We do not need to seek a deeper understanding of this process for our immediate purposes. It is sufficient to know that a low pressure centre normally develops at the tip of a warm sector. Figures 8.1(a) and (b) illustrate the typical pattern of a young depression formed in association with a warm sector. In this illustration, and the next three figures, the

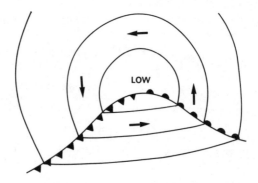

Fig. 8.1(a)   Typical pattern of a young depression formed in association with a warm sector in the northern hemisphere.

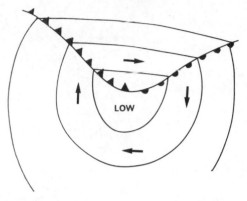

Fig. 8.1(b)   Pattern of a young frontal depression with a warm sector in the southern hemisphere.

cold fronts will be depicted as relatively simple anacold fronts. (Remember that unstable katacold fronts often have a trough of low pressure ahead of the original frontal trough.)

As a depression develops, the cold front tends to catch up with the warm front. The warm sector sandwiched between these fronts becomes narrower, and is eventually squeezed up by the occlusion process. The tail of the cold front often trails out some way behind the depression into a *cyclogenetic* zone in which another depression can form. The first sign of such cyclogenesis usually appears as a *wave* on the front. As the wave develops, so the pressure at the tip of the warm sector falls and another depression is born. This depression is called a *secondary depression*. As the secondary depression itself develops into a mature low pressure system, it is also likely to create, on its trailing cold front, a zone favourable for the birth of yet another low pressure centre. Meanwhile the original depression becomes weaker in the sense that it begins to fill up (i.e. the pressure at its centre begins to rise and its fronts become diffuse and less recognisable). Thus, in some regions, depressions tend to occur in families of between about two and five successive members. Each member matures and gives birth to an offspring before declining into obscurity. Figure 8.2(a) shows a typical pattern for the northern hemisphere. The old occluded depression is moving slowly towards the east while the next depression in the family line is still deepening and has a well-defined open warm sector. Farther

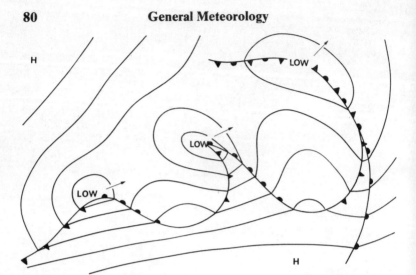

Fig. 8.2(a)   Typical pattern for a family of frontal depressions in the northern hemisphere.

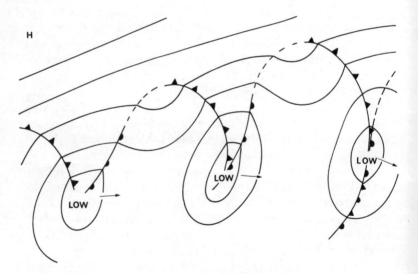

Fig. 8.2(b)   Family of frontal depressions in the southern hemisphere.

down the family tree the wave on the cold front forms the next embryonic depression. The distance between each low pressure system and its secondary depression in such a family system is usually about 1500 km or more, and each successive depression tends to move towards the east at a slightly lower latitude than its predecessor—although there are many exceptions to this tendency. The most favourable regions for families of depressions to occur are over the temperate latitudes of the Atlantic and Pacific Oceans, western Europe and the eastern half of North America.

In the southern hemisphere, the family pattern is not so well marked partly because the distribution of land and sea contributes to a slightly different style of frontal patterns, and partly because the associated warm fronts occur mostly over regions where meteorological observations are sparse. Figure 8.2(b) shows a typical sequence of frontal depressions in the southern hemisphere. The cold fronts (which are also known as *cool changes* in Australia) are often well marked in these situations, but, in contrast to the northern hemisphere patterns, the frontal linkage between one depression and the next is often difficult to trace in the southern hemisphere.

Breakaway depressions

Secondary depressions can develop not only on trailing cold fronts but also on the warm front in a frontal depression. The pattern of development is illustrated in Figure 8.3. Occasionally, when the frontal and pressure situation is like that shown on the left, a small wave and secondary low pressure centre forms suddenly on the warm front. This *warm front wave* or a *warm front breakaway depression*, as it is called, is often a short-lived, one- or two-day affair, which ripples quickly down the frontal zone away from the main depression—and often produces an inordinate amount of rainfall for such a small disturbance. When a frontal depression is somewhat elongated, like that shown on the left in Figure 8.4, there is often a tendency for a secondary low pressure system to develop at the tip of the warm sector. The subsequent pattern is like that shown on the right in this figure, but the general development is slower and lasts longer than the warm front breakaway wave sequence. This type of secondary low pressure centre is also known

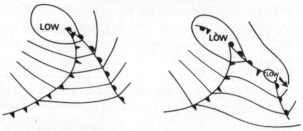

Fig. 8.3   Occasionally, when the frontal depression pattern in the northern hemisphere is like that illustrated in the left-hand section of this diagram and when the jet stream associated with the warm front is strong, a warm front breakaway depression forms on the warm front—like that shown in the right-hand section of the diagram. Warm front breakaway depressions in the southern hemisphere do not appear to be so common, but this may be due to the sparse observational network over the southern oceans.

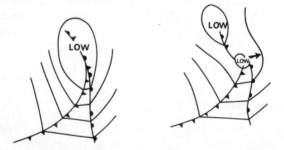

Fig. 8.4   When the frontal depression configuration is like that shown in the left-hand section of this diagram and when the jet stream associated with the cold front is fairly strong a secondary depression occasionally forms at the tip of the warm sector—like that shown in the right-hand section of this figure. This diagram depicts a northern hemisphere sequence. This occurrence does not appear to be so common in the southern hemisphere, but this may be due to the sparseness of observations over the southern oceans.

Plate 9   SATELLITE CLOUD PICTURES
This composite of four photographs taken by a *Nimbus* satellite covers an area from just north of the Great Lakes of North America to Venezuela. Notice the band or streaky structure of the clouds in many areas. Over northern Florida a hurricane (labelled *Cleo*) shows the typical pattern of cloud streets spiralling in towards the centre of such a storm.

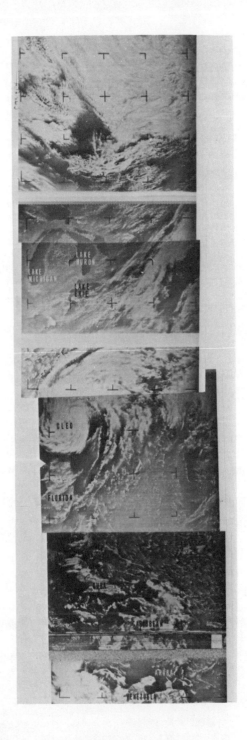

as a *breakaway depression*, but it is not unusual for this type of breakaway depression to grow while the primary low pressure centre gradually fills up.

Tracks of depressions

Frontal depressions move, in a very broad sense, from west to east. Superimposed on this general movement is a tendency for these systems to follow paths that curve mostly towards higher latitudes, and very occasionally towards lower latitudes.

Polar lows

Not all depressions are associated with the frontal patterns typified by the examples just described. In cold showery airstreams from polar regions it is not unusual to find a small depression (of about 100–200 km in diameter) moving towards lower latitudes. These small depressions are usually accompanied by showers of rain or snow and occasionally have what appears to be a cold front extending outwards from the low pressure centre towards the west. Such a depression is called a *polar low*. From the forecasting point of view, it is a troublesome phenomenon; it can develop suddenly; it is usually too small to be tracked through a coarse network of observations (such as that over the sea) yet it is often active enough to produce appreciable rain or snow in what might otherwise be a cold airstream with scattered showers and bright periods.

In the northern hemisphere polar lows occur occasionally in cold climatic regions, and they are also liable to develop over inland seas such as the Mediterranean and the Black Sea when cold showery airstreams sweep across their shores from the north in winter.

Thermal depressions

Stagnant low pressure systems, without fronts, tend to develop over land masses which become hotter than their neighbouring seas. A depression over the Iberian Peninsula is a common feature of the weather map from about May to September. Over England a small depression superimposed on the general isobaric pattern can sometimes be detected on a hot summer's day. Such depressions as these are called *thermal depressions, thermal lows* or *heat lows*.

Thundery depressions

Some thermal lows are associated with upper wind and temperature distributions which lead to the formation of widespread thunderstorms at medium and high cloud levels. These low pressure systems often develop as the extension of a trough of low pressure from a warm or subtropical region towards higher latitudes. Once developed, they move very slowly and somewhat erratically. They are usually non-frontal but nonetheless can produce prolonged periods of rain and thunderstorms, which is why they are called *thundery depressions* or *thundery lows*. These slow-moving thundery depressions are common summer-time features of the weather of central Europe where spells of fine hot weather are liable to be interrupted by periods of thundery rain lasting as much as several days at a time. They are also features of regions, such as north-east Australia, where the extensions of summer-time subtropical low pressure systems bring prolonged and heavy thundery rain southwards. Figures 8.5(a) and (b) show examples of thundery depressions.

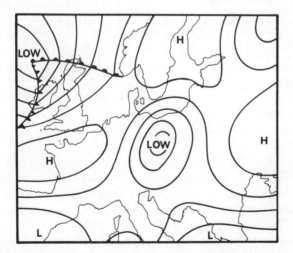

Fig. 8.5(a)   Thundery depression in summer-time over central Europe. Such a depression can produce broad areas of thundery rain for several days at least.

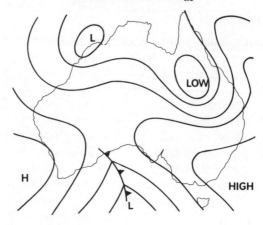

Fig. 8.5(b) An extension or development of a low pressure system
southwards over Australia in summer-time can often produce overcast
conditions with frequent thundery rain for periods of several days.

Lee depressions

When a fresh or strong airstream crosses a broad mountain range,
it is not uncommon for a trough of low pressure or a depression to
form on the lee side of the high ground. Such a depression is known
as a *lee depression* or *lee low*. Occasionally these depressions are
associated with fronts and they develop into frontal depressions, but
most lee depressions are small entities that do not have frontal
characteristics and last only as long as the main airstream blows
across or is partially blocked by the mountain range. Figure 8.6
illustrates a non-frontal lee depression created in a northerly airstream partly blocked by the Swiss Alps.

Air masses

It is natural that some regions of the world make better birth-
places for fronts and depressions than others. The general favourability of the region depends upon the distribution of land and sea,
the effect of mountain valleys, the ocean currents which largely
control the sea temperatures, and the very broad-scale global wind
systems. The eastern seaboard of North America happens to be a
favourable zone, so does the Norwegian Sea and the Mediterranean

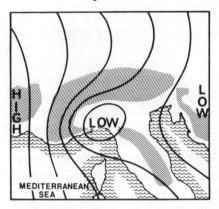

Fig. 8.6   A non-frontal lee depression created in a northerly airstream partly blocked by the Swiss Alps.

(though not so much in the summer). Fronts which originate in these regions are sometimes called *Polar, Arctic,* and *Mediterranean fronts* respectively while some of the air masses either side of them are given such labels as *Polar maritime* (to denote cold air from over the sea) or *Arctic* (even colder) or *Tropical continental* (warm from the land). These names are convenient labels for air masses that have distinctive broad-scale characteristics relating to their source regions and paths along which they travel. A complete knowledge of the labels used in air mass classification is not necessary for an understanding of meteorological phenomena; it is sufficient for our purposes to know that *Arctic, Polar, Tropical, Equatorial* virtually mean very cold, cold, warm, very warm and that *maritime* and *continental* denote moist (usually from over the sea) and dry (usually from over the land). Polar air that has moved to lower latitudes then turned towards higher latitudes again is sometimes labelled as *returning Polar air,* and an air mass which has had its distinctive characteristics changed slightly by moving over another type of terrain sometimes has the word *modified* included in its label; for example, cold damp air that becomes warmer or drier after it has moved some way inland may be labelled *modified Polar maritime.*

Climatologists often use the first letter of these air mass labels as a convenient shorthand. *Arctic, Polar, Tropical* and *Equatorial* are denoted by the letters *A*, *P*, *T* and *E* while *c*, *r* and *m* stand for *continental*, *returning*, and *maritime* or *modified*. For example, *rPm* means *returning Polar maritime*; *mPc* stands for *modified Polar continental*; *Tc* is *Tropical continental*. The letter *M* is occasionally used to indicate Mediterranean air or monsoon air (usually taken to be warm, moist, rain-bearing airstreams that invade some tropical land masses). A supplementary letter is sometimes tacked on to the abbreviated air mass labels to indicate whether the air mass is moving over relatively warmer or colder land or sea. The letter *k* is added to denote that the air mass is moving over relatively warm land or sea, and *w* is used to label an airstream moving over a relatively cold land or sea surface. Thus, *Pck* denotes Polar continental air moving over a warmer surface; *Tmw* indicates Tropical maritime air moving over cooler land or sea.

Although air mass labels are convenient for many purposes, they can surreptitiously instil into the unwary the misleading idea that a front is some sort of perfectly elastic membrane always and forever more separating discrete masses of air drawn from a few exclusive sources. The temperature and moisture characteristics of an air mass may be approximately uniform over some considerable area, but it is never normally completely uniform; it usually contains variations that may be slight in relation to the broad-scale weather pattern but significant in their effect on soaring conditions.

9

Anticyclones

Although the word cyclone is often thought of as referring only to strong winds, by definition it can be applied to the circulatory wind flow around any depression and, because the wind flows in the opposite direction around high pressure centres, the word anticyclone is a logical synonym for a region of high pressure.

An anticyclone is the antithesis of a depression in more than just wind direction. The particular features of anticyclones that are in direct contrast to the characteristics of low pressure systems are:

1 The build-up of a high pressure system (*anticyclogenesis*) is favoured by the weakening, rather than the strengthening, of a thermal gradient; that is to say, high pressure systems are more likely to form in air masses well away from active fronts.
2 The interaction between the high- and low-level winds in an anticyclone is such as to weaken the thermal gradient even more.
3 The development of a high pressure system is likely to be a decelerating process leading towards stagnation.
4 Inflow of air occurs at high levels over anticyclones while outflow occurs at low levels, the two flows being linked by a slow downward motion (*subsidence*) of the air in between.
5 Surface winds are generally light in an anticyclone (though they can be strong on the outskirts of the high pressure region).

Warm and cold anticyclones

Illustrated in Figures 9.1(a) and (b) are two types of regions favourable for anticyclogenesis. The principal difference between them is that one is on the warm side of the front and the other is in the cold air. When a high pressure centre develops it can be called a *warm anticyclone* or a *cold anticyclone* according to whether it contains warm or cold air. The distinction is not without some

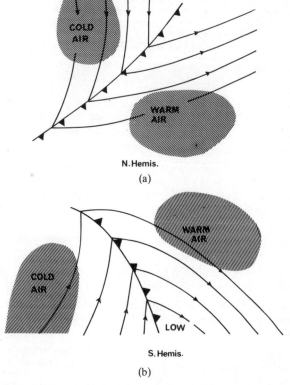

Fig. 9.1(a) and (b)   Anticyclones tend to form either in the warm air towards the Equatorial side of a warm sector, or in the cold airstream on the polar side of a cold front.

significance; upper winds are liable to increase with height over (and especially towards the cold side of) a warm anticyclone, while cold anticyclones are noted more for light winds aloft.

Another distinction between the two types concerns their persistence. By weakening the thermal gradients in its vicinity, an anticyclone tends to inhibit further pressure changes; so that once formed, a high pressure system tends to block the development and progress of the more active depressions, but the temperature and pressure of a cold anticyclone forms a much less efficient block than that of a warm high pressure cell. Therefore, while a warm high

pressure system may persist for days, weeks, or even months, a cold
anticyclone is more often seen as a relatively flexible and mobile
feature of the weather map. This is not to say that cold anticyclones
are never persistent; they do in fact persist for long winter spells
inland over large continents, but not without some fluctuations; a
cold winter anticyclone, such as the Siberian high, is liable to suffer
more low pressure incursions than a warm system such as the
Azores anticyclone. Figures 9.2(a) and (b) comprising average MSL
pressure maps for January and July, show both the winter tendency

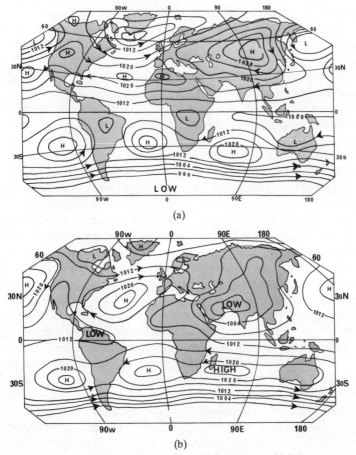

(a)

(b)

Fig. 9.2   Mean MSL pressure in (a) January and (b) July.

for high pressure to prevail inland over large continents and the general tendency for high pressure regions to predominate over the oceans in two subtropical belts which migrate north and south with the sun.

Effects of subsidence

Subsidence of air in an anticyclone usually takes place in a height range between 5000 and 20 000 ft (1500 and 6000 m). It is a very slow process—so slow that it is practically impossible to measure the downward airspeeds directly. However, rates of descent of the air have been inferred from various meteorological observations. Subsidence as slow as 100 ft (30 m) per day, or even less, is typical.

Slow though it is, subsidence is the vital link in the chain of events that leads to anticyclonic weather. The subsiding air is compressed and warmed—at the saturated or dry adiabatic lapse rate according to whether or not it is saturated with water vapour. Unsaturated subsiding air becomes appreciably warmer while its relative humidity decreases. Saturated subsiding air is warmed by compression more slowly than dry air. Therefore, if subsidence operates on a region containing a layer of cloud, a temperature inversion is likely to be established as the air above the cloud top is warmed by descent more than the air in the cloud itself. If this layer of cloud persists during the night and if, as is usually the case, the sky above it is clear, then the top of the cloud will cool by nocturnal radiation, just as the ground cools under cloudless night skies. So the inversion of temperature above the cloud top will be accentuated, and the cooling by radiation at the cloud top can easily counteract the warming by subsidence. Thus, the layer of stratocumulus that exists in such a situation tends to persist, particularly in winter-time anticyclones. The stratocumulus sheets are variable in horizontal extent and, being dependent on the state of balance or unbalance between several factors, the stratocumulus is liable to form or disperse somewhat erratically. Occasionally, however, the stratocumulus persists and covers the sky for one or perhaps several days and deserves its name *anticyclonic gloom*. Sometimes the stratocumulus sheet has a distinctive pattern of tongues, like those sketched in Figure 9.3. Such patterns are usually on too small a scale

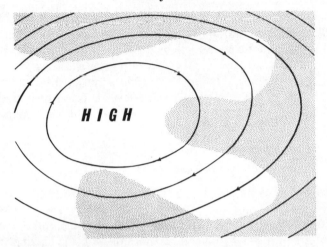

Fig. 9.3 This figure illustrates a northern hemisphere pattern. Sometimes cloud cover, mainly on the high-latitude side of an anticyclone has a
distinctive pattern of tongues like that indicated by the shaded area in this
figure. Such tongues are often about 100–200 km across.

to be identified on routine synoptic charts, but too large a scale to be
recognised by an observer at one spot.

In warm or hot weather the warming by subsidence in an anticyclone is far more likely to cause the cloud layer to evaporate,
leaving clear skies, apart from occasional incursion of cirrus or
patches of medium cloud. Then convection currents, or *thermals*,
are likely to develop which will eventually reach up to the base of
the subsidence temperature inversion. These thermals are often
dry, but they may be capped by fair weather cumulus especially in
warm or hot climates. In temperate latitudes about 20% of anticyclones limit thermal development to about 3000 ft (1000 m) or less;
65% confine convection motion to below about 6000 ft (2000 m);
and 15% permit some convection to heights over 6000 ft (2000 m).
In warmer climates, these depths of convection are usually higher;
convection to 6000–8000 ft (2000–2500 m) is frequent, and heights
of 10 000–15 000 ft (3000–5000 m) is not unusual in warm dry
climates—though we should note that even in hot climates there are
occasions when temperature inversions limit convection to below
3000 ft (1000 m).

As mentioned in Chapter 6, an inversion acts as a sort of lid on pollution injected into the atmosphere from below; the lower the height of this lid the poorer will be the visibility. Persistent haze or pollution in or near industrial or built-up areas is, therefore, common in anticyclonic conditions. With an inversion base at about 3000 ft (1000 m) visibility at ground-level is often restricted to 2–5 km over extensive areas in and downwind of large conurbations.

Transient ridges of high pressure

Broadly speaking, the higher the pressure in an anticyclone the greater the likelihood that prolonged subsidence has occurred and that the anticyclone will be particularly persistent. But the rate of rise of pressure has an inverse relationship with the likelihood of persistent subsidence and continued anticyclonic development. When the rise of pressure is fast, say over 4 mb in 3 hours (the conventional period of time for routine observation of pressure tendencies), there is practically no chance of persistent subsidence or a prolonged anticyclonic spell. But when the pressure rise is slow, about 1 mb in 3 hours, there is more likelihood of subsidence and the slow development of a persistent anticyclone.

The explanation of this apparent paradox that pressure rises are not good indicators of persistent subsidence, and anticyclonic development is that such rises are associated more with the movement of pressure systems than with the actual formation of an anticyclone. The pressure at a place in the path of an active depression falls quickly as the depression approaches and rises after it has passed, but experience shows that the rapid rise is likely to be short-lived; it soon gives way to a fall ahead of the next low pressure system in the family of depressions. Thus, the ridge of high pressure between two depressions is often as mobile as the depressions themselves. It must not be inferred that all ridges are mere passengers in the trains of successive depressions; the point being made here is that rapid pressure rises usually denote transient ridges of high pressure while the slower but more persistent pressure rises are better predictors of more durable anticyclones.

10

Tropical Weather

As we approach low latitudes the effect of the earth's rotation on wind speeds and directions decreases—it becomes zero at the Equator. Winds at latitudes less than about 15–20 degrees do not flow mainly along the isobars of pressure systems. They flow more across isobars from high to low pressure, but pressure gradients themselves are mostly weak and changeable; local pressure gradients are created by diurnal heating and cooling, while regional patterns of weak pressure changes are usually swamped by semi-diurnal and larger-scale pressure oscillations in the tropics. These semi-diurnal oscillations are a form of atmospheric tide which raises and lowers pressures in the tropics—from a minimum at about 04.00 solar time to a maximum at about 10.00 hours, then down to a low again at 16.00 hours, and up to a second high point at 22.00 solar time. (Solar time in this book is taken to be 12.00 hours when the sun is at its highest for the locality.) The range of the double pressure oscillation is 2–3 mb.

On the broad climatological scale, a weak trough of low pressure, known as the *Equatorial Trough*, girdles the earth close to the Equator, and migrates annually north and south following the sun. The climatological pattern of winds blowing in towards this trough is a convenient framework on which to build an overall picture of tropical weather. Figures 10.1(a) and (b) show the broad-scale wind systems for January and July. The converging north-easterly *trade winds* in the northern hemisphere tropics and south-easterly trade winds in the southern tropics flow from belts of high pressure sketched in Figure 9.2 of Chapter 9. The zone where these two sets of trade winds meet is called the *Intertropical Convergence Zone* (ITCZ) or *Intertropical Front* (ITF)—the ITCZ is the more appropriate of these two labels. In Figures 10.1(a) and (b) we see that the seasonal range of movement of this ITCZ varies considerably around the earth. Over south-east Asia it ranges from just south of the Equator in January to well north of the Tropic of Cancer in July,

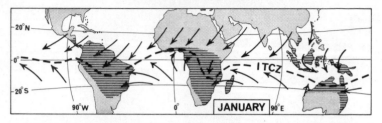

Fig. 10.1(a)   Typical January position of the Intertropical Convergence Zone (ITCZ). Areas shaded with the horizontal lines are those particularly prone to tropical rainfall associated with the ITCZ and moist tropical airstreams from the sea. Arrows show the prevailing trade winds.

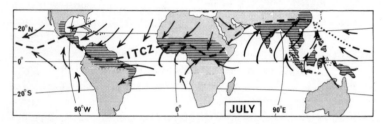

Fig. 10.1(b)   Typical July position of the Intertropical Convergence Zone (ITCZ). Areas shaded with the horizontal lines are particularly prone to tropical rainfall associated with the ITCZ and moist onshore tropical airstreams.

while over the eastern Pacific it does not move far from its mean position, just north of the Equator. Notice that when the trade winds cross the Equator they tend to turn towards the east; the SE trade winds over the Indian Ocean for example turn to become south-westerlies north of the Equator. Trade winds that have a long land track over a continent usually bring dry and sunny conditions, while winds blowing inland from the oceans mostly bring wet and cloudy weather—to the regions shaded in Figures 10.1(a) and (b). Clouds in the humid airstreams are mostly of the convective type— large cumulus, altocumulus and cumulonimbus—but widespread ascent of air in convergence zones and spreading out of convective cloud often produces layer clouds, while rainfall from those clouds often moistens the air at low levels sufficient to form ragged low stratus.

Although the ITCZ and the associated rainfall regions are sketched by the horizontal lines in Figures 10.1(a) and (b), the ITCZ should not be viewed as some sort of continuous elastic membrane neatly separating opposing trade winds; nor should the shaded areas be interpreted as regions of continuous tropical downpours. Figures 10.1(a) and (b) and the discussion so far should be seen as an introductory global framework on which to picture tropical systems. In reality the actual weather systems are more variable and less precise than the climatological patterns may suggest, and the individual continental and oceanic tropical regions each have their own superimposed characteristics.

Easterly waves

Before discussing individual regional characteristics we must supplement the introductory ITCZ concept with a look at a class of weather systems that are particularly significant in the tropics.

Over the Atlantic and Pacific Oceans in the Equatorial easterlies north of the ITCZ, weak waves—like those sketched in Figure 10.2—are liable to form at intervals of between about 4–6 days in

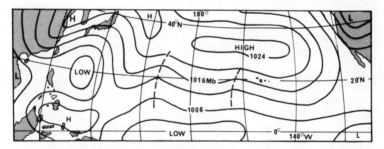

Fig. 10.2   The broken lines denote troughs of low pressure, otherwise known as easterly waves. The two easterly waves in this illustration are moving towards the west.

time and 1500–2500 km in distance in the summer and autumn. These waves are mostly known as *easterly waves,* but they are sometimes called *wave disturbances* or *transverse waves* in the trades. Moving towards the west at about 10 knots (20 km/h), these waves carry the weather and cloud characteristics shown in Figure 10.3 to the oceanic islands and the coastal zones of the downstream land masses bordering the two oceans.

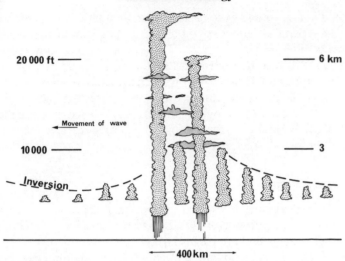

Fig. 10.3   A west–east weather and cloud cross-section across an easterly wave in the tropics. Away from the wave cumulus cloud is limited in depth by a temperature inversion in the trade winds.

Well ahead of the trough weather is fine with streets of scattered cumulus cloud whose vertical development is limited by a *trade wind* temperature inversion at about 4000–6000 ft (1300–2000 m).

Close to the trough line the cumulus develops in vertical extent and produces some showers.

Behind the trough line a veer (in the northern hemisphere) in the wind heralds large cumulus or cumulonimbus with thundery showers and a drop in temperature.

Well behind the trough the weather and cloud characteristics gradually revert to the small trade wind cumulus type.

During the winter and spring, anticyclonic subsidence over these oceanic regions tends to suppress deep convection and thereby inhibit easterly wave formation.

It is likely that easterly waves also develop occasionally over the oceans south of the ITCZ in the southern hemisphere summer and autumn, but they do not appear to be a common occurrence and have not yet been well documented. In the southern hemisphere winds would back at the passage of the trough line.

Tropical cyclones

Most easterly waves form, produce their characteristic wind weather and cloud pattern—some well marked, some weak—then fade away, especially if they move inland over a large land mass. But a few of these easterly waves mature into low pressure systems— like that mapped in Figure 10.4. At this stage convection clouds in the system are deep and widespread. Pressure in the centre of the convective region has fallen, and winds circulate around the low pressure centre—much as they do around a temperate latitude depression. These circulating winds become fresh or strong and the whole system is called a *tropical depression*.

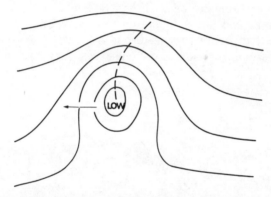

Fig. 10.4   Some easterly waves mature into low pressure systems, like that illustrated in this diagram. They continue to move towards the west.

A few of these tropical depressions become more intense. The central pressure continues to fall and wind speeds continue to increase. If the wind speed exceeds 33 knots (61 km/h) the system becomes conventionally known as a *tropical storm*.

If the intensification continues and the wind speed gets to 62 knots (115 km/h) or more the system is classed as a *tropical cyclone*—but the names adopted regionally are *hurricane* in the Caribbean, *typhoon* in the north-west Pacific, and *cyclone* in the southern hemisphere.

At this tropical cyclone stage, weather and cloud structure in the northern hemisphere are like that illustrated in Figures 10.5(a) and (b). Bands of deep convective clouds spiral in towards a central eye, which has relatively thin and sometimes well-broken cloud. The wind at low levels is strongest in a ring around this central, practically calm eye. Figure 10.5(c) shows the variation of wind speed across a line through the eye. In the southern hemisphere, tropical cyclones have the same kind of vertical cloud structure and the same characteristics such as the intense low pressure pattern and hurricane-strength winds around an almost calm eye, but the circulation is the opposite direction. The wind circulation and spiralling of the cloud bands in towards the storm centre are clockwise in a southern hemisphere tropical cyclone. Tropical cyclones do not bring gliding weather; they bring winds strong enough to tear roofs off houses and hangars that are not adequately designed for cyclones; they bring exceptionally high tides with destructive waves to lee shores and floods in the wake of torrential rain. So, to appreciate the precautions needed to safeguard themselves and their property, inhabitants of cyclone-prone districts should learn

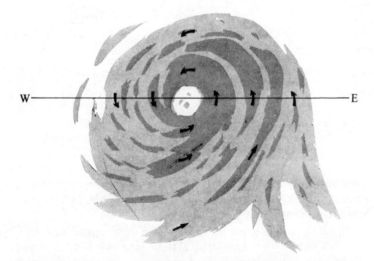

Fig. 10.5(a) Schematic sketch of cloud and rain areas associated with a typical northern hemisphere hurricane. The cloud and rain areas tend to form in bands spiralling around and inwards towards a central eye which is often comparatively clear of cloud. Arrows in this diagram denote the general wind circulation around the hurricane. Typical cloud and wind speed distributions along the transect labelled W–E are illustrated in Figs. 10.5(b) and 10.5(c).

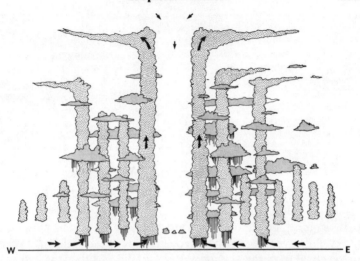

Fig. 10.5(b) Characteristic weather and cloud cross-section across a tropical cyclone. The central eye, with broken and relatively shallow cloud, is ringed by towering cumulonimbus clouds. In this schematic illustration the width of the central eye is somewhat exaggerated compared to the width of the tropical cyclone as a whole. Air at low levels spirals in towards the big convective clouds then up and out of the tropical cyclone at high levels.

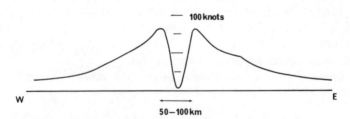

Fig. 10.5(c) Typical cross-section of wind speed distribution across a tropical cyclone. The W–E line corresponds to the similarly marked line in Figs. 10.5(a) and (b).

something of the structure and behaviour of these destructive weather systems.

Figure 10.6 shows the tropical cyclone regions of the world and typical tracks. These tropical cyclones normally move westwards while forming, then, when they are well developed, curve towards higher latitudes. As this curving of the track continues the cyclone's

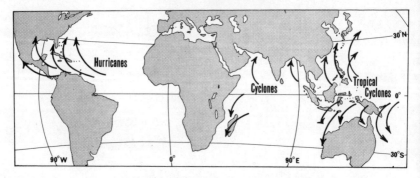

Fig. 10.6   Tropical cyclone regions of the world and typical tracks.

path acquires a component towards the east, but if this path takes
the cyclone over land the system begins to collapse; if the path keeps
the cyclone over the sea the system gradually broadens and may
dissipate slowly or acquire the characteristics of a deep temperate
latitude depression as it moves into higher latitudes. In the jargon of
tropical cyclone forecasting, the path of a tropical cyclone is often
said to *recurve* as it swings towards higher latitudes and turns
towards the NE in the northern hemisphere, or SE in the southern
hemisphere.

The reason why tropical cyclones do not persist far inland is that
the energy that keeps them going comes from the latent heat of
water evaporated from the sea. So when a tropical cyclone moves
inland its energy supply is quickly cut off.

Tropical cyclone seasons are summer and autumn (fall in North
America).

Continental effects

Because diurnal heating and cooling of land surfaces and the
availability of moisture play such significant roles in low latitudes
the distribution of land and sea superimposes continental characteristics on tropical climate.

Over the Indian subcontinent the contrast between the dry air
from the Asian interior to the moist summer air from the south is so
noticeable that the name *monsoon* (from the Arabic word *mausim*,
meaning season) is used to describe the climate. The transition

between the dry and rainy seasons, however, is not so sharp or predictable as implied in some popular misconceptions of tropical weather; monsoon rainfall can vary considerably from year to year.

The climatological flow pattern over south-east Asia in January is illustrated in Figure 10.7(a). This figure also shows the 10 000-ft (3000-m) wind pattern, which differs markedly from the low-level flow. The interplay between dissimilar high- and low-level winds and vertical air motion in the tropics is somewhat complex and makes it difficult to understand tropical weather systems by looking at a pressure or wind pattern at one level only.

Air subsiding in the upper westerly flow south of the Himalayas is a source of the dry northerlies over Pakistan and India, though the upper westerlies steer an occasional depression and cold front from the Mediterranean or the Middle East into Pakistan and northern India. Some of these depressions skirt the southern Himalayas and become rejuvenated as they approach eastern China. Winter-time China is also affected by depressions steered by the upper westerlies along the northern flank of the Himalayas. In the wake of these

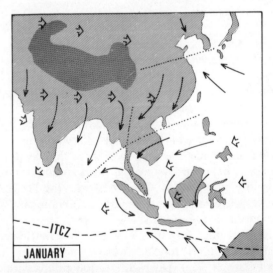

Fig. 10.7(a) Typical January position of the ITCZ south of south-east Asia and minor convergence zones (denoted by the dotted lines). The open arrows denote typical 10 000-ft (3000-m) wind pattern, which differs markedly from the low-level flow denoted by the long arrows.

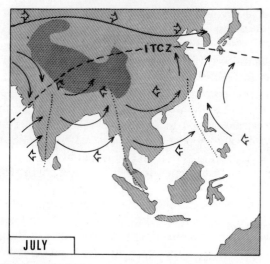

Fig. 10.7(b)   Typical July position of the ITCZ and minor convergence zones (dotted lines) over south-east Asia. Winds at low levels are denoted by the long arrows, while the high-level flow is indicated by the shorter open arrows.

depressions come the cold *buran* blizzards of Mongolia and Man-churia (comparable with the *northers* of central USA).

The easterly winds flowing between about 5 and 15°N produce convection clouds and convective storms over the Philippines, the Vietnamese coast and Malaysia, but inland, from central Vietnam to Thailand, they are mostly dry. Variations from the broad-scale flow sometimes produce bands or zones of convergence marked by convection clouds and occasional showers or thunderstorms. Con-vergence zones between low-level airflows from different sources are shown in Figure 10.7(a). Compared with the ITCZ these are minor convergence zones; they are not uncommon, but they are by no means permanent features of the flow pattern.

From January until July the ITCZ migrates northwards across south-east Asia, until, by July, it reaches its most northerly position shown in Figure 10.7(b). Deep convection clouds with thunder-storms are likely in and near the convergence zone—as sketched in Figure 10.8. Large convection clouds, and thunderstorms, are also likely to occur in the warm moist air south of the ITCZ—

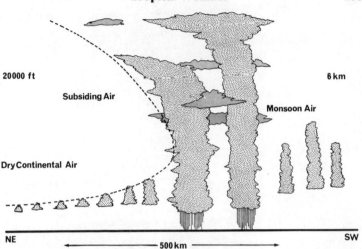

20000 ft   6 km

Subsiding Air

                                            Monsoon Air

Dry Continental Air

NE   SW
←——————— 500 km ———————→

Fig. 10.8 Typical NE–SW cross-section through the ITCZ over India. Close to the coast moist onshore winds are liable to produce somewhat more cloud.

particularly in subsidiary convergence zones also shown in Figure 10.7. These subsidiary convergence zones are less persistent than the ITCZ. They vary in intensity and position from day to day, and sometimes they appear to be associated with troughs of low pressure or *monsoon depressions*, which occur two or three times a month and move eastwards across India.

To the east, over China, the summer monsoon rains spread farther north, but the position and role of the ITCZ is not clear, as it is often distorted by, or merged with, the formation of thundery depressions.

Japan also has, in the *Bai-u* season, south-east monsoon rains from easterly waves, convergence zones and monsoon, or thundery, depressions. But the rainy season is interrupted by longer sunnier spells in July and August, before the *Shurin* season of September and October, when more thundery rain is likely to be supplemented by rain from low pressure systems, including typhoons.

The migratory ITCZ and subsidiary convergence zones are also features of the African continent. Figures 10.9(a) and (b) show typical January and July positions of these zones. Here, too, convection showers and thunderstorms occur mainly in or near these

Fig. 10.9(a) January position of the ITCZ and a minor convergence zone (dotted line) over Africa. The arrows denote the low-level flow pattern.

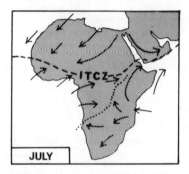

Fig. 10.9(b) July position of the ITCZ and a minor convergence zone (dotted line) over Africa. The arrows denote the low-level flow pattern.

convergence zones and in the warm humid airstreams from the ocean, but as in all other tropical areas, topography plays an important part; it superimposes both orographic rainfall and sheltering effects on the cloud and weather systems. Chapters 11 to 17 of this book deal with the effects of topography in some detail, but here, we can at least note that both high ground and coastlines have particularly pronounced effects on rainfall in the tropics where hot humid airstreams are frequent.

Between about 10 and 35° N and S, the western shores of the world's continents are bordered by cool sea-currents. Warm air flowing over the cold water is cooled, and, if the air contains sufficient moisture, sea-fog or very low stratus is likely to form by the time the air reaches the coast. Where mountain ranges such as the Andes tend to block a deep inland penetration of such air, the lowland coastal belts are subject to cool and foggy sea-breezes with local pollution concentrated under a temperature inversion at about 1500–4500 ft (500–1500 m). The Pacific coasts of Columbia, Peru, Chile and the coastal strip at the foot of the Namib Escarpment, in South West Africa, are particularly prone to such conditions. The Californian coast also experiences sea-fog and very low stratus at times in airflows coming from over the adjacent cold sea-currents. Thus, even though tropical and subtropical weather is mostly warm or hot, it also has its share of cloudy, clammy, non-gliding conditions.

Gliding Meteorology

11

Airflow over Hills

When the wind blows across a hill ridge air rises on the windward slopes. When such air rises fast enough to support a glider in flight it is called *hill lift*, and the technique of gliding in hill lift is known as *hill soaring*. As in most aspects of gliding, actual experience is the best guide to efficient hill soaring, but as a prelude to acquiring such experience, or as an aid to interpreting experience already accrued, it is instructive to consider the theoretical distribution of horizontal and vertical speeds of air flowing up and over a long hill ridge with a fairly simple smooth form. Figure 11.1(a) shows the pattern of streamlines for a 20-knot airstream flowing across a 300-ft high ridge. Figure 11.1(b) shows the associated distribution of vertical speeds in this airstream as it crosses the ridge. Notice that the lift, on the upwind side of the ridge, is strongest close to the windward slope and the zone of lift extends well above and upwind of the ridge. Allowing 1 knot (100 ft/min or $\frac{1}{2}$ m/s) for the sinking speed of his glider, a pilot in this hypothetical situation could soar up to about

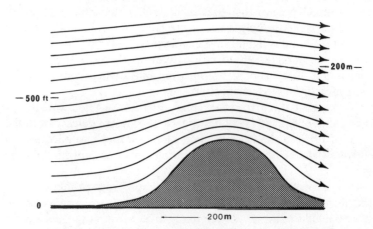

Fig. 11.1(a) Typical streamlines for an airstream flowing across a ridge.

111

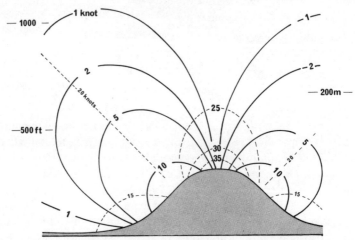

Fig. 11.1(b). Distribution of lift (full lines) and horizontal velocity component (broken lines) in an airstream as it crosses a ridge.

1000 ft above the flat ground-level. To maintain this maximum altitude he would need to keep about 200 m upwind of the hill crest. If he flies too far downwind towards the hill crest he is liable to emerge quickly from the zone of lift.

Compared to the vertical speed pattern the horizontal velocity distribution, also shown in Figure 11.1(b), is of secondary importance, but we should at least note that at the hill crest the surface wind is much greater than that of the flow some distance upstream and decreases with height above the hill crest, while at the foot of the hill the wind is lighter and increases with height. These effects, which are characteristic of many an airflow over hills of various shapes and sizes, should be borne in mind when contemplating launching or landing at hill sites.

Notice that if, in this particular situation, a pilot were to fly downwind of the hill crest, he would not only run quickly from the zone of lift into the downdraught but he would also encounter a relatively strong headwind when trying to fly back upwind into the lift.

Of course, the uniform airflow and simple ridge profile used for the illustrations in Figures 11.1 (a) and (b) are an oversimplification of actual hill soaring conditions likely to be encountered, but we can reason out some of the modifications necessary to obtain more realism. The surface friction effect, likely to retard all winds close to the ground, must be superimposed on the smooth flow depicted in Figures 11.1(a) and (b). This surface friction is greater over wooded hill slopes than over comparatively smooth grass- or snow-covered ridges; wooded slopes therefore tend to be somewhat poorer generators of hill lift than smoother slopes—although if the wooded slopes are steep enough they will nonetheless produce hill lift in fresh or strong winds.

The effect of the steepness of the hill slope is difficult to assess. Obviously hill lift is likely to be weak over gentle slopes, but too steep an escarpment is liable to induce windward eddies in a position such as that shown in Figure 11.2. The steep windward

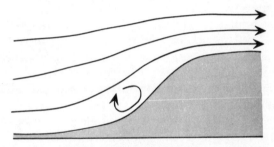

Fig. 11.2   Windward eddy in front of a steep escarpment.

escarpment may also create eddies on the immediate leeward side of the crest when the high ground profile is like that sketched in Figure 11.3, and a steep leeward escarpment is also likely to produce *bolster eddies* as indicated in Figure 11.4.

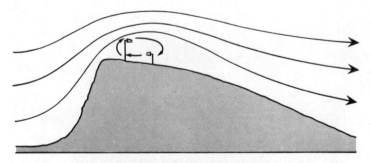

Fig. 11.3   Eddy in lee of the crest of a steep windward escarpment.

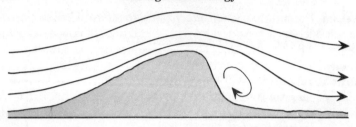

Fig. 11.4   Eddy downwind of a steep leeward escarpment.

There is no set of simple rules for guessing or predicting when, or precisely whereabouts, large eddies will form. But merely realising that they do exist and that they are mostly unpredictable should prompt caution in launching or landing, and while there is no adequate substitute for hill soaring tuition in the air, it is enlightening to use a few minutes of non-gliding weather or of a winter's evening to make speculative pencil sketches of the probable streamlines or eddies in the airflow across ridges of various shapes. An elementary concept of aerodynamic flow plus artistic intuition are usually all that is required to make the sketches broadly correct.

It is usually easy to guess the principal effects on hill lift of gullies and other irregularities in an escarpment, although it may surprise the inexperienced pilot to learn that upward vertical currents are

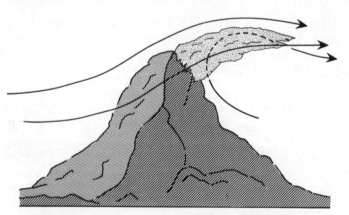

Fig. 11.5   The shape of the streamlines past a high mountain peak is sometimes betrayed by the 'smoking mountain' cloud streaming from the peak. This cloud forms in the air which is drawn up the leeward slopes before joining the main airstream.

sometimes found on leeward slopes of isolated mountain peaks. When this leeward air is relatively moist it may produce a cloud appearing to stream from the mountain peak, as illustrated in Figure 11.5.

Effects of temperature lapse rate

The tendency for eddies to form is related not only to the structure of the high ground but also to the temperature lapse rate in the airstream. In convective conditions the airflow is likely to be generally somewhat turbulent with randomly distributed eddies moving with the wind—as depicted in Figure 11.6—and hill lift is also likely to be compounded with thermal activity—which is the subject of Chapter 12.

Fig. 11.6   In convective conditions the airflow is likely to be generally somewhat turbulent with randomly distributed eddies moving with the wind.

When the airstream is more stable—as indicated in Figure 11.7— the general flow is smoother, and the zone of hill lift appears to extend further upstream from the hill ridge than is the case when the airstream is unstable. Semi-permanent eddies are more likely to form at the foot of any steep escarpment. These eddies can be turbulent, and the transition from the smooth airflow to the turbulence of the eddies can be quite sharp. Occasionally, such eddy formation is periodic, that is to say, an eddy develops and decays at fairly regular intervals of between a few minutes and about 20 minutes or so.

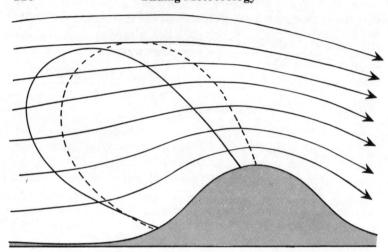

Fig. 11.7   In a stable airstream the general flow is often smooth, and the zone of lift appears to extend farther upstream from the hill ridge than is the case when the airstream is unstable, i.e. from the zone enclosed by the broken line to that bounded by the full line in this diagram.

Another feature of hill lift in fresh winds and stable airstreams is that such lift can be augmented or suppressed by lee wave phenomena that can occur in such airstreams. These phenomena are described in Chapter 17.

Wind gradient and gustiness

Potential danger in the gliding approach to landing is the usual increase of wind with height from ground-level up to at least a height of about 150 ft (50 m). During the final landing leg into wind this *wind gradient,* as it is called, has the effect of reducing the airspeed of a glider whose actual momentum changes only slowly as the aircraft descends into decreasing headwinds. Failure to make allowance for this effect can result in an inadvertent stall and an inelegant, possibly calamitous, landing, especially as the wind gradient is often most pronounced within a few feet of the ground. The wind gradient also calls for considerable prudence in making turns at low levels; in a steeply banked turn the lower wing may well be in an airflow several knots slower than that at the level of the upper wing and the dangers of this type of situation can easily be figured out by any glider pilot. Obviously the existence of a 'bolster' eddy can be an added hazard in a wind gradient.

In light or moderate winds the wind gradient itself usually deserves attention without being unduly worrying, but in a stronger flow the danger of stalling in a lull during an approach into wind is increased by the gusts and lulls in the winds at low levels. Wind speeds in these gusts and lulls, lasting for between about 3 and 30 seconds, are likely to range from about 170% to 30% of the mean wind speed averaged over 30 minutes or so; a 15-knot surface wind, for example, is likely to include gusts to about 25 knots and lulls in which the wind speed drops to about 5 knots.

Katabatic winds

Because the cooling of air by nocturnal radiation is greatest at ground-level, a feature of mountainous terrain on practically calm, clear nights is that the air close to the hill slopes becomes cooler and denser than air at the same level over the adjacent valleys. Therefore, this hill slope air tends to slide down into the valleys and in doing so creates a *katabatic wind.* Down gentle slopes of small hills these winds are often light and merely add to the difficulties of interpreting surface wind observations, but large escarpments and long steep valleys can produce fresh katabatic breezes. Snow-covered slopes or glaciers are particularly prone to katabatic winds, and on such slopes the cooling of air at the snow or ice surface frequently makes downslope winds liable to persist during both night and day—such a persistent katabatic flow has the alternative name: *glacier wind.*

The onset of katabatic flow is sudden, and the katabatic wind is normally confined to a shallow layer, often less than about 500 ft deep. Obviously, katabatic winds do not constitute soaring conditions, but the glider pilot should include them in his stock of meteorological knowledge in order to interpret local wind observations and to supplement his general ideas of airflow over mountains.

Anabatic winds

Of more direct concern to the soaring pilot are the winds urged upwards along hill slopes by daytime insolation. The mechanism is practically the converse of the katabatic variety; heating from the sun is communicated via the ground to air close to a hill slope quicker than it is to the air at the same level over the adjacent lowland, and the density variation produces an *anabatic wind* up the hillside. Figure 11.8 illustrates the nature of the flow. The

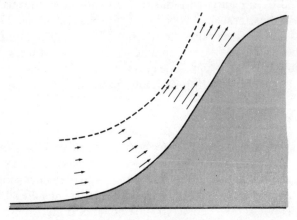

Fig. 11.8   Anabatic flow.

primary factors governing the depth and strength of the flow are the gradient of the escarpment and the temperature lapse rate of the air over the adjoining lowland. Gentle slopes and temperature lapse rates close to the DALR are favourable for deep but weak anabatic wind layers, while steep slopes and inversions produce stronger upslope winds in a shallow layer, confined to within 150 m of the face of the mountainside. In order to get the most lift out of upslope winds a pilot must often fly very close (within a few wing spans of the mountainside), and in such a position he must be particularly alert—especially when rounding a butte brings him on to a collision course with a glider coming the other way.

Occasionally anabatic winds attain speeds of over 15 knots, yielding a vertical component of 10 knots or more on a 45-degree slope, but all too often general anabatic soaring conditions along a mountain range are marginal, and some experience is needed, firstly to assess where and when to seek the best lift, and secondly, to avoid flying into newly formed cloud clinging to the slope or into the mountainside itself. The upward flow is usually strongest on the sections of the slope directly facing the sun. Bare rock which is readily heated by direct sunshine is a good generator of anabatic flow, while poor lift or even sink, may be found over a neighbouring surface of snow. Cloud cover needs watching as anabatic winds are quick to decline when the mountain slope becomes shaded by cloud. Sudden cloud formation in the upslope flow itself presents another hazard to anabatic soaring; the anabatic phenomenon is not exempt from the rule that ascent of air leads to cooling, and condensation if the air contains sufficient moisture. Furthermore, over mountainous terrain parcels of air have such diverse histories and trajectories that it is unwise to reckon on one single condensation level being appropriate to a large region; the condensation level in one valley may be quite different at times from that in the next, and it is dangerous to forget this fact when learning to fly in truly mountainous terrain such as the Swiss, Austrian or French Alps, where anabatic soaring is widely practised.

Mountain and valley winds

A valley can be considered to comprise three sloping surfaces: two steep mountain escarpments and the valley floor between them. All of these three slopes can generate anabatic or katabatic winds and the interplay between these winds often produces a recognisable daily sequence of events. Before sunrise the predominant katabatic flow takes the form of a steady wind (sometimes known as a *Bergwind*) down the valley. Soon after sunrise anabatic winds (*Hangaufwinde*) begin to flow up the steep escarpments flanking the valley and these upslope winds gradually intensify during the morning. By midday the anabatic flow up the valley has become well established and during the afternoon this up-valley wind increases at the expense of the mountain slope winds which gradually weaken. By late afternoon, the up-valley wind predominates, but comes the evening, and the katabatic flow down the mountain slopes (*Hangabwinde*) sets in and persists for a while until the nocturnal cooling is sufficient to restore the early morning flow down the valley. The details of diurnal changes vary, but the broad features of the sequence of events (illustrated in Figure 11.9) are often recognisable in wide and deep valleys. Experience suggests that the precise shape of the valley cross-section or the inclination of

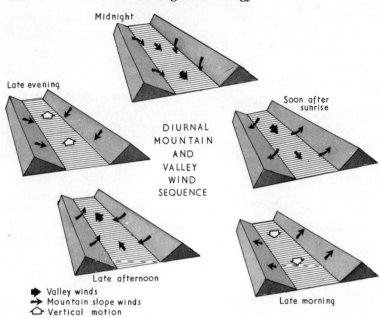

Fig. 11.9 Mountain and valley wind sequence.

the valley floor are of little consequence but the sequence is primarily a fair weather phenomenon and is best observed in deep and wide valleys such as those in the Swiss Alps.

Cooling by nocturnal radiation is often associated with generally light winds, but in rugged terrain with deep valleys it is not unusual for an airstream to maintain winds of moderate strength across the mountain ridges while cool air below tends to stagnate under a temperature inversion that forms in the valleys. In such circumstances hill soaring conditions over the upper slopes may continue into the late afternoon and evening while incipient katabatic conditions develop below the inversion. Figure 11.10 illustrates the flow pattern.

Orographic convergence lines

During the past decade it has become evident that bands of lift lying along the wind direction occasionally form in lee of hills or

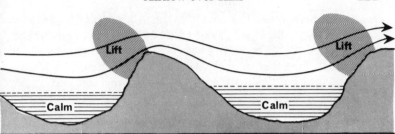

Fig. 11.10 On cloudless evenings over rugged terrain it is not unusual for pools of cold air to stagnate in deep valleys while winds aloft still provide hill lift higher up the mountain slopes.

mountains. The precise structure of the wind patterns is not clear, but in some situations, when two branches of an airstream converge after flowing on opposite sides around a mountain or small block of mountainous terrain, one branch tends to flow up and over the other—thus producing a band of lift stretching downstream from the mountain. John Aldrich, a gliding meteorologist, has described a particularly good example of this phenomenon. The Tehachapi Pass at 4000 ft above MSL in the USA separates the Sierra Nevada Mountains to the north from the Tehachapi Mountains that curve away to the south-west—as mapped in Figure 11.11. When air from

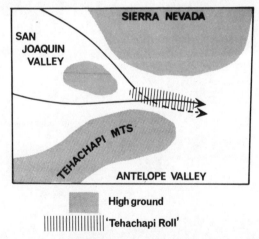

Fig. 11.11 The 'Tehachapi Roll' in which air flowing around opposite sides of high ground converges and produces lift as one branch of the airflow flows over the top of the other.

the west flows through this pass from the San Joaquin Valley to the Mojave Desert, the flow is boosted by upslope mountain breezes and reaches the Tehachapi Pass via two routes—one from the north-west, the other from the west across Cumming's Valley. As these branches of the airstream converge in the Tehachapi Valley the southern branch appears to flow up and over the branch from the north-west, thus providing a band of lift several thousand feet above the valley floor, and extending downwind for about 8 km. The branch of the flow from the north-west appears to descend in this convergence line and the convergence line itself appears to form a long roll. It is known as the '*Tehachapi Shear Line*' or '*Tehachapi Roll*', and occurs mostly in the afternoons during fairly clear weather regimes. When southerly winds prevail aloft the lift becomes weak and patchy, while with easterly winds the convergence line disappears.

12

Dry Thermals

To a glider pilot a *thermal* is any convective current of rising air in which he can gain height. Where the rising air is cloudless the thermal is called a *dry thermal.* Convection in the atmosphere can be considered in a general way as buoyant air rising through a relatively cold environment, but the thermals which constitute this convection are much less amenable to easy description.

However, we need not be too alarmed at the complexity of convection phenomena. Simple, logical concepts of thermal structure are adequate for extensive thermal soaring and these ideas can gradually be elaborated in the light of accumulated experience. Most top-class soaring pilots do not supplement their flying skill and experience with much more than elementary views on what thermals are and where to find them. Rather than confuse themselves with rigid or ultra-complicated ideas, these pilots are ready and quick to assess the characteristics of thermal conditions they actually encounter. An understanding of the meteorology of convection can ensure that such assessment is realistic.

Thermal structure

When the sun heats the ground most of the heat is quickly transferred to the air close to the ground surface. If the airstream that has been heated in such a way is relatively cool then air being heated in the shallow layer close to the ground will become buoyant and tend to rise—or convect—up into the cooler air aloft. The ascent of this buoyant air does not occur in a steady regular pattern; it is a mixture of chaos and coherence. The chaos is the eddy motion or small-scale turbulence; the coherence is found in the apparently more organised structure of thermals.

An incipient thermal rises from the shallow heated layer as a dome-shaped protuberance which develops into a column with a diameter of between about 150 and 300 m. Its initial velocity is usually about 2 knots (1 m/s), but in weak thermal conditions this initial velocity is often much less. The column accelerates as it rises and its diameter may decrease slightly. Higher up, the diameter gradually increases and the thermal begins to assume the shape of an inverted cone, as sketched in Figure 12.1. In weak or moderate

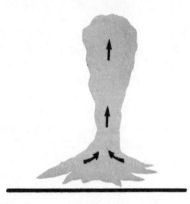

Fig. 12.1 At low levels a thermal rising from ground-level usually assumes the shape of an inverted cone.

thermal conditions the column may soon break away from the heated ground layer and form an isolated bubble of rising air. But in some situations, especially very hot and dry conditions, a thermal column may draw up air from the heated ground layer for several minutes before exhausting the temporary supply. As the column rises it spreads laterally by entrainment with the surrounding air; the bottom of the column rises up into the thermal as a whole, and the structure begins to acquire the characteristics of a vortex ring, like that illustrated in Figure 12.2. Isolated thermal bubbles also tend to spread laterally as they rise and acquire vortex ring characteristics, so that as the bubble and column types of thermals ascend well into the thermal regime they both tend to acquire the vortex ring characteristics. Thermals in the atmosphere are seldom isolated and are frequently distorted by wind shear, but the concept of the expanding and diffusing vortex ring is a useful basis for visualising thermal structure at cross-country soaring levels. A cross-section of the internal motion across a vortex ring is illustrated in Figure 12.3. The arrows in this figure show motion relative to the

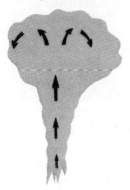

Fig. 12.2   As a thermal rises it begins to acquire the characteristics of a vortex ring.

thermal itself. The thermal as a whole will be rising—so the downward-pointing arrows in the illustration at the edges of the thermal do not necessarily represent sink. The thermal itself will be getting wider as it ascends. The region of lift appears to be between about 200 and 600 m in diameter at 1000–2000 ft above ground-level, and wider at higher levels.

A thermal may have a *thermal core* or narrow region, usually near the centre, where the lift is markedly stronger than that in the relatively broad surrounding region of thermal lift. Thermal cores tend to be narrow and relatively strong in very hot and dry conditions. In such conditions a soaring pilot should try to locate the core

Fig. 12.3   Vortex ring motion in an isolated thermal. The arrows indicate air motion relative to the thermal itself; so that the net vertical motion is that indicated by the arrows in this diagram plus the rate of rise of the thermal itself.

quickly and circle tightly within it, especially if he has located the thermal at a low level. In generally weaker thermalling conditions, on the other hand, gentle turns in a slowly developing incipient thermal may be more effective as such a thermal tends to have converging air at low levels which drift a circling glider into the developing core. There is no simple golden rule for predicting which technique to follow, but climatic and terrain features of a site tend to impose thermal characteristics which can be gleaned from careful observations and local experience.

The feature of particular relevance to thermal soaring is that the upward velocity of the air in the centre of the thermal is greater than the rate of ascent of the whole thermal. As long as this difference in velocity is greater than about 1 knot ($\frac{1}{2}$ m/s) a glider in the centre of a thermal will rise through the thermal itself; then, having climbed to somewhere near the top of the thermal, the glider will rise at the same rate as that of the thermal as a whole until the bubble of buoyant air becomes too dilute and slow moving to sustain soaring flight.

The most common difference between the vortex rings illustrated in this chapter so far and reality is that thermal vortex rings in the atmosphere are seldom perfectly circular; the ring is often somewhat more in the form of a meandering circuit which may be stretched in the direction of a wind shear, and which may embrace more than one thermal core.

Dry thermal layer

Atmospheric conditions usually impose a form of lid on the vertical extent to which dry thermals ascend. In this book the layer between ground-level and this lid will be called the *dry thermal layer*—or *thermal layer*. This layer contains shallower layers whose characteristics will be described by subsidiary names, but the term dry thermal layer will always be used to denote the whole layer through which a dry thermal regime is established. When thermals from ground-level extend up into cloud the layer from ground-level to the cloud base will be called the dry thermal layer.

Many a good dry thermal day follows a clear night, with little or no wind, and radiation cooling—that produces a low-level temperature inversion, and possibly early morning mist or fog or low stratus.

When the sun's heating has dispersed, or 'burnt off', the mist or fog or low stratus, the ground quickly warms up and small thermals begin to transport the heat from ground-level up into the air above. Initially these thermals are too small and shallow to use easily for soaring flight. But as the morning progresses, the depth of the thermal layer gradually increases and, by the time it is up to about 1200 ft (400 m) or so, some of the thermals will be sufficiently well organised for sporadic thermal soaring.

If the temperature inversion is strong (that is to say, the temperature increases markedly with height) the rate at which the dry thermal layer increases in depth will be slow. The *surface air temperature*, however, will increase fairly rapidly under a strong inversion. This rapid increase of surface air temperature may appear to be inconsistent with the slow development of the thermals, but the explanation is that because the sun's heating is distributed through only a shallow layer underneath the inversion the temperature of the air in this layer will rise quickly.

The breakdown of a temperature inversion can sometimes be deduced by taking a succession of surface air temperature measurements at a gliding site during a period in which thermal soaring conditions are expected to develop. The temperature rise slows down, and may even pause, at the trigger temperature, and, as thermals develop, fluctuations in temperature over one or two degrees within a minute or two may become noticeable—especially if a thermograph is available to show a continuous temperature record.

If the heating is sufficient to raise the top of the dry thermal layer above the top of the temperature inversion, the depth of the thermals will increase sharply—and the rate of rise of the air temperature will slow down because the sun's heating is now becoming spread throughout a greater depth. Thus, it is not uncommon for the depth of thermals to increase very slowly during the morning, then at some critical time (depending on the sun's heating and the temperature profile of the airstream) to increase rapidly. The surface air temperature at which this transition from slow to rapid development of thermals occurs is sometimes called the *trigger temperature*. After this trigger temperature has been reached the thermals usually become moderate or strong and may be somewhat rough.

As long as the thermals are buoyant relative to the air surrounding them they will continue to rise. When they reach a level at which the temperature of the surrounding air is not relatively cooler they will be no longer buoyant and their ascent will be checked. Therefore, conditions favourable for thermals include strong sunshine to heat the ground surface and an airstream that is relatively cool up to a height sufficient for thermals to develop and soaring to take place.

The height to which a dry thermal layer develops is usually limited by a stable layer, or temperature inversion. Figure 12.4 illustrates the nature of this thermal layer. Incipient thermals

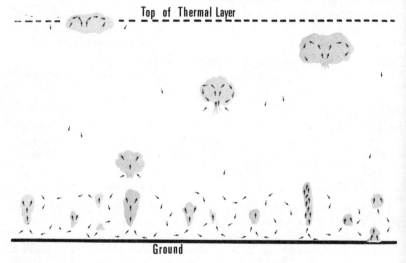

Fig. 12.4   The nature of the thermal layer.

develop in the shallow layer with a superadiabatic lapse rate. The depth and degree of instability of this superadiabatic layer are determined mainly by the intensity of the sunshine, low-level turbulence and the nature of the ground. Blazing sunshine with light winds over a desert can produce a superadiabatic layer several thousand feet in depth, but in temperate maritime climates superadiabatic layers are more likely to be several hundred feet deep on warm sunny days, and scarcely discernible if the sun's heating is either distributed upwards too readily by turbulence or used up in evaporating moisture from wet and soggy ground.

The superadiabatic layer is unstable for both upward and downward displacements of air, that is to say, ascending thermals accelerate upwards while any parcels of air that are displaced downwards in the general turbulence accelerate downwards.

The strengths of both the thermals and the downdraughts depend mainly on the depth of the superadiabatic layer and its degree of instability. On many a convective day in temperate maritime climates the superadiabatic layer is only just unstable, and both thermals and downdraughts at very low levels are of only weak or moderate strength, but it can be taken as axiomatic that whenever superadiabatic layers produce strong thermals they are also liable to harbour disconcertingly strong downdraughts.

The interplay between ascending thermals and downdraughts in the superadiabatic layer is usually such that neither species has the chance to reign supreme. A large proportion of both types lose their identities in the general convective confusion but the thermals that do manage to preserve their identities to, say, half-way up through the superadiabatic layer have more than a 50% chance of developing into mature thermals; the higher a thermal gets in the superadiabatic layer, the bigger it becomes and the lesser are the chances of it being diluted and nullified by turbulence and downdraughts. Thus, the superadiabatic layer acts as a sort of filter from which relatively durable thermals emerge into the layer above.

Above the superadiabatic layer the temperature lapse rate is usually very close to the DALR. In this adiabatic layer there are fewer thermals than at lower levels but they are more organised. They tend to develop the vortex ring characteristics and become broader as they ascend.

When these thermals reach the top of the dry thermal layer they spread and lose their buoyancy quickly by entrainment with the surrounding air. Usually a slight increase in small-scale turbulence is a sign that the thermal is approaching the top of the dry thermal layer. The top of the dry thermal layer is usually fairly sharp and it is often visible because it also marks the top of haze or pollution trapped in the well-mixed air below. If a thermal is particularly buoyant it may penetrate about 100 ft or so into the relatively warmer air above but it soon subsides back into the dry thermal layer.

The effect of thick pollution in the thermal layer weakens the sunshine reaching the ground and modifies the vertical distribution of thermals; the pollution itself absorbs some of the insolation and some of the generally weak thermals form within the polluted layer—they do not all come from ground-level.

Heated thermal sources

One of the factors contributing to the characteristics of convection at low levels is the type and distribution of thermal sources. We can talk of *heated thermal sources* as those spots over which the air close to the ground tends to become warmer than that over the immediate surroundings. This excess warming of the air over a thermal source depends on the rate at which the temperature of the ground surface itself rises, and on the length of the time the air remains close to the surface before being carried away in the general wind flow. For a given intensity of sunshine the rate of which the ground surface temperature rises is controlled by several factors which include:

1 *The angle of incidence of the sun's rays.* The temperature of sun-facing slopes will rise faster than adjacent horizontal but otherwise similar surfaces, and indeed such slopes are often efficient sources of thermal activity.

2 *The dampness of the ground.* The wetter the surface the bigger will be the proportion of incoming radiation wasted in evaporating some of the moisture—especially in strong winds.

3 *The moisture content of the soil.* The wetter the earth the bigger will be the proportion of incoming heat wasted by absorption within the soil itself. Chalky soils drain quickly and usually provide more thermal activity than such soils as clay and loam.

4 *The nature of the soil surface.* Dry, rocky or sandy surfaces heat up rapidly because their conductivity is low and the heat does not penetrate far below the surface. Granite is slow to warm up because it readily absorbs heat, but by storing the heat it remains warm until late in the day.

5 *The crop or foliage cover.* A thick crop or dense trees will intercept much of the incoming insolation before it reaches the ground, and usually a large part of this intercepted heat is used up in transpiration, that is, evaporation from the leaf surfaces

of moisture which makes its way up through the plant from the ground. The amount of moisture evaporated in this manner is very considerable—a large tree transpires about 3 tonnes of water per day. During periods of drought, however, the water content of the ground may not be enough for adequate transpiration and some crops become overheated and shrivel up. On the other hand, thick crops and wooded areas tend to retain their heat longer and sometimes release this heat in the evening when open ground has begun to cool down. Wasteful evaporation from a freshly cut grass meadow uses much of the incoming insolation, but when the cut grass dries and mats, it forms a heat insulator and barrier to evaporation—thus improving its prospects of becoming a thermal source. Leaf litter also acts as a thermal insulator and evaporation barrier.

6 *The wastage of incident solar radiation by reflection from the ground.* The power of a surface to reflect heat is difficult, if not impossible to estimate, but it is instructive to compare some actual measurements relating to a few types of surfaces. Here they are:

Type of surface	Insolation wasted by reflection
Various cereal crops	5-15%
Coniferous forest	10-15%
Black mould	10-15%
Patches of damp sand	10-15%
Bare ground	10-20%
Dry ploughed fields	10-25%
Patches of dry sand	15-25%
Various grass fields	15-40%
Desert	15-40%
Snow or ice	40-90%

The length of time the air remains close to the surface of a particular field or potential thermal source depends on the general wind speed and the effect of local sheltering. The airflow through, say, the plants of a wheatfield is usually slowed down by the crop foliage and on a sunny day the temperature within the crop is often about 3°C higher than in the faster airflow just above the top of the crop. Mid-afternoon temperatures within a potato crop are some-times about 1-5°C higher than the air temperature just above, and it seems probable that, on sunny days with light to moderate winds, locally high temperatures are attained at the foliage level of trees in woods.

Group of buildings, towns and steep leeward escarpments in hilly country offer similar, though larger-scale shelters to the general wind flow, and the last type has acquired the name *wind shadow*. A wind shadow, however, is probably active as a thermal source mainly when the lee escarpment is also a sun-facing slope. Buildings and small towns are often efficient thermal sources; they are usually dry, their reflective power is often low, and they usually have some internal heating. It needs but little imagination to appreciate the difficulties of predicting the efficiency of heated thermal sources; for example, we may argue that since the reflective power of patches of damp sand is low, then, in very light winds, the exposed sandy banks of an almost dried-up river may be useful thermal sources, but with fresh winds the air close to ground-level would not remain over the sand long enough to gain excessive heat; furthermore, evaporation, with its wasteful consumption of insolation, would be greater with fresh winds, and it is practically impossible to predict just how slow the wind must be to allow particular sandy banks to become efficient thermal sources in particular weather conditions.

To consider another illustration, we can argue that a dry wheatfield is likely to be a more productive thermal source than a neighbouring ploughed field, but if the crop is wet, and if the wind is very light, it is open to conjecture whether or not the air tempera-ture within the wet wheatfield would be higher or lower than that close to the surface of a ploughed field. Of course, we could theorise on the combined effects of sun-facing slopes, wetness of the surface, moisture content of the soil, transpiration, heat reflection and wind shelter (to say nothing of the effects of irrigation) at great length, but since it is practically impossible to know how much of each effect applies to particular places at particular times such theorising is mainly inconclusive. However, this sobering inconclusiveness is no cause for pessimism; it merely means that we must be wary of forming preconceived notions of where and when to find thermal sources. Instead we must be aware of the factors which create such sources and let nature reveal how these are combined on particular occasions. Then if we can deduce the reasons for the efficiency, or lack of efficiency, of one heated thermal source, there may be a better chance of predicting where to find the next.

Cellular source patterns

Recent research, including observations by Australian research meteorologists, Eric Webb and Derek Reid, indicates that over flat terrain heated fairly uniformly by the sun, surface wind and temperature fluctuations tend to occur in cellular patterns. Each cell is about 1–5 km across and usually has three, four or five sides. Deviation from the mean wind is fairly uniform within each cell but it differs from one cell to the next.

The walls of adjoining cells are often zones of converging (and rising) air or diverging (and sinking) air. Temperature records and gliding research flights suggest that thermals rise mostly from the junctions of three or four of these convergence zones between adjacent cells. Thus an incipient thermal appears to be fed by air converging into and along three or four narrow channels radiating like spokes of a wheel from the thermal. The incipient thermal is often one or two degrees warmer than the surrounding air, but this excess temperature is quickly reduced as the thermal ascends and mixes with the air aloft.

A cellular pattern at very low levels usually moves with the low-level mean wind, and as it moves its detailed structure changes slowly.

Complete thermal source patterns are normally a mixture of a topographic pattern of heated thermal sources and some mobile cellular source pattern, associated mainly with the airstream characteristics and the general rate of heating. As already suggested, complications of thermal source behaviour need not daunt the pilot who is quick to simplify the picture by discerning or guessing the dominant features in the thermal patterns he finds.

Late thermal sources

As already mentioned, thick crops, dense trees, and rocky surfaces (especially granite) tend to retain their heat and become *late* (or *residual*) *thermal sources* late in the day. The thermals they produce appear to be smoother and easier to use, though more widely spaced, than the more vigorous variety triggered off by strong midday sunshine.

The difference in character between midday and late thermals appears to arise from a basic difference in the activation of the thermal sources; as the day warms up, thermal sources are heated more than their surroundings, whereas residual thermal sources are created because they do not cool down as quickly as their surroundings.

Heated thermal sources do not suddenly cease to be active as soon as the residual sources begin to work, but sometimes there appears to be a *thermal pause*—for about half an hour between about 16.00 and 18.00 LST—after the heated source mechanism has passed its peak but before the residual thermal sources become fully active.

Spacing between thermals

Over uniform terrain and in light winds the spacing between thermals depends largely upon the depth of the dry thermal layer. The life of early morning thermals is brief and their vertical extent usually much less than will be achieved later in the day, but this lack of size is balanced by closer spacing. Both the size and lifespan of thermals increase during the day, but the distances between them also become greater.

Towards the end of convection the distances between thermals become greater and the strengths slowly decline, but the vertical extent usually remains nearly the same as it was during the heat of the afternoon. A guide is that the distance between adjacent thermals is about $1\frac{1}{2}$ to $2\frac{1}{2}$ times the height to which the thermals ascend.

Dust devils

Since the thermal capacity and conductivity of loose sand are low, insolation is especially effective in raising the temperature of the surface of a desert, and over such regions the superadiabatic layer is particularly unstable and often extends upwards for a few thousand feet. Thermals and downdraughts in this layer are vigorous. As air flows in towards the bottom of a thermal it tends to circulate around the thermal core—just as bath-water circulates around an open plughole. Usually this circulation is insignificant and not readily detectable, but a vigorous thermal can concentrate an incipient circulation into a tight vortex that can stretch up as a spinning column-type thermal for several hundred and occasionally a few thousand feet above ground-level. If such a vigorous rotating thermal picks up enough dust or sand to reveal its whirling motion it is called a *dust devil*, or *willy willy* in Australia.

The column of dust or sand in a dust devil is more visible when viewed through polarised glasses. Lift within it is strong, but tight circling is needed to stay in the core, especially at low levels. The dust devil often persists for at least several minutes as it drifts slowly with the wind, and as it ascends to higher levels in the dry thermal regime it usually develops into a less vigorous but nonetheless good thermal.

At ground-level passage of a dust devil is accompanied by an unpleasant whirl of dust about 10–15 m in diameter and gusts of wind strong enough to move insecurely parked gliders.

The effect of wind and wind shear

Although thermals might be well formed in hypothetically calm conditions, a wind favours the production of more frequent, though perhaps distorted, thermals. The reasons for this are that the turbulence created by the wind triggers off incipient thermals and that a thermal displaced by the wind may travel over the shallow, heated surface air and draw into its circulation a greater volume of air than is available in calm conditions. On the other hand, winds tend to reduce the rate of rise of surface temperature by distributing heat up through the deep turbulent layer likely to exist in such a flow. Therefore, winds of moderate strength or more tend to inhibit the creation of thermals from ground-level sources. As if to partially compensate for this thermally disruptive action, the turbulent motion itself displaces parcels of air vertically, and, if the temperature lapse rate is superadiabatic (even only slightly), parcels displaced upwards will become incipient thermals. Hence, there may well be an appreciable number of thermals in moderate or strong winds, but many of them will originate above rather than at ground-level, and although some buoyant bubbles may also rise from the land surface, it is usually difficult to relate fixed thermal sources with the thermals actually encountered in the air. This distorting effect of the turbulence also adds to thermal soaring difficulties in such conditions.

The term *wind shear* is used usually to describe a sharp change of wind with height. It used to be thought that wind shears would not normally persist in a thermal layer because of the thorough vertical mixing that was believed to occur in the layer. In the past decade, however, glider pilots have discovered that marked wind shears occasionally do persist in thermal layers, and that these wind shears distort the thermal structure. The effect is illustrated in Figure 12.5. Such wind shears are not frequent, but they occur often

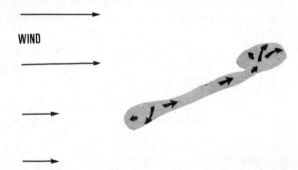

WIND

Fig. 12.5 Vertical cross-section of a thermal rising through a wind shear. The core of the thermal is moved in the direction of the shear.

enough to be noticeable and troublesome to soaring pilots, and they appear to be most noticeable in hot dry inland climates. The existence of such a shear is not normally apparent without detailed meteorological information on the spot. Often, the first clue a soaring pilot has that such a shear exists in a dry thermal layer is an apparent weakening or turbulent dissipation of the thermal in which he is climbing. In this situation, the best chance of remaining with the rising thermal is for the pilot to move in the direction of the wind shear. Wind shear direction is illustrated in Figure 12.6. If a wind shear is suspected but the direction not known, it may be necessary for the pilot to widen his circling to search for the shift of

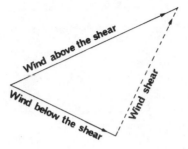

Fig. 12.6 A wind vector can be depicted as an arrow drawn in the direction towards which the wind is blowing and of a length proportional to the speed of the wind. Wind shear is the vector difference between the wind vectors above and below the shear.

the thermal core—then, if he detects the apparent direction of shear, use this direction again during the next hour or two whenever he is trying to climb in a thermal up through the level of this wind shear.

This thermal shift due to wind shear, that has just been discussed, occurs in very shallow layers, usually about 100 ft deep. The more general change of wind with height through the dry thermal layer also affects the structure of thermals. When the wind change up through this layer is greater than about 2-3 knots per 1000 ft, soaring in dry thermals on a good convection day is likely to be possible, but difficult, due to turbulent distortion of the thermals.

Thermal streams and thermal streets

Occasionally thermals appear to be organised into streams or streets orientated in the direction of the wind. *Thermal streams* are likely to develop downwind of quasi-continuous sources such as small towns, factories, or isolated hills, as drawn in Figure 12.7, the principal condition for such streaming being that the wind direction does not change radically up through the dry thermal layer. The length of streams which stem from particularly active thermal sources is often between 5 and 15 km. When several parallel streams form, the spacing between them is determined primarily by the distribution of the thermal sources. Therefore, in general, the lengths of thermal streams and the spaces between them will not be regular.

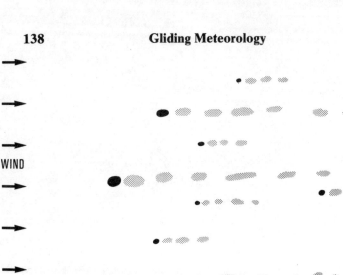

WIND

● Thermal Sources   ◞ ◞ Thermal Streams

Fig. 12.7   Thermal streams are likely to develop downwind of quasi-continuous sources such as small towns, factories, or isolated hills. The spacing between the streams is not normally regular.

Certain types of wind and stability conditions, however, are favourable for the organisation of thermals into much longer and more evenly spaced *thermal streets*, which do not spring from individual thermal sources. The stability condition is that the convective layer should be capped by a very stable layer. This stabilisation will impose a firm limit on the ultimate sizes of the largest and most significant thermals in the convection layer, and it is the control of these ultimate sizes that allows the regular spacing between the streets to be maintained. The distance between adjacent streets is usually about two to three times the general depth of the convective layer. The wind condition favourable for regular street development is that the wind speed should increase from ground-level up to about two-thirds the depth of the dry thermal layer and then become constant or even show a slight decrease towards the top of the convection layer. The wind direction should not change much with height. Figure 12.8 illustrates this type of

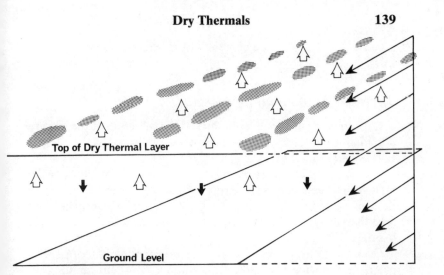

Fig. 12.8 Thermal streets and a wind profile favourable for street formation.

wind profile. As mentioned in Chapter 2, variation of wind with height is linked to temperature gradients through or between air masses. The air mass gradient required to produce the wind profile suitable for thermal streets is such that if you face into wind the colder air will be on your left in the northern hemisphere (right in the southern hemispere).

Truly broad systems of very long, regularly spaced thermal streets are not uncommon features of convection structure over large, flat, or uniform regions. Convection in the trade winds over the oceans is very frequently organised into evenly spaced streets. Even over the arctic pack-ice as far north as 80° N convection at low levels is characterised by the regular street pattern during the prolonged solar heating of the summer months.

The soaring potential of organised lines of thermals is easily realised in flights directly into winds or downwind, but when flying on cross-wind routes it is wise to anticipate considerable downdraughts likely to be induced between adjacent streams or streets.

Thermal streets are more common than is generally supposed; it is often worth while to look for lift along the wind direction through a thermal, rather than be content with traditional circling in thermals.

Thermals in mountainous terrain

Over mountains the topography and the direction of the sun are dominating influences, but their effect is complicated by the interaction of local winds with the general airstream.

It is common for atmospheric haze to decrease with altitude; so high ground receives a greater proportion of the sun's energy than the valleys. Slopes which face the sun get more insolation per unit area than flat ground particularly during the early and late parts of the day.

Ground surface in mountainous terrain is usually more variegated than on the lowlands. Rock surfaces heat up rapidly, but higher snowfields experience little change of temperature. On the lower slopes woods are slow to warm up. An isolated wooded area may produce a few thermals very late in the day, but extensively wooded areas rarely produce strong thermals, especially when the woods are in narrow valleys with steep sides.

Diurnal changes in mountain valleys

During the night air cooled by nocturnal radiation flows down the valleys as katabatic winds, and by dawn the valley air is usually very cold with a marked temperature inversion above it.

After sunrise the eastward-facing slopes are warmed rapidly by insolation, but little change of temperature takes place over wooded lower slopes, and the valley, part of which may still be in shadow, remains under the strong temperature inversion. Thermals begin to rise from the heated upper slopes—especially the east-facing slopes. The influence of hill slope on heating is greater than is generally realised; Figure 12.9 illustrates the magnitude of the slope effect for sunshine at 40° latitude.

As the morning wears on, the flow of thermals from the upper slopes becomes almost continuous, while the lower slopes and eventually the valley floor begins to warm up. The air flowing up the mountainsides is fed by an anabatic flow up the valley from lower ground, but there is also gradual subsidence over the middle of the

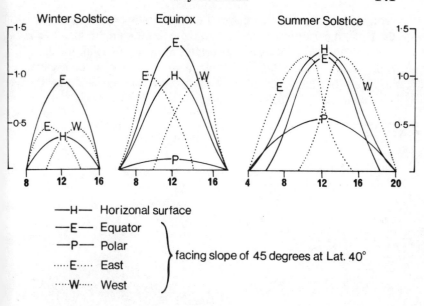

Fig. 12.9 Comparative insolation received by horizontal and sloping surfaces at the solstices and equinoxes. The vertical scale of units is such that 1.0 indicates the heating received at midday on a horizontal surface at the equinox at latitude 40°. The effect of slope is very significant; notice, for example, that at the time of the equinoxes the east-facing slope at 08.00 hours and the west-facing slope at 16.00 hours receive as much heat as a horizontal surface at midday. Local Solar Times are labelled on the horizontal base-lines.

valley. This maintains an inversion over the valley throughout the day, preventing any thermals from rising directly up from the valley floor.

Not all the up-currents are due to flow up heated slopes. Some of them are triggered by the wind flowing up the valley being deflected by spurs jutting out into the valley. The pattern of flow up the mountains changes steadily as some slopes come into sunshine and others become shaded. By sunset only the higher westward-facing slopes are able to produce thermals.

Cooling on the shaded slopes produces a slow downward flow from the slopes into the valley and is often associated with a slow gentle rise of air over the valley floor. This rising air sometimes produces just enough lift for soaring, and pilots can sometimes prolong their flight by flying over the valley in the evening. But soon the general cooling produces a katabatic flow down the valley as a whole. This sequence of events relates to generally calm, or light, wind conditions with little or no cloud—in other words, conditions in which sunshine and night cooling by radiation can play the dominant role in diurnal weather changes.

13

Cumulus Convection

As a dry thermal rises it cools at approximately the dry adiabatic lapse rate of 3°C per 1000 ft. If the thermal reaches a height at which the cooling lowers the temperature of the air in the thermal to its dew point, the thermal becomes saturated, and any further cooling by ascent will produce cloud. Thus weather conditions for fair weather cumulus development are similar to those required for dry thermal development; the only real difference is that depth of convection has to be sufficient for the thermals to reach their condensation level. The cloud that forms will have a cumulus outline, indicating the shape of the tops of a collection of thermals. The thermal will be called a *cloudy thermal*, or simply a thermal in cloud. (It is not normally called a wet thermal in contrast to the dry thermals which are not strictly dry—they are merely not saturated.) A cumulus formed by one thermal, however, will be little more than an ephemeral puff of cloud in the sky. It takes a succession of thermals to form and maintain a firm-looking cumulus cloud. Over a lowland plain the height of fair weather cumulus clouds is usually fairly uniform and the individual cloud bases are fairly flat. The cloud base ranges from about 2000 ft (600 m) in cool and moist weather conditions to about 15 000 ft (5000 m) in very hot and dry situations. (There is a world-wide tendency for professional meteorologists to underestimate rather than overestimate the height of fair weather cumulus cloud base but this almost traditional error is gradually being eliminated as co-operation between meteorologists and glider pilots increases.)

On some days small cumulus forms quickly and looks promising, then disappears, but this does not mean that thermals have weakened; it will normally mean that the air above the level of the small transient cumulus is somewhat stable but not sufficiently stable to prevent the depth of thermals continuing to increase. The short-lived cumulus is colloquially said to have been 'burnt off'.

Plate 10   SMALL CUMULUS OVER WAIKERIE
These small cumulus clouds have a slightly ragged outline, due to wind
shear near the top of the convective region, but thermal lift is strong.

Much of the discussion of dry thermal structure in the upper half
of the dry thermal layer can be tentatively applied to thermals in
cloud by substituting the words saturated adiabatic for dry adiabatic; for example, the buoyancy of an adiabatically ascending thermal
will tend to increase, or decrease, according to whether the temperature lapse rate of the surrounding air is greater than, or less than,
the saturated adiabatic lapse rate. (Figures 3.5 (a) and (b) in Chapter
3 illustrate the stability concept.) The structure of the cloudy

Fig. 13.1   Nature of the general motion of air within and at the sides of a
small convection cloud.

thermal, however, has additional complications in that it is influenced by the effects of condensation and evaporation.

Bright sunlit sides of well-developed cumulus clouds reflect appreciable amounts of sunshine, and some of this reflected sunshine is directed obliquely towards the ground. So, cumulus clouds impose on the ground an ever-changing pattern of both cloud shadows and augmented sunshine—where the ground receives both direct and reflected sunshine.

Cloudy thermal structure

When condensation of moisture takes place, a large amount of latent heat is released and the cloudy thermal is virtually given a boost to its buoyancy. It grows laterally, as it entrains surrounding air, and maintains vortex ring characteristics. The diameter of a thermal at cloud base is of the order of one-third of the height of this cloud base; for example, at a 3000-ft (1000-m) cloud base the thermal diameter is likely to be about 1000 ft (300 m).

When a cloudy thermal rises above the main body of the cloud, into the clear air above, the cap of the thermal mixes with the relatively dry environment. During this mixing some of the cloud evaporates and the resultant cooling reduces the buoyancy of the thermal. The sides of the cloudy thermal are also likely to be cooled by evaporation of the saturated thermal air into the relatively dry surroundings, and descent of air, or *sink*, is likely just within the sides of the cloud as sketched in Figure 13.1. The net result of these buoyancy changes is that a well-developed cloudy thermal exhibits a fairly clear-cut outline at its leading surface as it penetrates into a dry and stable environment, while the contrasting vertical velocities at the sides usually produce small-scale turbulence. So, when a dry thermal becomes a cloudy thermal the lift is likely to become stronger at first, but the entrainment of air and evaporation will subsequently weaken the thermal by dilution and evaporation.

For a cumulus cloud to persist for more than a few minutes the cloud needs to be fed with a number of thermals. However, once a small cumulus cloud has formed, it will act as a tenuous shield protecting successive thermals entering its base from such rapid mixing with, and evaporation into, the surrounding dry air. Thus, if a small puff of cumulus formed by an isolated thermal is not quickly

Plate 11   CLOUD STREETS
Although these convection clouds are not deep, they are orientated in
lines along the wind direction and are fairly sure signposts of long bands of
lift under the clouds. Long bands of downdraught are also likely in the
clear air between the cloud streets. Cloud, or thermal, streets are more
frequent than is commonly supposed.

reinforced by at least another thermal, it will soon disappear; but, if
it is reinforced by at least another thermal, the chances of it growing
even more are considerably increased. Even so, a typical fair
weather cumulus cloud normally has a lifespan of only 20 minutes
or so. This is seldom obvious from a cursory look at a sky dotted
with apparently well-formed small cumulus clouds. But, if we watch
carefully, we will see that most of the individual clouds are in the
process of forming or disappearing. New growing clouds can be
discerned by their brightness and fluffiness, due to the high concentration of small water droplets; whereas the dying cloud is ragged
and acquires an off-white coloration because the smallest droplets
have evaporated leaving a smaller concentration of larger droplets
to reflect the sunlight.

Not all of the thermals entering a cumulus cloud base necessarily
come from the ground. It is not uncommon for some of the
surrounding air just below cloud base to be sucked into the cloud, as
shown in Figure 13.2. The water vapour in this air condenses; the
release of latent heat causes this air to acquire buoyancy, and so it

Fig. 13.2   It is not uncommon for some of the surrounding air just below cloud base to be sucked into the cloud. When this happens the cloud is not necessarily maintained by a stream of thermals from ground-level, and it is sometimes difficult for a glider pilot to thermal soar from low levels up to cloud base.

becomes a thermal. Thus, a well-developed cumulus cloud can become self-stoking. Such a convection cloud does not necessarily decay when its supply of thermals from ground-level is cut off, and a significant, if perhaps vexing, corollary is that convection clouds in the sky are not necessarily guarantors of abundant thermals from ground-level. It is often easy to maintain height just under the base of a self-stoking cloud but surprisingly difficult to reach cloud base by thermalling up from much lower levels.

The subcloud layer

On a sunny day with fair weather convection clouds floating in the sky the total cloud averaged over, say, 40 000 sq km (10 000 sq miles) usually covers less than half the sky, and the widespread descent of environment air which usually, but not necessarily, compensates for the ascent of thermals is, on average, very slow. Nevertheless, this descent is important because the environment is adiabatically warmed in the process, thereby reducing the chances of thermals from low levels reaching their condensation level. This means that thermals have a better chance of rising up past their condensation level into cloud that already exists than into a cloudless region—as may be observed when a large convection cloud virtually damps down convection around it, or when persistent and vigorous convection from the sun-facing slopes of a mountain escarpment inhibits the development of cumulus over the adjoining lowland. The process is often very noticeable when convection occurs over very large areas of an ocean or a continent, and in such regions the convection clouds may virtually organise themselves into bands, streets or groups between which the subsidence of the environment produces a stable layer down to about 200–600 ft (60–200 m) below the general level of the cloud base. Such a layer is frequently referred to as the *subcloud layer*. It appears that this subcloud layer is more likely to form in an anticyclonic MSL pressure pattern than in a low pressure situation. When a subcloud layer exists it is usually difficult to climb with a dry thermal through this stable layer into cloud. In such a thermalling situation it is usually wise to tighten the thermalling within the core of the thermal, because it is the core that is most likely to penetrate the subcloud layer and reach cloud base.

Spreading out of cumulus

One of the principal factors governing the life history of a convection cloud is the humidity of its environment. In a fairly dry environment evaporation at the periphery of the cloud will considerably reduce the chances of small individual clouds persisting for longer than about 15 minutes, but if the environment is very humid then not only will the rate of evaporation be reduced, but its effect may be to increase the water vapour content of the immediate environment of the thermal to the saturation value. The cloudiness will spread out from the thermal, and the cumulus cloud will degenerate into a large patch of stratocumulus which will literally cast a shadow over thermal soaring prospects for anything between 15 minutes and a few hours. This spreading out of cumulus to form large patches of stratocumulus is usually called overclouding. It is not uncommon in moist temperate climates for overclouding to occur towards midday and last for an hour or two, after which substantial breaks in the cloud are sufficient to allow sun's heating to penetrate to ground-level and trigger off more thermals.

The development of cumulus followed by a spreading out of the cloud before a regeneration of convection is sometimes referred to as a *recycling* of thermal soaring conditions. This name is useful in that it expresses the process in one word, but it should be used with caution. On long midsummer days the spreading out and regeneration process may occur at about midday and be repeated later in the afternoon—which means two cycles (good–poor–good–poor–good soaring conditions). But on most occasions the process is not a repetitive sequence that is repeated over several cycles. Shorter period cyclical changes can and do occur in the atmosphere, and they can influence thermal soaring conditions, but the variations they produce are usually too small to detect, predict and use with sufficient accuracy and confidence for soaring tactics.

Effects of wind shear

Winds and wind shear exert much the same effects on cloudy thermals as on dry thermals; wind shear up through the convection cloud layer causes the cumulus clouds to lean in the downshear direction. The upshear side of the cumulus tends to be more favourable for lift than the downshear region which may include a marked downdraught at the edge of the cloud. In practice, it is not easy to discern the direction of a slight wind shear, but when a cumulus cloud has a noticeable tilt and the upshear side appears to be freshly formed compared to the downshear side, lift sometimes

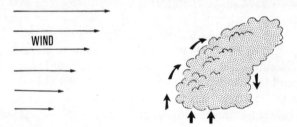

Fig. 13.3(a)   Lift sometimes exists outside a convection cloud on the upshear side. The wind shear is indicated by the tilt in the cloud profile.

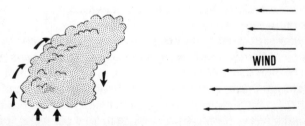

Fig. 13.3(b)   When the wind decreases with height convection clouds appear to slope backwards with height, i.e. backwards in relation to the direction in which they are moving. Lift on the outside of such a cloud is still likely to be on the upshear side.

exists not only within the cloud but also outside the cloud on the upshear side, as indicated in Figures 13.3(a) and (b). When the wind shear is very strong, however, it is likely to distort the cloud structure and lift pattern so much that the clouds are scarcely worth exploring for lift.

Cloud streams and cloud streets

Conditions favourable for cloud streams or cloud streets are similar to those that organise thermals into thermal streams or streets—ideally a wind whose direction is fairly constant with height and, for cloud streets, the additional condition that the convective layer should be capped by a stable layer. Cloud streams are likely to develop downwind of quasi-continuous thermal sources. The lengths of streams stemming from particularly active thermal sources are often between 5 and 25 km; the spacing between parallel streams is determined primarily by the distribution of the thermal sources, and is therefore not necessarily regular.

When the convective layer is capped by a stable layer, more regularly spaced cloud streets are likely to form. The distance between adjacent streets is usually about two to three times the general depth of the convective layer; in other words, if the tops of small cumulus clouds are mostly at, say, 10 000 ft (3 km) the space in between the cloud streets is likely to be between about 6 and 10 km. Because the cloud street formation is a regional-scale feature, the location of the streets is not necessarily, or easily, related to the location of active thermal sources. Sometimes, the street pattern overrides the effect of local thermal sources; sometimes, a particularly active local thermal source superimposes its effects on the street pattern.

Regular patterns of cloud streets are more common and can cover bigger areas than is generally supposed. Cloud street regions with a length of more than 800 km along wind and a width of 400 km or more are not uncommon, particularly in oceanic trade wind areas and in high latitude regions such as Finland. Within such a region the cloud street pattern is usually made up of a number of parallel streets of lengths up to about 100 km rather than a simple set of streets running the whole length of the region. Very long streets are seldom straight along their entire length. When they form in a

NORTH

Plate 12 SATELLITE VIEW OF CLOUD STREETS
This photograph taken from an *Apollo* satellite shows long cloud streets
over south Georgia, USA. Although this pattern is evident to the spaceman, it is seldom quite so clear to the glider pilot flying just beneath the
cloud base. But if the cloud base is high, the pilot can sometimes see the
pattern revealed by cloud shadows on the ground.

region where the MSL isobars curve around a low or high pressure region the streets will be aligned approximately along the curved isobars.

Very occasionally, after cloud streets have formed they break up then reform in a slightly different direction. This change of direction normally means that the depth of convection has suddenly extended upwards through a wind shear and that the general wind flow in the convective layer has been changed by the wind above the shear.

Thermal and cloud streets have occasionally been observed to drift slowly sideways across the line of the streets. Detailed observations in such occurrences are too sparse to justify an unequivocal explanation of the drift, but it seems likely that, when the wind direction above the streets differs from that in the convection layer below, the streets are liable to drift in the direction of the wind shear.

Downdraughts between cloud streets are usually more marked than those between dry thermal streets. When streets form it is usually possible to fly for considerable distances along the streets just under cloud base. But the view of a pilot flying just under cloud base is too restricted to see the street pattern by looking at the clouds; from such a viewpoint the pattern is better revealed by cloud shadows on the ground.

Thermal waves

A stable layer capping a convection layer below is a favourable condition not only for cloud streets but also for waves, which will be discussed in Chapter 17. The additional condition for waves to form in an airstream that is also suitable for cloud streets is the existence of a strong wind shear in the stable layer just above the convection layer. Figure 13.4 illustrates the type of wind structure needed. When these conditions are fulfilled, the cloud streets can act as a series of parallel mountain ridges, across which the air aloft flows in a wavelike pattern, as sketched in Figure 13.4. When this occurs it is sometimes possible to climb, not only along the upshear side of the clouds, but also in the clear air above the clouds. It appears that this type of airflow pattern, known as a *thermal wave*, has been discovered only in the last decade. Like all recently discovered soaring patterns, it is likely that they occur more often than is generally

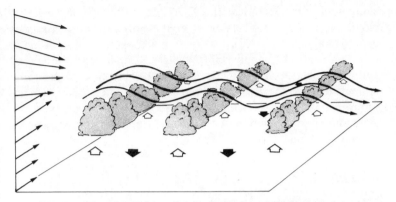

Fig. 13.4   Thermal waves can occur when the wind direction changes markedly above a layer in which cloud streets exist. The air over the top virtually rides over the cloud streets as though the streets were a series of hill ridges. Thermal streets can also trigger off waves above the streets when such a wind shear exists. The waves are known as thermal waves. They are not precisely stationary; they, together with the thermal or cloud streets, sometimes appear to shift slowly across the line of the streets.

supposed. In 1967 I climbed over the top of cumulus to 9000 ft over Narromine (northern New South Wales) in thermal waves without realising what they were; by 1975 Ingo Renner and other pilots had soared to over 20 000 ft in thermal waves in this region.

Thermal streets without convection cloud can also trigger off thermal waves if a wind shear exists at the top of the thermal layer, but thermal waves are more likely when cloud streets exist.

Thermal waves are not always stationary; they often move slowly—along with a sideways drift of the underlying thermal or cloud streets usually associated with the thermal waves.

Group structures

In light wind conditions groups of thermals have been observed to form a cluster in the shape of a ring whose diameter is about five times the height of the convective layer. Although the individual convection cells in such a ring usually last for less than 30 minutes, the ring as a whole can sometimes be identified for a few hours.

When convection begins cumulus clouds are generally small and evenly distributed, unless there are no clearly dominant thermal sources. However, it has been noticed that as the sizes of individual clouds increase and the total number of clouds decreases, groups of clouds tend to cluster together to form a conglomeration of many cumulus clouds of widely differing sizes, usually with the largest cumulus near the focus of development. This type of grouping appears to assist the growth of large cumulus. When this occurs the group becomes self-sustaining, and tends to draw in air from the surrounding zone, thereby continuing to grow at the expense of individual clouds outside the group.

Cumulus in mountainous areas

Where a mountain range is set in an area of wide plains, the pattern of convection changes during the day. The sun-facing slopes are usually the first to trigger off thermals but this does not prevent the development of thermals over the plains during the morning. For some time, convection, indicated by small cumulus clouds, occurs over both high and low ground. Later in the day, as the

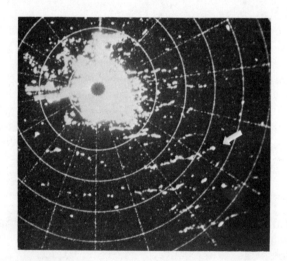

Plate 13   RADAR VIEW OF SWIFTS IN DRY THERMAL STREETS
On 12 July 1956 conditions over England were suitable for the formation of dry thermal streets. Swifts flying on food-collecting missions in these streets were revealed by the lines of radar echoes shown in the photographs. The range circles are at 10-mile intervals.

airflow towards the mountains increases, the cumulus over the slopes becomes dominant, while slow subsidence over the plains suppresses the cumulus over the adjacent low ground.

When the speed of the airstream over the top of the mountain peaks is moderate or fresh, cumulus clouds that develop from heating over the slopes are likely to be small and soon carried away downwind. When the upper wind is light, or is blowing on the shaded side of the ridge, the anabatic flow up the sun-facing slopes can form a convergence zone over the peak where it meets the upper wind flow. An almost steady circulation then develops with persistent cumulus over the peak.

Because parcels of air flowing amongst mountains follow such tortuous paths and have such diverse histories, it is unwise to reckon on one single condensation level being appropriate to a mountainous region. The condensation level in one valley may be quite different at times from that in the next, particularly during the early part of the day when entirely different circulations are separated by low level and valley inversions. During the afternoon, when convection has produced more mixing, the cloud base tends to become more uniform, and is usually considerably higher than over the adjacent plains.

14

Convective Storms

When convection occurs in an airstream that is cool and fairly moist over some considerable depth, some of the convection clouds can grow to great heights. The broader and deeper an individual cumulus cloud becomes, the better are its chances of it developing even more because it tends to draw thermals in through its base and protect these thermals from dilution and evaporation into the surrounding clear air. When the convection cloud is deep enough for one or both of the basic rainfall production mechanisms (described in Chapter 4) to function, some of its moisture will begin to fall as raindrops. Because these rainmaking processes are sudden, rainfall from a convection cloud is normally in the form of a local sharp shower, rather than the more gentle, prolonged, but lighter rainfall from layer clouds.

A cloud can extend to well above the freezing level without its water drops freezing. There is a general shortage of freezing nuclei in the atmosphere on which water droplets can freeze; droplets become supercooled. As described in Chapter 4, the freezing process is slow to start, but once started it can spread through the cloud above the freezing-level very quickly. The outline of the convection cloud is a good indicator of whether or not this glaciation process has occurred. Before glaciation the water droplets produce the hard cauliflower appearance that is characteristic of cumulus clouds. After glaciation, the ice crystals give the upper reaches of the cloud a fuzzy profile. Glaciation also helps to prolong the life of the cloud. Ice crystals evaporate much more slowly than water drops so that when a convection cloud becomes glaciated it suffers less shrinkage and cooling at its sides by evaporation into its environment. This also adds to the chances of the cloud growing even more, and, in a particularly unstable airstream, it may grow many thousands of feet vertically to become a cumulonimbus. Depths of over 20 000 ft for cumulonimbus clouds are not uncommon. Usually the tropopause is the level at which tops of cumulonimbus clouds level out, but vigorous cunimbs have been observed to penetrate several thousand feet into the stratosphere.

As this development process goes on, the big convective cloud becomes more and more self-stoking—usually at the expense of thermals and small cloud development in a wide surrounding area. The cloud begins to develop its own flow system, including updraughts and downdraughts that are more organised than the thermal currents of the smaller convective systems. The updraught in one or more of the developing cells in the cumulonimbus is likely to be in the form of a deep column of air rising at speeds of between 20 and 60 knots (40 and 120 m/s). Even higher vertical speeds, exceeding 100 knots (50 m/s), have been estimated in some severe convective storms.

Plate 14   LARGE CUMULUS
These large cumulus, in this picture, are also showing some signs of cloud street formation. Cloud streets are more often associated with smaller convection clouds.

This tremendous lift is not always turbulent. Sometimes it appears to be fairly smooth because the updraught is broad in relation to the circling diameter of a glider within it. However, the edge of the lift is likely to be very rough, especially if it is at the transition between the updraught and a neighbouring downdraught in the cloud.

Downdraughts in a cumulonimbus cloud are also likely to be strong and deep. They are more likely to occur when the precipitation is heaviest, but precipitation is not a sure sign of downdraught; precipitation can also occur in lift where the cumulonimbus is developing.

Although a moderate or strong wind shear may be disruptive to dry thermals and small cumulus formation, such a wind shear through the much greater depth of a cumulonimbus cloud is a positive aid to the development of the larger convective storm system. The wind shear is usually strongest near the top of the cumulonimbus cloud and its visible effect is the plume of cirrus that stretches out from the top of the cumulonimbus. This plume of ice crystal cloud gives the whole cumulonimbus structure its characteristic anvil shape, as illustrated in Figure 14.1.

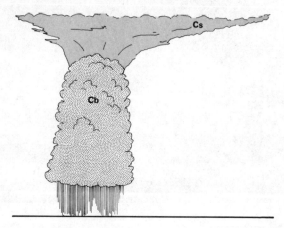

Fig. 14.1   Characteristic anvil shape of the top of a cumulonimbus cloud.

Ice accretion

Supercooled water droplets in cloud above the freezing-level freeze readily on contact with a solid object, and are therefore likely to form ice on a glider, especially at the leading edges of the aerofoils and at exposed joints. Very often this ice accretion is not serious, but it is feasible for a glider to have its windscreen covered and its control surfaces jammed by ice while still being carried aloft

Plate 15 CUMULONIMBUS DEVELOPMENT

These four photographs taken at approximately 5-min intervals show cumulonimbus clouds moving from left to right in the pictures. The anvil cloud in the top photographs reveals that the wind speed increases with height. The top of the large cumulonimbus in the foreground rose very quickly and the cloud produced a shower of rain, but by the end of the 15-min period this cloud was beginning to decay while the rapid growth of new convection cloud was apparent, both on its upshear side (in this case on the left) and the downshear side. Notice the relatively firm outlines of the cumiliform tops of the new convection clouds compared to the more fibrous top of the older cumulonimbus cloud. Such outlines indicate that the new clouds are still composed mainly of water drops, while the older convection cloud has matured past the glaciation stage.

in a thermal, and then to enter a strong downdraught in which it descends to a dangerously low level before the ice has melted. To minimise the danger of icing it is wise to try to avoid lingering only just above the freezing-level too long—this is where the ice accretion is likely to be rapid. At higher levels where the cloud is composed mainly of ice crystals rather than supercooled water droplets the icing hazard is reduced.

To realise fully the extent of the hazard of descending through cloud base in an iced-up glider, we must also remember that cloud base usually lowers considerably in precipitation.

Thunder and lightning

Lightning is the electrical spark discharge which takes place in a strong electrostatic gradient between oppositely charged regions of cloud or between cloud and the ground. Within range of about 40 km the noise of this spark may be heard as thunder.

Since the flash and the noise originate simultaneously, the nearness of the discharge may be determined by noting the time interval between the lightning and the thunder, and remembering that sound travels about 1 km in 3 seconds. The lightning flash itself may be a kilometre or more in length—intercloud discharges of over 80 km in length have been observed during radar studies of long lines of cumulonimbus clouds. The sound from the whole length of a flash may therefore continue to be heard for several seconds, and echoes from hills or buildings add to the reverberations.

A gradient of about three million volts per metre is required to trigger off a lightning discharge, and many thousands of volts per metre to extend the length of the spark. Such electrostatic gradients in the atmosphere are built up by individually minute but collectively potent events in the life histories of raindrops and ice crystals in a cumulonimbus cloud. The differential electrostatic charging of various regions in the cloud is particularly efficient if the cloud contains an abundant supply of both liquid water and ice particles, and observations confirm that neither clouds which do not extend far above the freezing-level nor clouds which are entirely above the freezing-level are efficient generators of thunderstorms.

Although the electrical potential associated with lightning is measured in millions of volts, the electric current is very small and

Plate 16   LARGE CUMULUS WITH DISTANT CUMULONIMBUS
Anvil cirrus cloud from a distant cumulonimbus is spread out towards the
gliding field in this picture. As air at low levels will probably be sucked into
this major development of the distant cumulonimbus it is likely that local
convection conditions over the airfield will weaken as the storm
approaches. There is also a possibility that a downdraught from the
convective storm will spread out towards the airfield.

the structure of a thoroughly bonded metal glider is adequate to
conduct a lightning discharge with little or no damage. Safety in a
basically non-metallic glider, however, often rests on the statisti-
cally small chance of it actually being struck by a powerful discharge. A protruding or trailing radio aerial increases the risk of the
aircraft being struck; should this occur it is almost certain that the
aerial will be damaged or destroyed and there would be a risk of fire
breaking out in the equipment. The most common electrostatic
manifestations in soaring in thunderstorms are *St. Elmo's fire*
(myriads of small spark discharges associated with instruments and
other metal fittings) and a hissing or crackling which may build up to
a crescendo before a somewhat bigger discharge takes place somewhere in the thundercloud.

As with ice accretion and small-scale turbulence, the region of the
freezing-level seems to be particularly prone to these electrostatic

Plate 17   MAMMATUS CLOUD
These bulges of cloud hanging from the rain-bearing bulk of cloud are
known as mammatus clouds. They are a sure sign of downdraught which
has been triggered off by precipitation.

manifestations. A lightning discharge usually causes electric currents to flow in diverse parts of the storm and a glider pilot in a
non-metallic aircraft may receive from the controls electric shocks
which range from mere twinges to painful spasms. Bonding the
aircraft nose to tail and wing-tip to wing-tip increases the chances of
it being struck, but considerably enhances the structural safety of
the aircraft in the thousand-to-one chance of it being struck by a
really powerful stroke of lightning.

Just over 200 years ago, in an age when electric experiments were
a drawing-room novelty, Benjamin Franklin dabbled with atmospheric electricity by obtaining sparks from a wire stretching up to a
kite flying below a thundery cumulonimbus. Wisely, perhaps, he
used an assistant to perform the experiments! He was virtually
prodding the thunderstorm with an efficient lightning conductor. A
glider launching wire stretching from a winch or tow car on the
ground to a glider at several hundred feet is also an efficient
lightning conductor; if a thunderstorm is practically overhead the
risk of lightning striking a glider during the launch is very considera-

ble and the effect of such a strike would probably be to damage the
aircraft and, if the winch or tow car were not earthed, to harm the
operator.

People struck by lightning are not charged with electricity. They
can be touched at once and, if they are still alive, may need artificial
respiration if, as is often the case, their breathing mechanism has
been temporarily paralysed.

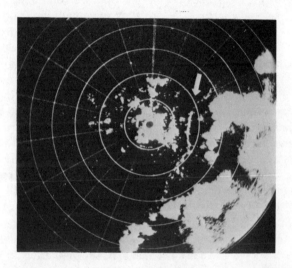

Plate 18 RADAR ECHOES FROM SWIFTS IN A LINE SQUALL
Bright patches in the centre of this radar picture are due to reflections from
buildings and other obstacles, but the larger echoes to the east and
south-east are caused by heavy showers in a broad band moving from the
east. This band was preceded by line squall effects which included the
wedgelike advance of cold air at low levels. The thin line of echoes
indicated by the arrow are due to the large number of swifts feeding on
insects in the narrow belt of lift associated with the line squall effect. The
range circles are at 10-mile intervals.

The normal zigzag pattern of a lightning stroke with its various
branches is appropriately described as *forked lightning*, while *summer lightning* is a popular though unscientific description of visible
lightning which is too far away to be heard, and *sheet lightning* is
another colloquial name applied to the illumination of the sky by a
distant concealed stroke. The rare *thunderbolts* which are observed
appear as slowly moving balls of some glowing form of electrical

activity, but both descriptions and understanding of them are very sketchy.

Hail

Static and lightning can be frightening, but the worst hazard to modern gliders in a cumulonimbus is hail. In vigorous convection clouds growing hailstones encounter, and are sometimes carried aloft by, several thermals before they eventually fall out of the cloud, and, with accumulated coatings of opaque or glazed ice, their ultimate size is comparable to that of peas or small marbles. In the powerful updraughts in violent convection clouds some hailstones may not fall out of cloud until they have grown to the size of golf balls or even larger. Hailstones with diameters of 5 cm (2 in.) have been encountered at ground-level in freak showers in the British Isles, while in some warmer climates hailstone diameters of 15 cm (6 in.) have been recorded. Hailstones of about 1 cm (nearly half an inch) in diameter fall through the air at about 30 knots (69 km/h) and are therefore formidable missiles capable of inflicting expensive damage on parked gliders. Gliders in the air, of course, will collide with hailstones at the vector sum of their airspeed and the falling speed of the hailstones. Fortunately, most hailstones are somewhat smaller than this, and hail showers themselves are usually short lived; such showers usually become rain showers after the initial short sharp burst of hail. It is not easy to predict whether or not a shower will precipitate damaging hailstones. Obviously hail will not fall from an isolated convection cloud whose top does not extend up

---

Plate 19   DOWNDRAUGHT FROM CONVECTIVE STORM
In the top picture a Blanik is about to take off from Benalla (Australia) gliding field as a heavy convective storm approaches. Soon after the take-off more ragged fractostratus formed (as shown in the centre picture) in rain which was still fairly light over the airfield itself. But soon after this the extent of the downdraught of the storm was evident in the cloud formation shown in the bottom photograph. This picture shows the downdraught effect just behind the storm. It was stronger and more widespread just ahead of the storm, but the cloud pattern ahead of the storm could not be photographed so clearly at this stage. However, the returning Blanik pilot found a very strong wind shear on the approach to the airfield and such a strong headwind at very low intervals that he only just managed to reach the field.

to or above the freezing-level. Nor is hail likely in a convection cloud which is so cold that it cannot contain an abundance of water drops to coat the falling ice pellets with a number of shells, and a convection cloud which lacks really strong thermals is likely to let raindrops fall out before the incipient hailstones can grow.

Precipitation downdraught

Lift is frequently located in precipitation underneath or inside cumulonimbus clouds, but precipitation also exerts a frictional or downward drag on the air, and, in some parts of the cloud, it can trigger off a downdraught that accelerates downwards and keeps going right down to ground-level where it spreads out in a shallow layer, as illustrated in Figure 14.2.

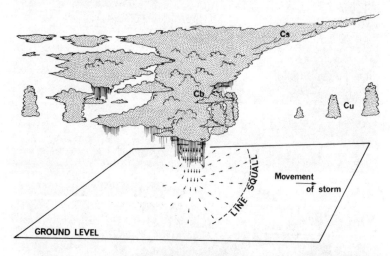

Fig. 14.2   Precipitation downdraught flowing down in precipitation from a deep convection cloud and spreading out as a shallow layer of cold air over the ground.

This spreading out of a precipitation downdraught into a shallow layer adds very considerably to the low-level wind gradient hazard. Such a spreading out is often extensive, especially when the stormcloud is anchored over a mountainside. A particularly sharp wind shear can exist between the light winds blowing towards a stationary cumulonimbus situated over a windward escarpment and the precipitation downdraught which flows down the mountainside and spreads out over the adjoining plain. On 11 July 1952, during the World Gliding Championships, the depth of this undercutting cold air, illustrated in Figure 14.3, was only about 120 ft (40 m) at Madrid (about 70 km from the mountains). R. Ortner who signified his completion of the day's task by swooping his Sky Sailplane low over the airfield, suddenly found his airspeed rising from 75 to 110 knots (with alarming downward flexure of the Sky's wing-tips) as he entered the shallow cold air. Another, and this time tragic experience, was that of a pilot whose two-seater glider stalled and crashed on descending into, and in the same direction as, the undercutting cold flow.

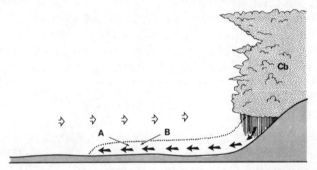

Fig. 14.3 The schematically illustrated spreading out of a downdraught and the associated low-level wind shear at Madrid on 11 July 1962, during the World Gliding Championships. A and B show the approach paths of gliders mentioned in the text above.

Since the extensive spreading out of such precipitation downdraught may not be easily detectable from the air, it is wise for ground-crews or controllers to be alert for signs of the cold air and to try to communicate their observations by radio or signals to pilots flying in the locality. Of course, the spreading out of the downdraughts are not always as extensive as that just described; in many situations the downdraught and the spreading out causes little more than a temporary slight wind shift with some gustiness. However, the glider pilot should always be on the alert for this type of phenomenon whenever he is in the vicinity of convective storms. Sometimes the cumulonimbus cloud provides a clue to the existence of a downdraught by having mammatus cloud formation under the cloud base. These hanging bulges of cloud which comprise a sort of upside-down cumulus formation are sure signs of downdraughts coming down through the cloud base.

The thunderstorm high

The initiation and development of a strong downdraught in a precipitating cumulonimbus is often so sudden that the near balance between the net inflow of air into the cloud base and outflow at high levels is tilted sharply in favour of net accumulation of air with an accompanying rise in the MSL pressure immediately under the storm. The resultant dwarf anticyclone is called a *thunderstorm high* and, though the majority of such anticyclones are too weak to be obvious, it is not unusual for a group or line of vigorous storms to produce pressure surges of a millibar or two and to produce pressure patterns like those illustrated in Figure 14.4.

Line squalls

In spreading out at ground-level a thunderstorm downdraught acts as a wedge forcing up the air in its path, and if, as a result of wind shear in the convective layer, the spreading out is concentrated mainly in one direction, then this lifting may well be sufficient to trigger off convection on the downshear side of the main storm centre. Thus a thunderstorm over flat countryside can propagate itself roughly in a downshear direction without being fed by a supply of thermals from fixed ground-level sources.

Convective storm studies suggest that fresh convective development in self-propagating convective systems tend to occur in the locations sketched in Figure 14.5. The details of these arrangements of development probabilities will vary somewhat according to the local topography and the prevailing wind shear, but these variations will not detract from the general conclusion that once a few neighbouring storms are arranged into a line across the general wind direction they tend to consolidate and perpetuate the line formation. If, as is commonly the case, the line is preceded or accompanied by severe gusts of wind, it is called a *line squall*.

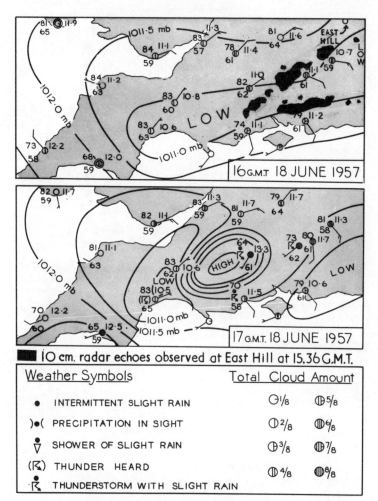

Fig. 14.4 At 16 GMT the principal thunderstorms over southern England were between the observing stations, and a weak low-pressure system covered the whole region. But within the next hour a thunderstorm high developed suddenly in association with a precipitation downdraught. Temperatures (°F), dew points, pressures, winds, weather and cloud amounts are plotted in the system shown in Figure 19.1. The thunderstorm high, together with its cold downdraught, maintained its identity for several hours as it moved westwards at about 25 knots (40 km/h).

Northern Hemisphere

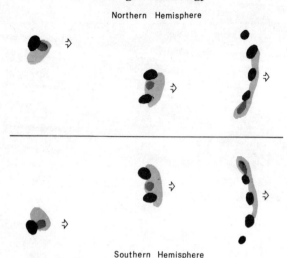

Southern Hemisphere

Fig. 14.5   In general there are likely to be wide areas of no lift or slow sink around dominant convective clouds, but when precipitation downdraughts occur they are likely to trigger off more convective developments in the hatched areas in front of, between, or towards the low-latitude side of the existing large convection clouds, illustrated by the very dark patches in this diagram.

In its most pronounced state the passage of a line squall is marked by:

1 a sudden slight pressure rise during the approach of the thunderstorm high (which is often masked by a broader scale troughing of the isobars across a line squall);

2 a very sharp veer (back) in the wind direction in the northern (southern) hemisphere;

3 considerable gustiness which reaches a peak at about the same time as

4 a drop in temperature and a rise in humidity, which precedes

5 a burst of heavy precipitation followed by between about 10 and 30 minutes' lighter rainfall.

Line squalls which form either on or parallel to and just ahead of cold fronts are often a few hundred kilometres in length, but when the organisation of cumulonimbus clouds into a line is the result of local topographical effects (such as the preferential heating on sun-facing slopes of a mountain range) then the line squall is often less than 300 km in length and may even be too short to be clearly distinguished on routine weather charts.

The wedgelike action of the cold air advancing at ground-level is often sufficient to produce a belt of lift just in front of the zone of heavy precipitation. Using such lift as this, Hanna Reitsch flew her Zugvogel glider at an average speed of 51 knots (102 km/h) over a 46-naut. mile (92-km) course from Orlinghausen to Dortmund, Germany. A schematic cross-section of the cloud structure is sketched in Figure 14.6. Luckily the line squall moved westwards

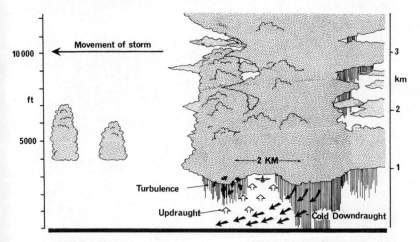

Fig. 14.6 Observations made by Hanna Reitsch suggest that the line squall she encountered was being displaced eastwards by both movement and fresh development of convection cloud and rain in advance of the main storm system.

across the course with the right speed to allow a long straight soaring flight in about the position indicated in the sketch. Visibility towards the east was considerably reduced by heavy precipitation, and from time to time the port wing plunged into this precipitation, which occasionally included hail and snow. To the west small cumulus clouds illuminated by bright sunshine were still visible but gradually thickening streaks of rain suggested that some development of the cloud and precipitation system was taking place along a line just to the west of the flight path. In order to reduce the possibility of being cut off from visual flight conditions by this development, an attempt was made to fly the Zugvogel westwards to beyond the newly formed leading edge of the precipitating cloud, but such severe turbulence was encountered in the development zone that a return to the remarkably smooth flight conditions of the rain-free channel was preferred. The strength of the continuous lift in this narrow

Plate 20 FUNNEL CLOUD
After extending from cloud base at 2600 ft obliquely downwards to about 1300 ft above ground-level, this funnel cloud developed close to the Dunstable site of the London Gliding Club on the afternoon of 12 October 1958. During the half-hour before the phenomenon gradually faded away several gliders flew in strong lift and in reasonable comfort close to the rapidly rotating funnel of cloud. John Costin felt a violent jolt when he flew quickly through the tip of the funnel. Although this rapidly rotating vortex was only a mild species of tornado, winds at ground-level were locally strong enough to damage a few farmyard buildings. The practice of flying in the vicinity of such clouds is not, of course, recommended.

channel may be gauged by the fact that a constant altitude could be maintained at soaring flight speeds of between 60 and 85 knots (120 and 170 km/h).

In hot dry climates it is not uncommon for downdraughts from convection storms to create sandstorms which start suddenly and have a well-defined leading edge—especially if the downdraught is associated with a line squall. The sand is raised to heights of several hundred feet and occasionally to 1000 ft or so. Often the convection storms that trigger such a downdraught have a high base and the associated precipitation evaporates before it reaches the ground. The best-known sandstorms of this type are the *Haboobs* of Sudan.

Tornadoes

With a mechanism somewhat similar to that of a dust devil, a tornado is a rotating funnel of cloud pointing downwards from a convection cloud. A tornado, however, has an additional source of energy in the form of latent heat released during the condensation of water vapour in the ascending and rotating air. Therefore this phenomenon is usually more vigorous and persistent than a dust devil.

The funnel cloud does not necessarily hang vertically from its parent cloud; it may be tilted, or it may swing rather erratically below the main cloud base. It may or may not reach the ground and in some cases (especially at line squalls) several funnel clouds may reach down from the same convection cloud.

The diameter of the tip of a funnel cloud is usually in the range from several metres to a few hundred metres, but extreme widths of over 2000 m have been observed. The winds are very strong within and close to the funnel cloud, and in extreme cases their speeds have been estimated to be over 200 knots (400 km/h). Outside the destructive central core the wind speed decreases very sharply; even only 100 m away from the rapidly rotating core the winds can be light and not at all destructive. The risk of destructive winds, nonetheless, will be great because of the tendency of some tornadoes to meander along their path of travel.

The passage of a tornado is often accompanied by a temporary but very sudden pressure drop whose magnitude is approximately 30 mb per 1000 ft height of the funnel cloud (10 mb per 100 m). For example, if the tip of a funnel cloud is 1500 ft below the base of its parent cloud the pressure at the tip will be about 45 mb less than that at the same level outside the tornado. Thus, as a tornado passes over a building the outside pressure drops so suddenly that the walls and the roofs are liable to be blown outwards unless doors and windows are left open to allow a freer flow of air. Most tornadoes persist only for a few minutes but a 'twister', as the Americans call it, maintains its identity for an hour or more and leaves a narrow trail of destruction along a path that can range from 100 to 500 km long.

The Great Plains of the USA, stretching from the Gulf of Mexico to Canada, have more tornadoes than anywhere else on earth. The zone comprising Texas, Oklahoma, Kansas and Missouri has been called 'Tornado Alley'. Kansas is nicknamed the 'Cyclone State', but Oklahoma is more tornado-prone considering its smaller size. Although tornadoes are mostly isolated and sometimes referred to as 'loners', a dozen or so may form in a region on a tornado-prone day. In such conditions tornadoes sometimes form in families and move in the same direction along a belt several kilometres wide.

Tornadoes occur in many regions and more often than is generally supposed. The British Isles, for example, is not normally considered as a tornado-prone country, but destructive tornadoes appear to occur on an average of about once in two years and funnel clouds not reaching ground-level are reported in meteorological literature several times a year inland in the southern half of England. It is practically certain, however, that a number of funnel clouds are not brought to the notice of meteorologists and aviators. The majority of the British Isles' tornadoes have moved towards the north-north-east in slow, unstable air masses on the forward side of a trough of low pressure.

The tornado season extends roughly from early spring to late autumn and they occur mostly in the afternoon, but they are not confined to these seasons and times; tornadoes occasionally occur in winter-time and at night.

Conditions favourable for tornado development include:

1 the presence of a cold front;
2 moist, unstable air from ground-level up to a few thousand feet, capped by

3 a very shallow stable layer under a
4 deep and relatively dry, unstable layer of air.

Tornadoes formed by local convective processes are mostly weak but those associated with cold fronts or line squalls are more likely to be of the more powerful and persistent variety. Convection over the sea or lakes can also give rise to funnel clouds which often extend downstream to link up with spray whirled up from the water surface. The resultant column of spray and cloud is called a *waterspout*.

Medium-level convection

Convective instability is sometimes produced within an extensive layer of slowly rising air. Such instability is often confined to medium levels and is indicated by the presence of altocumulus castellanus. Because the updraughts associated with the individual clouds are usually weak and confined to medium levels, this type of convection is not normally suitable for thermal soaring. Occasionally altocumulus castellanus forms in straight lines, looking like medium-level cloud streets, but in some situations, particularly those associated with hot summer-time depressions, medium-level instability produces convection cloud over such extensive regions that the cloud mass looks more like altostratus from below. Sometimes this type of medium-level cloud is many thousands of feet deep and produces prolonged showers or thunderstorms. These thundery depressions are usually slow moving and can persist for many days. The general conditions can be correctly described as convectively unstable, but this type of instability and convection is useless for thermal soaring at lower levels.

Radar views of convection phenomena

Precipitation from convection cloud is usually detectable as a bright patch on the radar screen, and, by watching these echoes, the progress of showers can be followed within a range of about 150 km from the radar apparatus. This radar picture is a valuable aid to predicting the local likelihood of showers up to about 2 hours in advance, but the speed of development and the change of pattern of precipitation within the zones of convective activity make longer period forecasting difficult. The radar picture, nevertheless, provides a view of the precipitation pattern in considerably more detail than can normally be gleaned from routine weather charts; a short line squall conspicuous as a line of precipitation echoes on the radar screen may be indistinguishable from an isolated shower on the routine weather chart and the radar observer will often have a better overall view of the precipitation in a cluster of convective clouds than a pilot flying in or near the actual clouds.

Because the most commonly used 10-cm radars detect precipitation and not cloud, the radar screen does not show a comprehensive view of thermal activity. On some occasions, echoes are received from flights of birds who happen to be soaring or searching for insects in convective updraughts. Such echoes may be caused by swallows, martins or gulls but the swift is the most interesting radar indicator of organised thermal updraughts. When their young are in the nest and must be fed throughout daylight hours of good weather, the adult swifts fly mainly between 20 and 100 ft, but occasionally as high as several thousand feet above ground, collecting insects carried aloft by thermals. They fly in such large numbers that, when the convection is organised into a pattern of thermal streets, concentrations of birds along these streets have been evident as radar echoes showing the streets. Concentrations of swifts have also acted as radar markers delineating a band of updraught along a line squall.

Higher resolution radar can reveal more details of a convective pattern but such radar facilities are not normally available for routine operational use; they are used mainly for research and special investigations.

15

Thermal Soaring Prospects

Before leaving the subject of convection it may be useful to extract from the last three chapters the main points to remember when considering thermal structure and thermal soaring prospects. We can note that:

1 A dry thermal layer can be considered as two layers:
   (a) a superadiabatic layer from ground-level up to between a few hundred feet (in temperate climates) and several thousand feet (in blazing sunshine over arid country);
   (b) a dry adiabatic layer from the top of the superadiabatic layer up to the base of a stable layer or temperature inversion.
2 The superadiabatic layer is a somewhat turbulent breeding layer both for incipient thermals and downdraughts.
3 Thermals tend to leave ground-level as columns, but as they ascend in the atmosphere they tend to acquire a vortex ring structure—though the ring is not necessarily circular.
4 In a dry thermal layer the temperature lapse rate above the superadiabatic layer is usually very close to the DALR. In this adiabatic layer there are fewer thermals than at lower levels, but they are more organised. They tend to develop vortex ring characteristics and become broader as they ascend.
5 On reaching the top of a dry thermal layer a thermal often exhibits slight turbulence before it is dissipated.
6 A steady wind with little or no change of direction with height coupled with a fairly definite lid to the top of convection is favourable for thermal streets with downdraughts between the streets.
7 A wind shear through a very shallow layer within the thermal layer is likely to produce slight turbulence in a thermal and a shift of the thermal core in the direction of the shear.

8 A pronounced wind shear throughout the thermal layer is likely to distort the thermal structure into chaotic forms difficult to use for thermal soaring.

9 Sun-facing slopes are particularly good thermal sources, except when they are heavily wooded. During much of the day thickly wooded slopes are likely to be poor thermal sources, but they may produce a few thermals late in the day. Don't forget to distinguish between sunlit slopes and sun-facing slopes; at some times of day and in some seasons some sunlit slopes are less sun-facing than flat ground.

10 Thick crops, woods and hard rock surfaces tend to produce isolated but well-organised thermals late in the day. Between The afternoon and late thermals there may be a thermal pause.

11 In heavily polluted airstreams some thermals develop within the pollution—they do not all start from ground-level.

12 On entering an existing convection cloud the thermal is given a boost.

13 Occasionally, in anticyclonic conditions, a shallow layer of stable air—called a subcloud layer—makes it difficult to climb in a thermal through the 200 ft (60 m) or so just below cloud base.

14 Some turbulence and descending air is likely at the sides (and especially the downshear side) of a convection cloud.

15 Soaring outside of convection cloud is often possible on the upshear side of the cloud.

16 A combination of thermal or cloud streets and lee wave conditions can produce thermal waves over the top of the thermal or cloud streets. Subtropical climates (where wind shear at the top of a convection layer is common) produce more thermal wave conditions than is generally realised.

17 Cumulus cloud is likely to spread out to form large patches of stratocumulus when the humidity of its environment is high.

18 A decaying cumulus whose supply of thermals is cut off is likely to have a ragged base, whereas a steady supply of thermals into a convection cloud will keep the base fairly well marked and approximately flat.

19 A well-developed convection cloud may persist even after supply of thermals from ground-level is cut off; the cloud can induce, and be maintained by, a horizontal inflow underneath its base.

20 A frequent, but not always essential, prerequisite for shower development is that the convection cloud should extend to a height above the freezing-level.

21 The spreading out of a precipitation downdraught can produce a landing hazard in the form of low-level wind changes.

Neither this summary nor the preceding three chapters provide an unequivocal answer to the question: 'Where and when will the next thermal appear?' but nature ensures that such an answer is not possible; if it were then thermal soaring would not be the intriguing sport it is.

Coherent, if somewhat flexible, ideas on convection allow the glider pilot to be more specific in his request for meteorological advice, and it is appropriate to supplement our summary with notes on thermal soaring forecasts.

Forecasts for thermal soaring

To facilitate discussion we can classify forecasts for thermal soaring into three types, namely:

1 Casual forecasts—usually in the form of impromptu replies by a forecaster to telephone inquiries from glider pilots.

2 Routine gliding forecasts—issued by a meteorological office to a nearby gliding centre according to a mutually convenient schedule.

3 Special gliding forecasts—usually prepared at a meteorological office temporarily established for events such as a gliding championship.

When making a casual inquiry the pilot should announce that he wishes to have a thermal soaring forecast for a specific place or region for a specified period of the day. Such vague questions as 'Is it unstable today?' or 'When will the cold front arrive?' are worse than useless as opening queries. The forecaster and the glider pilot are likely to differ unwittingly in their interpretation of the significance of such questions and their answers. The response to a specific question on thermal soaring prospects will vary according to circumstances; the forecaster may or may not be extremely busy fulfilling his routine forecasting commitments and, since the majority of his commitments do not entail more than elementary ideas of convection, he may not have studied details relevant to the inquiry. Not many forecasters have much opportunity to build up experience in forecasting for thermal soaring. (In meteorological jargon, the word 'thermal' relates to thermal wind charts rather than to convection currents.) However, the forecaster's initial reply usually reveals how prepared he is to give a comprehensive thermal soaring forecast, and it is for the pilot to judge what supplementary questions are necessary. Bearing in mind that forecasters usually only have limited time to deal with each casual inquiry, the pilot should try to obtain, either directly or by inference, the answers to the most appropriate, if not all, of the following questions:

1 *Will convection from ground-level occur?*
2 *Will convection cloud form?*
3 *What will be the height* (above sea-level or ground-level, whichever is specified) *of the convection cloud base at various times of the day?*
4 *How much convection cloud will there be?* (Remember that small amounts of cumulus cloud provide better cross-country thermal soaring conditions than abundant convection cloud which is likely to reduce the chances of bright sunshine.)
5 *Will the convection cloud spread out to form large patches of stratocumulus?* (If the humidity of the environment of cumulus is high then occasional spreading out is likely.)
6 *How much medium or high cloud will there be to reduce the chances of bright sunshine?* (Weak, diffuse sunshine can be sufficiently intense to produce thermals active enough to form convection cloud but not strong enough to allow thermal soaring.)
7 *How high will the tops of the convection cloud reach?*
8 *What will be the height of the freezing-level?*
9 *Are showers expected? If so, how frequently, and will they be of rain, hail, sleet or snow? Is thunder likely?*
10 *How much will the cloud base lower in showers?*
11 *Will there be dry thermals even if convection cloud does not form? If so, to what height will the dry thermals reach?* (In other words, to what height will insolation create a DALR?)

12 *What will be the wind velocities at several levels in the convec-tion layer?* (This information is required for navigation and to assess the likelihood of thermal shear or turbulent distortion of thermals.)

13 *Are thermal streams or streets likely to develop?*

14 *At about what time will active convection at low levels die out?* (Not much forecasting experience has so far been built up around this question and, unless the synoptic situation reveals specific evidence to the contrary, the answer will usually suggest about 2–3 hours before sunset.)

15 *Are any regional convective phenomena such as line squalls or sea-breeze fronts expected?*

16 *What will the visibility be?* (For navigation and warning of pollution that may affect thermal strength and structure.)

17 *How will the large-scale synoptic features such as approaching fronts or anticyclonic subsidence affect thermal soaring pros-pects for the place or region specified?*

Some gliding clubs arrange to collect (usually by telephone) gliding forecasts from a near-by meteorological office according to a mutually convenient schedule. Such an arrangement has several obvious advantages. Prior to its inception the forecasters usually acquaint themselves with the nature of the particular forecasting problem; they can allocate sufficient routine time to prepare the forecast; they usually assess and try to improve their services and, with the forecasts available at the gliding club, there are fewer non-routine gliding inquiries to deal with.

At meteorological offices temporarily established for events such as gliding championships forecasts are usually derived from a careful watch on the local weather, temperature measurements on local flights, a detailed study of local observations within the area of operational interest, and the broader-scale analyses and forecasts issued by a central forecast office. Thus the forecaster on the spot can be reasonably well equipped to give moderately detailed fore-casts at individual or mass briefings of the assembled glider pilots and the organisers of the daily events. Much depends on the forecaster's interest and experience in gliding. His interest can be encouraged by his becoming involved in the operational aspect of gliding, and, even though he may not fly himself, he can acquire considerable experience by accruing, collating and analysing information and impressions he receives from glider pilots. The method and form of presentation of a gliding forecast are also critical factors in communication between forecasters and gliding pilots, but this subject is best discussed later in Chapter 21.

Thermal strength

A standard question put by the glider pilot to the weather forecaster is, 'What will be the thermal strength?' This is not an easy question to answer, mainly because of the variability of thermal strength and structure in any particular situation. However, attempts to amplify the question and find answers have suggested that the best single indicator of the average strength of thermals is the depth of the thermal layer. The approximate relationship for dry thermals has been noted by meteorologist Charles Lindsay to be:

Depth of dry thermal layer (height to which the DALR extends)	Mean thermal strength during climb (for a modern high-performance glider)
3000 ft (approx. 1 km)	2 knots (1 m/s)
6500 ft (approx. 2 km)	4 knots (2 m/s)
10 000 ft (approx. 3 km)	6 knots (3 m/s)

When thermals are capped by cumulus cloud the mean thermal strength appears to be greater than that for dry thermal conditions. The relationship between mean thermal strength of thermals below cumulus clouds and the height of the cloud base is:

Height of cumulus cloud base	Mean thermal strength of dry thermals below cloud base
3000 ft (approx. 1 km)	2.5 knots (1.25 m/s)
6500 ft (approx. 2 km)	5.0 knots (2.5 m/s)
10 000 ft (approx. 3 km)	7.0 knots (3.5 m/s)

It should be noted that these thermal strengths are mean rates of climb over a number of minutes rather than seconds. Thermal strengths will vary from thermal to thermal and in any one thermal there are likely to be surges of much stronger lift and occasional distortion in the thermal structure.

Thermal sensors

Because thermals are often thought of as bubbles of relatively warm buoyant air, attempts have been made to detect thermals during flight by measuring temperature differences between the air at the wing-tips of a glider. The idea has been that a thermal could be located by turning towards the wing-tip in the warmer air. Very sensitive and fast-response devices, such as thermistors, have been developed to measure air temperatures accurately enough to detect very small differences between one wing-tip and the other. However, developments on these lines have not yet produced an efficient inflight thermal location system. The main reason for the failure so far is that, above a few hundred feet or so from ground-level, temperature differences between thermals and the surrounding air are difficult if not impossible to distinguish from the very small-scale apparently random temperature fluctuations that occur anyway. Furthermore, a thermal is not necessarily warmer than the air around it. Water vapour in the air complicates the question of buoyancy. Because water vapour (which is a gas) is less dense than dry air, buoyancy in a thermal can also be the result of the thermal having slightly more water vapour than the surrounding air. Experiments indicate that at heights of more than a few hundred feet or so above ground, thermals often do have more water vapour than the surrounding air, and it appears that the buoyancy of a thermal is more likely to be due to this slight excess of water vapour than a slight excess of temperature. At low levels, within a few hundred feet or so of the ground, thermals are often measurably warmer than the surrounding air. Therefore, if we seek to develop a thermal location system based on buoyancy, we should use sensors to measure both temperature and water vapour differences between wing-tips. A small built-in computing system would be needed to convert these measurements to air density differences between the wing-tips, but at low levels (say, in the superadiabatic layer of the thermal regime) the temperature differences would predominate, while, in the dry adiabatic layer above, the humidity differences would probably be the more significant factor in the computations. Successful development of instrumentation to make and process these measurements would not necessarily guarantee the success of the thermal location system as a whole; experience at using the instrumentation would be required, and it is not yet known whether this complication of combining temperature and humidity measurements will still be too oversimplified for the problem of thermal location.

16

Sea-Breezes

On a sunny day the temperature at the surface of a land area rises more quickly than that of an adjoining sea surface. Therefore, in calm, light or possibly moderate winds, the air over land is heated more quickly than that over sea, and if the sea air is colder than that over the land then the temperature gradient across the coastline is intensified.

An early consequence of the differential heating of air across the coastline is a slight rise of pressure over land at height of about 3000 ft (1000 m) or above, accompanied by an almost imperceptible seaward flow of air at about the same level. As a result of this upper air movement, the MSL pressure over land decreases very slightly and air at low levels flows inland from the sea. At first this landward flow, called the *sea-breeze*, flows almost directly across the coast, but as the MSL pressure inland continues to fall (still only slightly) the sea-breeze increases in strength and begins to veer (in the northern hemisphere) or back (in the southern hemisphere). At the coast it is often at its strongest and is directed at about 30–50 degrees to the coastline by mid-afternoon, but from then on the speed decreases although the direction continues to change until by late afternoon the breeze is almost along the coastline, as illustrated in Figures 16.1(a) and (b).

The distance inland to which the sea-breeze penetrates depends on the duration and strength of the sunshine, on the height to which the heat from the sun is distributed, on the direction and strength of the superimposed general wind flow, and on the sea temperature. In hot climates sea-breezes are felt at distances of up to 400 km inland from the shore; in temperate latitudes about 100 km is considered a deep penetration, but this is only a rough guide. Figure 16.2 shows the deeper inland penetration that can be expected in a hot climate. Isochrones in this figure denote typical positions of the leading edge of sea-breezes that move inland over the extreme south-west of Australia. Sea-breezes in this region are so well known locally that

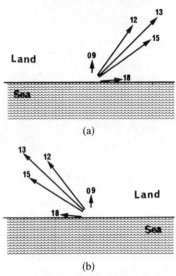

Fig. 16.1 Typical variation of wind near the coast during a day favourable for sea-breezes, (a) in the northern hemisphere and (b) in the southern
hemisphere. Numbers denote times of day in hours LST.

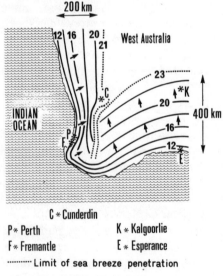

Fig. 16.2 Penetration of sea-breezes inland over the extreme south-west
of Australia. Numbers on the sea-breeze frontal positions are local times
of day.

they have acquired the name of 'Doctors'—because they bring cool relief from the summer heat. Locally these *'Doctor'* breezes are labelled by the names of the town from which they appear to come; for example, inland of Fremantle the southwesterly sea-breeze is known as the *'Fremantle Doctor'*; at Kalgoorlie the name for the cool southerly sea-breeze is the *'Esperance Doctor'*.

The arrival of a sea-breeze is often sudden—with sharp changes in wind, temperature and humidity. Figure 16.3 illustrates some of

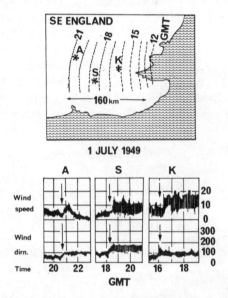

Fig. 16.3   Observations from meteorological offices were used to plot the hourly isochrones of the position of a sea-breeze front which advanced inland from the Thames Estuary on 1 July 1949. The autographic records illustrate the changes in wind speed and direction at the passage of the front.

the sharp wind changes that accompanied the arrival of a sea-breeze that moved inland from the Thames Estuary on a hot July day in England in 1949. Before the arrival of this sea-breeze, winds were light and mostly northeasterly, but the air from the sea spread inland with a slightly stronger flow from between 060 and 130 degrees, and at those stations equipped with pressure-tube anemometers the rapidity of this change and the gustiness of the sea-breeze were well marked on the autographic wind records—part of which are reproduced in Figure 16.3. Abrupt changes were also registered in the measurements of temperature and humidity, and it was apparent that the transition zone between the cool moist sea air and the dry air inland was very narrow. In fact this transition zone was frontal in that it comprised a horizontal temperature gradient which, after an initially gradual tightening, had triggered off a self-accelerating process which tightened the temperature gradient even more and persisted for a while—even after the original cause (in this case differential heating) had disappeared. Thus a *sea-breeze front*, as the phenomenon is called, can be considered as a shallow ephemeral species of cold front. Warm inland air rises ahead of the wedgelike advance of cool air from the sea, and, if the inland air is not too dry, the ascending air is marked by a line of cloud, usually cumiliform. Evidently some ascent also takes place close to the front and in the cool moist sea air, for, on

Plate 21   FRAGMENTS OF SEA-BREEZE FRONTAL CLOUD
Occasionally a sea-breeze front has a tattered curtain of patchy cloud in the narrow band of lift along the front. In this episode John Williamson is using such patches to guide him along an otherwise fairly clear sea-breeze front over southern England.

occasions, this ascent of air is marked by cloud with a peculiar vertically striated form resembling a tattered translucent curtain.

Whether marked by cloud or not, the upward motion at the sea-breeze front is usually strong enough for soaring flight. On 6 July 1956 J. K. Mackenzie soared in sea-breeze lift for most of a late afternoon 3-hour flight in the neighbourhood of Lasham, England. With the sea-breeze front orientated ENE–WSW and moving inland from the south coast at about 5 knots, lift, mostly 3–5 knots, but occasionally as strong as 15 knots, was located in a belt just north of the advancing air from the sea. The belt was a narrow one, only 100–250 m wide, but it was possible to climb to about 4000 ft (1300 m) provided that the glider was flown straight along the landward side of the sea-breeze front. Circling flight was tactically useless for soaring since downdraught existed immediately to the north (as sketched in Figure 16.4) and all but a thin slice of the cool sea air was void of lift. The thin, steeply inclined wafer of sea air which did rise was significant not only for its weak

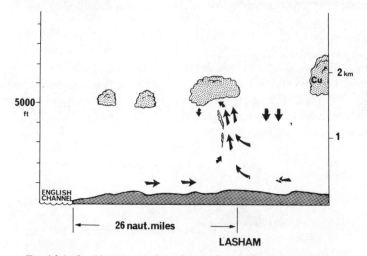

Fig. 16.4 In this cross-section of a sea-breeze front, over southern England on 6 July 1956, the vertical motion and cloud structure are illustrated schematically and not to the horizontal scale indicated. The structure, which was first sketched by J. K. Mackenzie, is almost identical with that noted by E. A. Moore on 21 May 1958. On this latter occasion, however, sections of the front were marked by a visibility contrast rather than by a distinctive cloud pattern.

lift, but its wisps of cloud which, having formed in the cool, moist, rising sea air, clearly marked the sea-breeze frontal zone. With such a visible guide as this, soaring close to a sea-breeze front resembles anabatic soaring, the wispy curtain of cloud taking the place of the mountain slope. Unlike the mountainside, of course, the cloud is liable to move and may disappear.

Smoke and haze can also be useful indicators of sea-breeze fronts. Smoke from ground sources on opposite sides of the sea-breeze front can sometimes be seen to converge towards the front, and many a weather situation produces pronounced haziness on one side of the front with relatively clear air on the other side. The contrast between the hazy air and the clearer air is usually sharp when the smoke or haze is in the sea air.

Sea-breeze prediction

A number of studies have been made in attempts to devise simple rules for forecasting sea-breeze phenomena. An early study was made at Thorney Island (close to the south coast of England) of the relationship between the temperature difference between land and sea and the local wind at 3000 ft (1000 m) with the sea-breeze from the south coast. The results for off-shore 3000-ft (1000-m) wind directions are illustrated graphically in Figure 16.5, but these results should be interpreted with caution; they have been deduced only for Thorney Island and the wind direction stated. Nevertheless such a study as this illustrates the relative power of horizontal temperature gradients and off-shore wind speeds in controlling sea-breeze effects.

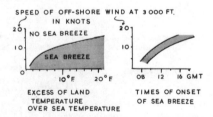

Fig. 16.5 A sea-breeze study at Thorney Island, southern England, showed that when wind and temperature conditions are represented by points in the shaded section of the diagram on the left, then a sea-breeze is likely to reach Thorney Island sometime in the interval indicated by the shaded band on the right.

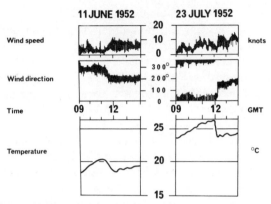

Fig. 16.6 Autographic record showing sea-breeze effects on a day of shallow convection (11 June 1952) and deep convection (23 July 1952).

The Thorney Island study also suggested that the depth of the inland convection is related to the abruptness with which the sea-breeze sets in. Figure 16.6 shows a sudden change in wind direction and an abrupt fall in temperature as the sea-breeze of 23 July 1952 replaced the inland air in which convection had distributed the sun's ground-level heating up to 8000 ft (2500 m). This figure also shows the more gradual sea-breeze changes associated with inland convection to only 4000 ft (1300 m) on 11 June 1952. These two examples accord with other observations that the arrival of a sea-breeze front is likely to be established suddenly (in about 10 min) on days of deep convection, but gradually, with perhaps fluctuations over a period of 1–2 hours, when convection from the ground is limited (say, by anticyclonic subsidence) to a relatively shallow layer of the atmosphere.

The effects of wind speed and direction relative to the coastline and the depth of inland convection on sea-breeze characteristics can be summarised as follows:

Wind

Off-shore airstream component of 15 knots or more

Sea-breeze unlikely because the off-shore speed of the airstream is likely to swamp the effects of differential heating.

Off-shore airstream component of 10–15 knots
If inland heating is good and the thermal convection layer deep, a sea-breeze front is likely to develop off-shore, then penetrate inland late in the day.

Off-shore airstream component of 5–10 knots
A sea-breeze is likely to cross the coast by midday.

Off-shore airstream component of 0–5 knots
The sea-breeze is likely to cross the coast soon after inland convection starts and may penetrate well inland.

On-shore airstream component of 0–5 knots
If inland convection is deep, a sea-breeze front is likely to develop during the late morning but it is not likely to be evident as a front close to the coastline; the frontal characteristics, if any, are more likely to become apparent as they develop inland.

On-shore component of more than 5 knots
The steady flow of air from the sea is likely to bring in cool stable air, which will damp down thermal soaring prospects.

Airstreams along the coastline
Airstreams that flow approximately along the coastline are the most favourable for development of sea-breeze fronts, especially if the inland convection becomes deep. Both light winds and moderate winds along the coastline are favourable for sea-breeze frontal development. Stronger winds in this direction are not necessarily unfavourable, but it may be difficult to distinguish between a sea-breeze frontal effect and thermal streets in such conditions.

Inland Convection

Inland convection restricted to 1500 ft (500 m)
Such a shallow depth for the convective layer will not stop air from the sea flowing across the coastline, but a marked sea-breeze front is not likely to develop.

Inland convection to between 1500 and 3000 ft (500–1000 m)
A weak sea-breeze front may develop, but is likely to be diffuse in places and not particularly persistent.

Inland convection to between 3000 and 6000 ft (1–2 km)
Provided the airstream direction is suitable (i.e. the cross-coastline component not too great) a well-defined sea-breeze front is likely to develop and penetrate well inland.

Inland convection to over 6000 ft (2 km)
Provided the airstream direction is satisfactory, a well-marked sea-breeze front is likely to develop, but if the convection is particularly deep, convection along the sea-breeze front will develop into convective stormclouds which may then become self-propagating and set up their own local wind systems (such as those described in Chapter 14 on convective storms).

Case histories

On 6 July 1956 surface temperatures inland in England rose to about 20°C (6° higher than the average July sea temperature in the middle of the English Channel) and cumulus at about 4500 ft (1500 m) with tops to 8000 ft (2500 m) formed in the westerly airstream which covered most of the British Isles. In Figure 16.7 the

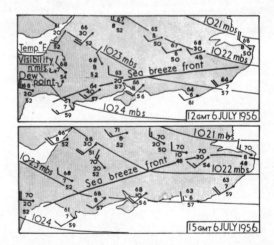

Fig. 16.7 Two of the hourly charts on 15 July 1956. Note that the visibilities are plotted in naut. miles while the temperatures and dew points are in degrees Fahrenheit (which were the units used in 1956). Each full feather of the wind arrows represents 10 knots.

weather charts show wind and dew point differences between the inland and the sea air, but neither the sharpness nor the precise positions of the front can be deduced from these charts alone. A clearer indication of the sea-breeze frontal progress can be gleaned from the autographic records copied in Figure 16.8, which, together with other records, were used to determine the isochrones of the sea-breeze front mapped in Figure 16.9. Towards the limit of its penetration inland the front slowed down to a mere 1–2 knots, but its movement and existence up to 22.00 GMT was still consistent with recorded changes in wind direction and relative humidity at South Farnborough, the sudden increase in wind speed and rise in humidity at Boscombe Down, and the change in wind direction at Blackbushe. However, during the early evening the line of small

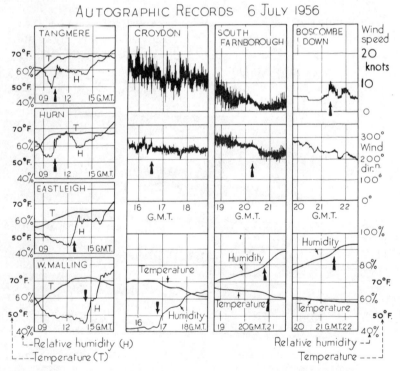

Fig. 16.8 Large arrows indicate sea-breeze effects on the autographic records. The positions of the recording stations are marked in Fig. 16.9.

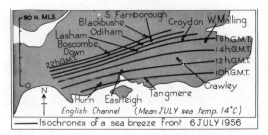

Fig. 16.9   Isochrones of the sea-breeze front on 6 July 1956.

cumulus associated with the sea-breeze front appeared (at Lasham) to have its progress not only retarded but reversed, and by 20.30 GMT this cloud could be seen about 7 km south of Lasham. Thus the front appeared to be in two places at once and the explanation of this double existence may well be linked to the observed tendency for some sea-breeze fronts to progress inland in a series of pulsations rather than with a steady movement; on occasions the sea-breeze frontal effects appear to decline in one belt while intensifying in another belt about a kilometre or so further inland. Sometimes in this region of southern England a sea-breeze front in the westerly or west-northwesterly airstream penetrates so far inland in the east of the country that it moves into the Thames Estuary as a paradoxical sea-breeze from the land. Sea-breeze fronts are also likely to extend further south-westwards than marked in Figure 16.9. A narrow belt of sea-breeze lift may well have developed south of the coast before moving north. It is very likely that soaring flights over the sea have been sustained by off-shore sections of sea-breeze fronts, but when exploring such soaring conditions it is wise to remember that the lift in a well-marked sea-breeze front often occurs in a narrow belt sandwiched between broader belts of downdraught.

Another case history worth using as an illustration of sea-breeze frontal phenomena occurred on 30 May 1962 in a light easterly airstream over southern England. Figure 16.10 shows the change of pressure pattern over England, from an anticyclone in the morning to a thermal low pressure system as temperatures inland rose to about 15°C. Surface winds, dew points and observations from several glider pilots revealed the existence of the sea-breeze front from about 10.30 GMT onwards. Figure 16.11 shows the extent of

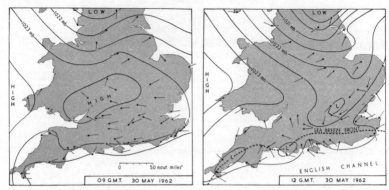

Fig. 16.10   MSL pressure patterns and surface winds at 09 and 12 GMT on the day of the sea-breeze flight. Surface winds indicated by the arrows were mostly about 5 knots. Temperatures inland rose from about 9°C to 15°C during the morning.

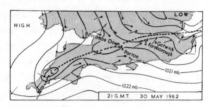

Fig. 16.11   The dotted line marks the sea-breeze front at 21 GMT.

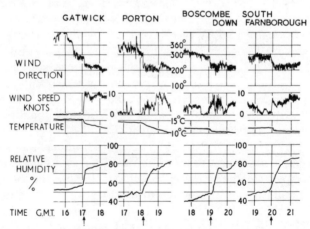

Fig. 16.12   Autographic records for stations whose locations are marked in Fig. 16.11. Times of passage of the sea-breeze front are indicated by the arrows.

the inland penetration by 21.00 GMT, and Figure 16.12 illustrates the sharp rise in humidity, the wind changes and the slight fall in temperature that marked the passage of this front.

I was fortunate enought to be at Lasham as the front approached. At 17.00 GMT thermal soaring conditions appeared to be on the wane, but to the south tattered wisps of cloud indicated the front. After being aerotowed to 2000 ft (600 m) I headed south and soon located rising air. Two other gliders joined me and it soon became apparent that the air was rising smoothly up some sort of sloping surface, as depicted in Figure 16.13.

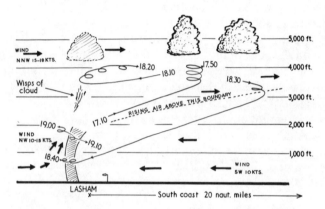

Fig. 16.13   A schematic cross-section of the sea-breeze wind and cloud structure on 30 May 1962 as revealed by gliding. The horizontal extent of the structure illustrated was about 8 km, but the clouds and width of the shaded turbulent zone are not drawn to scale. Sections of the main features of the glider flight path are shown by the thin lines with times in GMT at intervals.

The timetable was:

17.10–17.50	Initial climb
17.50–18.10	Exploring the extent of the rising air
18.10–18.20	Flying north to the bar of the cloud (shaded with dotted outline) and circling under this cloud as it drifted south
18.30	Set course back to airfield
18.40–19.00	Climb during straight flight on east to west course

The wisps of cloud appeared and disappeared just before the development of the bar of cloud above. The left-hand half of the picture was not apparent until the flight path had entered the narrow (100-m wide) turbulent mixing zone between the land and sea air. The position of Lasham is marked in Fig. 16.10.

The three of us flying above 2500 ft (800 m) had no difficulty in remaining airborne in the north-northwesterly wind of 15–18 knots at our flying levels, but to the south of the airfield other pilots found no lift in the south-west wind below. The wisps of sea-breeze frontal cloud to the south had disappeared and isolated wisps had formed just north of the airfield. But these wisps soon disappeared and an east-west bar of cloud began to form at a slightly higher level. The lift under this freshly formed bar was strong, but soon weakened as the cloud drifted towards the south and began to dissipate. On the descent back to Lasham there was no lift until the glider entered what was apparently a transition zone between the moist sea air and the flow from inland. This zone was very narrow—only about 100 m wide—and noticeably turbulent. One half of a circle on the edge of the zone would be in smooth air, on the other half the aircraft would be buffeted by small-scale turbulence. Immediately inland of this frontal zone there was a narrow band of lift. Figure 16.13 illustrates the main features of the sea-breeze frontal structure on this occasion.

Although these case histories are for particular days over a particular region, they are illustrative of noticeable characteristics of sea-breeze frontal structure that can occur anywhere in the world.

Secondary sea-breeze fronts

Occasionally a day's autographic records or observation indicate the passage of two sea-breeze fronts, a primary front in the late morning followed by a secondary sea-breeze front during the afternoon. The explanation of this double effect appears to be that, after changing direction at the passage of the primary front, winds near the coast gradually revert to the earlier direction, thereby restoring conditions suitable for sufficient differential heating across the coastline to create a second sea-breeze front. Usually when such a secondary sea-breeze front forms it is rather weak.

Pseudo sea-breeze fronts

Coastlines are not the only regions that can give birth to the sea-breeze type of phenomenon. The edge of a sheet of cloud, or a well-defined boundary of thick haze, or the edge of a plateau of high ground can also give rise to differential heating that leads to a sea-breeze type of flow or convergence line that resembles a sea-breeze front.

On 29 April 1958 in the situation shown in Figure 16.14 a westerly airstream across England was moist enough to bring low

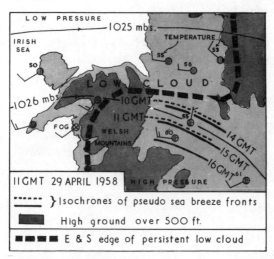

Fig. 16.14   Pseudo sea-breeze fronts appear to move southwards from the southern edge of a persistent low cloud cover, which persisted north and west of the heavy broken line.

stratus from over the Irish Sea into the Cheshire Plain and, with the Welsh Mountains blocking the advance of the low cloud immediately to the south, the low cloud over the north-west Midlands was bounded by a fairly sharp edge south of which bright sunshine was able to warm the air at low levels sufficiently to produce small cumulus clouds. The low stratus was thick enough to prevent a rise in temperature in the area it covered, and so conditions were ripe for a *pseudo sea-breeze front* to develop and move southwards. In fact there appeared to be a double frontal effect which produced weather changes like those mentioned above, and it is quite feasible that the soaring conditions were somewhat similar to those found at genuine sea-breeze front.

After crossing Tern Hill between 10.00 GMT and 10.35 GMT the first pseudo sea-breeze front appeared to weaken to the extent of becoming only just detectable as a slight temperature drop and deterioration in the visibility at Shawbury just before 11.00 GMT. The passage of the secondary pseudo front, however, was well marked by changes in wind direction, visibility and temperature at Tern Hill between 14.00 GMT and 15.00 GMT and at Shawbury about an hour later.

Cases of pseudo sea-breeze front from edges of thick haze and edges of plateaux are not so well documented but are nonetheless real. Figure 16.15 illustrates the theoretical nature of the pseudo

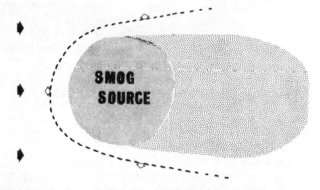

Fig. 16.15   Thick haze in a densely polluted area and in the pollution plume that is likely to drift slowly downwind reduces the insolation reaching ground-level, while surrounding pollution-free areas may be appreciably heated. Such differential heating can cause pseudo sea-breeze fronts to develop that tend to move outwards, sometimes even upwind, from the thickly polluted area. Such pseudo sea-breeze fronts are usually weak, but they can be particularly noticeable where the contrast between the polluted source and the surrounding pollution-free countryside is particularly sharp.

sea-breeze frontal effect that may be associated with a pall of thick haze or smog. In most situations of this type the pseudo sea-breeze frontal effects are weak because the air is generally stable and heating outside the smoggy area is confined to a fairly shallow layer. However, in regions such as the urban areas of southern California both the smog and the heating can be deep enough to produce noticeable pseudo sea-breeze fronts.

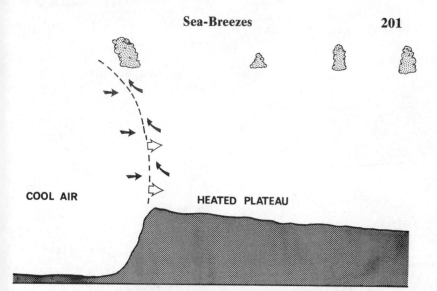

Fig. 16.16 The plateau type of pseudo sea-breeze front. While air over the plateau is being heated from the ground-level which receives insolation, air at a similar height over the coastal plain receives much less heat from convection over the plain further below. The differential heating produces a pseudo sea-breeze front that forms near the escarpment of the plateau and moves over the high ground.

The differential heating and pseudo sea-breeze frontal effect arising from the edge of a plateau of high ground is illustrated in Figure 16.16. The pseudo sea-breeze front that moves over the high ground from the edge of the high ground is practically identical in character to a genuine sea-breeze front. It is almost as though the lowland plain were filled with water up to the level of the plateau with the temperature of the surface of this imaginary sea being less than the ground-level temperature by 3°C per 1000 ft (1°C per 100 m) height of the plateau above the lowland plain. Where a plateau or tableland borders a coastal plain, as in eastern Australia, the pseudo sea-breeze effect is particularly likely when cool air from the sea or from higher latitudes flows over the coastal plain.

Effects of mountain barriers

A long unbroken mountain range just inland of a coastline will act as a barrier to the penetration of a sea-breeze front further inland.

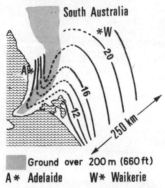

Fig. 16.17   Penetration of a sea-breeze front inland can be blocked by high ground—just as the sea-breeze fronts over South Australia are blocked by the range of hills shown in this illustration. Numbers on the sea-breeze positions are local times of day.

Figure 16.17 illustrates the characteristic progress of sea-breeze fronts partially blocked by a range of hills in South Australia.

If there are gaps in the range of mountains sea-breezes are likely to funnel through these gaps and spread out over the leeward lowland. Particularly interesting examples of this effect, together with examples of orographic convergence lines, can be found in the region of Los Angeles. The pattern of convergence lines and sea-breeze frontal effects (described by John Aldrich in the 1965 *Soaring International Yearbook*) is particularly useful to illustrate the nature of orographic effects on sea-breezes and convergence lines.

When sea-breezes invade the coastal plains in the region of Los Angeles they are forced to flow around the Santa Monica and Santa Ana Mountains, as illustrated in Figure 16.18. This creates two convergence lines in lee of these mountain ranges, something like the Tehachapi Shear Line described in Chapter 11. The northern line is known as the '*San Fernando Convergence Zone*'; the southern line is called the '*Elsinore Shear Line*'. Incidentally, these convergence lines are also known as *shear lines*.

The San Fernando Convergence Zone is not normally used for soaring because of the population density in the valley and heavy air traffic. The Elsinore Shear Line, however, has been used extensively for soaring. This shear line extends towards San Gorgonio Pass. The shear line persists for much of the day during summer and

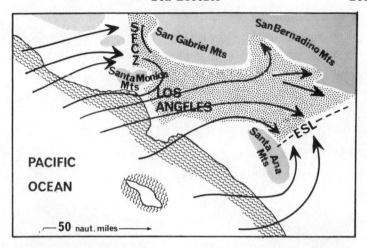

Fig. 16.18   When sea-breezes invade the coastal plains in the region of Los Angeles they are forced to flow around the Santa Monica and Santa Ana Mountains, as indicated by the arrows in this diagram. The smog area is denoted by the dotted shading. In the wind conditions illustrated there is a fairly sharp edge to the smog at the San Fernando Convergence Zone (SFCZ) and Elsinore Shear Line (ESL).

autumn, but in the meantime a sea-breeze front develops on the south-eastern edge of the Los Angeles smog. This front appears something between a genuine sea-breeze front and a pseudo sea-breeze front associated with the edge of the smog, but it does not matter which we call it. It behaves much like a classical sea-breeze front, though locally it is known as the '*smog front*'. As this smog front approaches Elsinore the pre-existing shear line remains almost stationary. So the orographic convergence zone effect is reinforced by the sea-breeze frontal effect and the net result is often excellent lift up to between about 6000 ft and 12 000 ft (2000 m and 4000 m) above sea-level.

Another convergence line is formed in the Mojave Desert as a result of cooler air flowing through the Cajon Pass, as illustrated in Figure 16.19. This feature of the flow appears to be partly the result of the orographic effect chanelling wind through the Cajon Pass, and partly the plateau type of pseudo sea-breeze frontal effect—as it is produced by the morning's heating of the high desert area. The shear line that goes through El Mirage is known as the '*El Mirage*

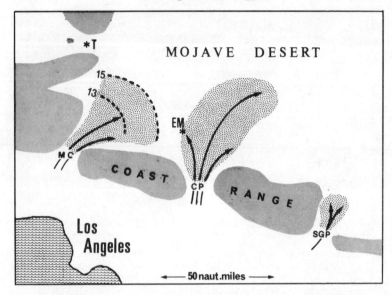

Fig. 16.19 Air flowing through Mint Canyon (MC), Cajon Pass (CP) and the San Gorgonio Pass (SGP) usually brings smog into the Mojave Desert. Sometimes the smog has a sharp leading edge which reaches the dotted lines in this diagram at about 13.00 and 15.00 hours. Tehachapi and El Mirage are denoted by the letters T and EM in this diagram.

Shear Line' or the *'Adelanto Shear Line'*. It is a regular characteristic of the weather at El Mirage Dry Lake. Within the cooler air there is little or no lift, but around the periphery thermals and dust devils begin to form and are useful indicators of the line of lift. A similar orographic-cum-plateau heating effect induces cooler air to move through Mint Canyon from the south-west before midday, spreading out north-eastward and creating a pseudo sea-breeze front at its edge. Thermals within the cold air are, of course, suppressed. Because this cool air flowing through Mint Canyon also brings the Los Angeles smog the shear line is also known locally as the *'smog front'*. As this shear line spreads it pushes back the El Mirage Shear Line, so, in the late afternoon, El Mirage is likely to find itself in the cooler air that has spread out from Mint Canyon.

  The phenomena just described are not unique to the Los Angeles region. Wherever differential heating (associated with coastlines, edges of cloud sheets, the edge of a plateau, or the edge of thick

Plate 22 CUMULONIMBUS AT SEA-BREEZE FRONT
On 18 June 1957 conditions over England were ideal for the formation of
deep convection, particularly in association with sea-breeze frontal
effects. This photograph taken at 14.20 GMT from an aircraft east of
Brighton on the south coast of England, shows the stormclouds associated
with the radar echoes illustrated in Plate 27 and Fig. 14.4. The tops of
those cumulonimbus clouds extend to about 40 000 ft (13 000 m).

smog) occurs there is the possibility of a sea-breeze frontal effect,
and wherever there are mountains and valleys airflow will be
blocked, diverted or chanelled. There are many more soarable
convergence line and pseudo sea-breeze frontal effects than are
generally realised, but even before flying in a region it is possible to
make a first guess at the possibilities of convergence line or pseudo
sea-breeze front by remembering the basic features of these
phenomena.

17

Lee Waves

Have you ever watched the ripples in a shallow brook as the water flows over a submerged rock? The water rises over the rock, dips sharply on the downstream side and, if the rock is in the form of a ridge placed across the stream, the water surface will rise and fall a second, third or several more times downstream. The crest of the ripples form a series of bars parallel to the rock and, with the water flowing through them, these bars remain in almost stationary positions in the stream.

Substitute an airstream for the brook, a mountain for the rock, and we begin to visualise lee waves in the atmosphere. Figure 17.1 indicates the nature of the flow. The *lee wavelength* is a measure of

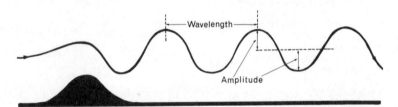

Fig. 17.1 In lee wave flow the air usually dips sharply down in lee of a hill ridge before undulating up and down for some considerable distance downstream. The wavelength of the lee wave is determined entirely by wind and temperature conditions in the upstream flow, while the lee wave amplitude depends on both airstream conditions and the size, shape and surface nature of the ridge. The true wavelength is normally greater than the distance between the summit of the hill ridge and the first lee wave crest downwind.

the distance from one wave crest to the next, or from trough to trough. Usually between 5 and 50 km, this wavelength is determined almost entirely by the winds and temperatures at various levels in the airstream. It is not normally the same as the distance between the summit of the ridge and the first lee wave crest. Some glider pilots refer to the first, second and third wave crest downstream from a mountain ridge as the primary, secondary and tertiary waves.

The lee wave *amplitude* is half the vertical distance from wave trough to crest. The amplitude normally varies with height. Often it is small at low levels and at very high levels, and has some maximum in between.

Wave cloud

Air rising in the updraught of a wave cools adiabatically. If this cooling is sufficient to cause condensation then cloud will form. Subsequent warming in the downdraught causes the condensed water to evaporate; so, by a continuous process of condensation at its leading edge and evaporation at the trailing edge, a cloud formed in a wave crest appears to be stationary in the sky. Wave clouds are most commonly observed at medium levels, and they frequently have the *lenticular* shape of a double-convex lens, like that sketched in Figure 17.2. When the wave cloud forms at low levels it is often

Fig. 17.2   Patches of lee wave cloud that form in the crests of waves often have an approximately lenticular shape.

torn into ragged patches by low-level turbulence. The patches as a whole remain more or less stationary but their detailed outline changes quickly and erratically. At high levels cloud is usually composed of ice crystals, and, because these crystals form quickly but evaporate slowly, high-level wave cloud forms readily in the updraught of a wave but does not always disappear in the descent; it tends to stretch out some way downstream.

The presence of wave cloud does not necessarily mean that the wave has a big amplitude; it indicates that near the level of the cloud this amplitude is enough to lift the air to its condensation level. Thus a wave cloud can indicate anything from weak waves in humid air to large-amplitude waves with low humidity. The lee wave amplitude is not necessarily at a maximum at the level of the cloud.

An airstream with, say, strong waves but low humidity at 6000 ft (2000 m) and weak waves but moist air at 10 000 ft (3000 m) may have wave cloud at the upper level but no visible sign of the larger amplitude below. Not all wave clouds have the characteristic lenticular shape. When the airstream below a wave cloud is fairly dry the wave cloud is more likely to form an arch with a concave base like that sketched in Figure 17.3. Many a wave cloud has a rather

Fig. 17.3   If the air below clouds is particularly dry the base of wave clouds may have a concave shape.

flat base, and when the airstream is particularly humid the visible clue to the existence of a wave flow is more likely to take the form of stationary gaps in the cloud cover. Figure 17.4 illustrates some typical wave-cloud configurations. Occasionally a vertical stack of thin wave clouds forms in a wave. The French call such a stack a 'pile

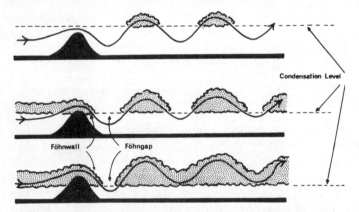

Fig. 17.4   If the general condensation level is high lee wave clouds may form in isolated patches while there is little or no cloud over the mountain ridge itself. If the condensation level is below the top of the mountain ridge cloud over the mountain (and possibly upstream) is likely to evaporate in the downdraught before forming again in the downwind crests of the wave. Cloud descending and evaporating on the lee escarpment sometimes looks like a cloudy waterfall. It has the name 'föhnwall'. The gap between the cloud over the mountain and the first wave cloud is known as the 'föhngap'. If the condensation level is even lower the föhngap may be the only visible clue to an observer on the ground to the existence of the wave flow. The lee wave cloud may have a continuously flat base downwind of the ridge.

of plates'. Such a formation denotes marked variation of humidity with height—it is not due to any peculiar variation of wave amplitude with height.

Wave conditions

Thanks to pioneer work by Professor R. S. Scorer on wave theory, the meteorologists' understanding of the nature of lee waves made rapid progress in the early 1950s.

Conditions favourable for lee waves with appreciable vertical currents comprise:

1 a layer of low stability (high lapse rate) at low levels;
2 a stable layer (e.g. isothermal layer or inversion) above the lower layer;
3 an upper layer of low stability in the troposphere;
4 a wind of about 15 knots (30 km/h) or more across a hill or mountain ridge.

An increase of wind speed with height without much change of wind direction adds to the likelihood of wave formation. These conditions, illustrated in the left-hand side of Figure 17.5, will produce a wave pattern like that shown on the right-hand side of the figure. Notice that the lee-wave amplitude is at its maximum in the stable layer.

To understand why stable air sandwiched between two layers of lesser stability favours the formation of significant lee waves it may be helpful to resort to an analogy. An unstable atmosphere can be compared with a weak flimsy spring because it offers little resistance to vertical motion within it, and a stable atmosphere can be likened to a tough heavy spring which tends to suppress internal vertical motion. With the aid of Figure 17.6 it is not difficult to imagine that, although the lower coils of the flimsy spring would move easily up and over a mountain ridge, the jolt received at ground-level would not be transmitted far upwards. Nor would it stretch the imagination too far to suppose that if the heavy spring were forced over a ridge it would be too tough for oscillations to be set up.

But consider now a few strong coils sandwiched between two weaker springs, as depicted in the lower section of Figure 17.6. With this arrangement it is conceivable that the tough coils will continue

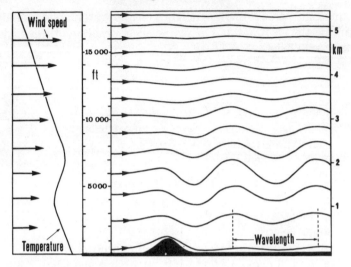

Fig. 17.5   Lee waves are often associated with a stable layer sandwiched between air of lesser stability together with an increase with height of wind components across the ridge. The lee wave amplitude usually increases with height to attain a maximum in the stable layer. Above this stable layer the amplitude tends to decrease slowly with height, although in some conditions another (longer) wave exists at high levels.

to bounce up and down for some time after the structure has crossed a mountain ridge.

The atmosphere works in a somewhat similar fashion. Neither a completely unstable nor a uniformly stable airstream can produce appreciable lee waves, but a stream containing stable air between layers of lesser stability is both flexible enough to be set in vertical motion and resilient enough to maintain this motion as a series of vertical oscillations.

The spring analogy has flaws and we must be cautious in drawing conclusions from it. Nevertheless, it illustrates several features of the flow. It seems reasonable to suppose that the heavy coils dominate the leeward oscillations, and indeed lee waves in the atmosphere usually do have their maximum amplitude in the stable layer which contributes to their existence.

The amplitude and frequency with which the coils bounce up and down are related in a close but complicated way to the precise depth

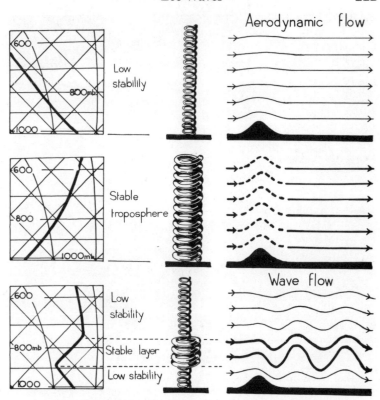

Fig. 17.6   The atmosphere may be likened to a vertical coiled spring. An unstable airstream can be compared with a weak, flimsy spring because it offers little resistance to vertical motion within it, and a stable atmosphere can be likened to a tough, heavy spring which tends to suppress internal vertical motion. The best structure for persistent oscillation is a sandwich of a few strong coils (shallow stable layer) between two weaker springs (deeper layers of lesser stability). Thick lines in the diagrams on the left denote temperature profiles (corresponding to the spring structures) plotted on an aerological diagram (described in Chapter 20).

and resilience of each part of the spring, and the lee wavelength is determined by the speed with which these vertical oscillations are propelled downstream. It should be no surprise, therefore, to learn that the lee wavelengths and amplitudes in the atmosphere are determined by the winds and the temperatures at various levels in the airstream. Out of the intricate relationships between winds, temperatures, and lee wavelengths and amplitudes, two deductions

Plate 23 THIN WAVE CLOUD
High over the tree in this picture is a thin wave cloud in lee of the 500-ft Black Mountain in Canberra, Australia. The narrow clear channel through the cloud with slightly thicker cloud either side is an illustration of aerodynamics and atmospheric physics. A Super Viscount airliner had just flown through this cloud leaving a double vortex wake—with downdraught in the centre and updraught on either side. The downdraught and adiabatic warming was just sufficient to clear the thin wave cloud, while the updraught and cooling thickened it slightly.

which emerge as useful though not infallible supplements to the wave flow conditions already listed are:

1 The stable layer associated with a wave flow produces larger amplitudes when it comprises a shallow layer of great stability than when only moderate stability extends over some considerable depth.

2 Long waves are associated more with strong upper winds than with light winds aloft. (Observations indicate that, for

wavelengths in the range 5–25 km, the wavelength in kilometres is about one-quarter of the mean speed in knots of the wind through the layer from ground-level up to the tropopause.)

Wave lift

Vertical currents in the wave flow depend on the amplitude, the wavelength and the wind speed. Strong updraughts and downdraughts are favoured by:

1 large amplitudes—the larger the amplitude the farther the air moves up and down;
2 short wavelengths—the shorter the wavelength the steeper the ascents and descents in the undulating airflow;
3 strong winds—the stronger the wind the faster the air moves through the wave pattern.

Lift in waves ranges from being almost imperceptible to about 20 knots (10 m/s) for good waves, but really big wave systems with 40-knot (20 m/s) lift have been recorded.

The distribution of lift and sink in a wave flow pattern is illustrated in Figure 17.7. The egglike structure representing vertical speeds is characteristic of the basic lee wave pattern. Of course, details vary from one situation to another but it is useful to have this basic pattern in mind.

Diurnal variation of lee waves

In the neighbourhood of Cross Fell in the Pennines of England the local folk assert that 'the bar never crosses the Eden' and if you appear no wiser for this odd piece of information they would explain that the bar refers to a cigar-shaped cloud (the *Helm bar*) sometimes observed downwind of and parallel to the steep escarpment of Cross Fell, and that the Eden is the river in the leeward valley. During the mornings the bar usually moves slowly downwind, towards the south-west, but later in the day just as the cloud seems about to cross the river it apparently changes its mind and retreats back towards the escarpment; thus 'the bar never crosses the Eden', or translating the story into meteorological English: there is a tendency for lee wavelengths to increase during the morning and

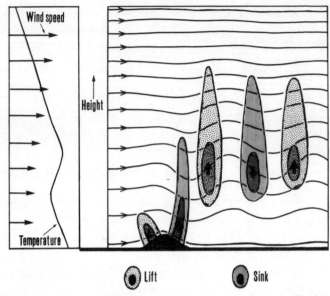

Fig. 17.7   Patterns of lift and sink in wave flow are best visualised as egg-shaped patterns like those illustrated by the shading and arrows in this diagram.

decrease during the afternoon. An explanation of this diurnal effect starts with insolation or heat from the sun, which warms the ground, which warms the air near the ground at low levels, and the subsequent increase in lee wavelength is a consequence of the intricate relationship between lapse rates and wave formation. In a complementary manner the subsequent decrease in wavelength stems from the low-level cooling which occurs in the late afternoons and the evenings of fairly clear days.

Lee wave amplitude is also affected by diurnal heating and cooling. Its variation is such that, in temperate climates and in areas of small mountains, wave conditions are at their best between about one and three hours after sunrise and during the late afternoon and evening. The middle of the day is the least likely period for soarable waves.

This sequence does not apply to regions where diurnal heating is more intense and where large mountain masses are involved. In the Owens Valley of California, for example, heating tends to increase the wave amplitude in the mid-afternoon.

Plate 24   LEE WAVES AND CUMULUS
Because lee waves are usually associated with stable layers, there used to
be a widespread misconception that lee waves and convection clouds
could not exist at the same time. But a well-defined convective layer
capped by an inversion can often produce ideal conditions both for
thermal soaring and wave lift. This photograph, taken over Canberra,
Australia, clearly shows the coexistence of lee waves and convection
clouds in a suitable airstream.

Although these diurnal effects are important they play only a
subsidiary role in the creation of lee wave conditions. It is the
broader-scale weather systems that can provide the wind and
temperature conditions suitable for wave flow.

Lee wave situations

A weather system suitable for lee waves is simply one in which the
airstream conditions in the locality being considered satisfy the
wave conditions already listed. These conditions can be fulfilled in a
variety of ways.

Warm sectors in temperate latitudes often include fresh winds
whose variation with height shows an increase in speed but little or
no change in direction. The well-stirred air at low levels usually has
little stability from ground-level up to between about 2000 and
6000 ft (600 and 2000 m) and above this layer the stability increases

sharply before falling off with height. So warm sectors are likely to promote a wave flow in lee of mountain ridges whose axes lie across the flow. But in cool moist climates it is unlikely that these waves are fully exploited; warm sectors in these climates often bring a complete cover of low cloud, which not only conceals its own wave top from observers below cloud but which may mask the hilltops with drizzle and fog. Warm fronts are often preceded by winds and temperature conditions which, for limited spells during the prefrontal changes, are suitable for wave flow. As the front approaches the changing upper wind and temperature structure goes through phases of varying favourability for wave formation. Some distance ahead of the front there are likely to be rather short waves of only mediocre amplitudes sufficient to produce patchy wave clouds at high or medium levels, but probably too weak for soaring. However, the wavelength and amplitude of the waves tend to increase and their most effective level descends. Wave soaring may be possible from about 12 to 18 hours before the front is due, but these

Plate 25 ROTOR CLOUD
This patch of rotor cloud, triggered off by hills in the background, was not large, but its turbulent nature was clearly indicated by the ragged patches of low cloud. The smoothness of the thin wave cloud above the rotor cloud suggested that the transition from the turbulence up into the smooth air just above was very sharp.

waves are likely to fade away before re-forming much closer to the front.

Anticyclones, with their subsidence aloft, usually have a temperature structure made to measure for lee waves; a shallow, extremely stable layer centred somewhere between 4500 and 10 000 ft (1500 and 3000 m) is a common feature of high pressure systems. But the centre of an anticyclone also features light and variable winds; so to locate the wave flow conditions we must search towards the outer fringes—far enough from the centre to pick up winds of 15 knots (30 km/h) or more, but not so far that the stabilising effect of the subsidence is lost.

Although warm sectors, the fringes of anticyclones, and pre-warm frontal regions have been mentioned as favourable zones for wave formation, lee waves are by no means confined to a few types of weather systems. They can occur in any type of situation that brings the favourable wind and temperature conditions already listed.

Hill shape and size

Two requirements are needed for waves to form: the wind and temperature conditions must be suitable for wave flow and there must be a hill or some trigger to set the waves in motion. The amplitude of the waves depends partly on the airstream conditions and partly on the size and shape of the hill. If an airstream suitable for waves crossed the three ridges outlined in Figure 17.8 we should find that although these ridges are of equal height they would not set off waves of equal amplitudes. In this particular illustration the ridge of medium width produces the best waves.

Fig. 17.8 Of the three hill profiles sketched in this diagram, the middle ridge has the best width for setting off lee waves of the particular wavelength illustrated.

The jolt received by the airstream passing over the narrow ridge is not nearly so effective. Nor does the gentle ascent and descent of air over the wider ridge lead to large amplitudes. There is a resonance effect between lee wavelength and hill width. It is not an effect which can be easily fc₹mulated and all we can do is to appreciate that short waves are best set off by narrow ridges and long waves are at their best over broader mountains. A corollary from this is that large mountains are not necessarily better than small hills for setting off waves. In Figure 17.9, for example, the larger ridge produces only feeble waves because its width is much too great for resonance with the lee wavelength.

Fig. 17.9   A big mountain (such as that on the left in this diagram) whose width is large compared to the lee wavelength does not necessarily trigger off bigger waves than a smaller ridge like that sketched on the right.

A symmetrically shaped ridge, such as those so far described, has its best lift about one-half of a wavelength downwind of the summit of the ridge, but for asymmetrical ridges with relatively gentle upwind slopes, such as that sketched in Figure 17.10, the best lift is

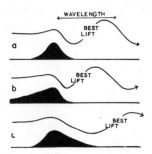

Fig. 17.10   A symmetrically shaped ridge has its best wave lift about one-half of a wavelength downwind of the summit of the ridge, but for an asymmetrical ridge with a gentle windward slope leading to a steep escarpment the best lift is closer to the lee slope of the mountainside.

closer to the lee slope of the mountainside. Furthermore, this type of ridge, with its steep lee escarpment, is particularly favourable for setting off soarable lee waves.

When an airstream suitable for lee waves flows past two ridges in succession the eventual amplitude of the waves depends on whether or not the ridges are in or out of phase with each other for the prevailing lee wavelength. If the distance between the ridges is equal to, say, 1, 2 or 3 wavelengths then the lee waves from the first ridge will be reinforced by those of the second ridge. As shown in Figure 17.11, the net result will be lee waves of larger amplitude than that due to each ridge by itself. If, on the other hand, the ridges are out of phase, say $1\frac{1}{2}$ wavelengths apart, then the second ridge will tend to cancel out lee waves set of by the upstream hill.

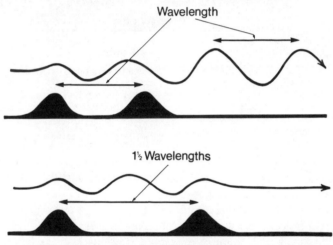

Fig. 17.11 When two ridges are in phase for the lee wavelength in force the second ridge in the flow augments the lee waves due to the upstream hill, as in the upper section of this diagram. If, on the other hand, the ridges are out of phase the second ridge will tend to cancel out the lee waves set off by the upstream hill.

In such a situation as this, the lee wave flow may well augment hill lift in front of the second ridge, but there will be no soarable train of lee waves farther downstream. Figure 17.12 shows an example of this out-of-phase effect that occurred in one of the lee wave investigations made in the neighbourhood of the Sierra Nevada, a Rocky Mountain range in California.

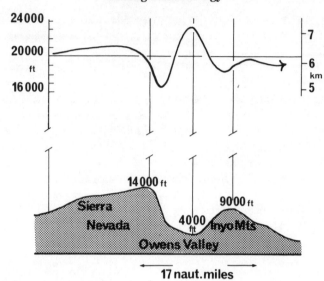

Fig. 17.12   On 1 April 1955 the lee wave flow over the Owens Valley, California, started with a descent immediately to the lee of the Sierra Nevada then passed through 1½ wavelengths before being practically cancelled out by the out-of-phase effect of the Inyo Mountains. The streamline drawn was deduced from temperature measurements made during a flight through the waves.

Because the lee wave effects of successive ridges are additive, even slow changes of lee wavelength can lead to rapid fluctuations in the resultant flow as the lee waves from various ridges are brought in or out of phase with one another. Figure 17.13 shows some of the variety of forms a lee wave flow can take over rugged terrain. When the lee wavelength changes, in response to changes in the temperature or wind structure in the airstream, the resultant wave pattern over hilly or mountainous country shifts erratically from one configuration to another.

The regular sinusoidal form of the lee wave flow is not apparent until the airstream reaches ground-level (or open sea) in the lee of the mountainous regions—but once over a flat plain or sea the wave train can extend for great distances—200 km or more—downwind.

It is not uncommon for hill lift to be augmented or confused by wave flow from an upstream escarpment. This effect has been noted particularly at Camp Hill, the site of the Derby and Lancashire

No Lee Waves

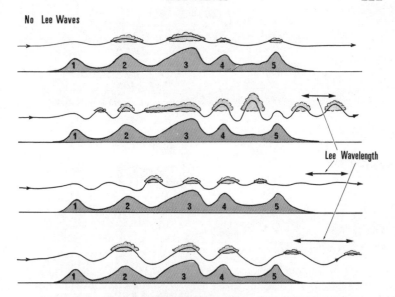

Fig. 17.13 Schematic sketches of the flow over rugged terrain for no lee waves and for the indicated wavelengths. In a flow without lee waves the orographic cloud is confined to caps right over the mountain peaks themselves. The combined resonance and phase effects of the five princi-pal ridges complicate the flow over the mountains themselves; the simple sinusoidal lee wave flow is not apparent until the flow reaches flat ground.

Gliding Club in England. Sometimes the hill lift over the steep escarpment forming the western boundary of the flying-field is boosted by a wave flow from the upwind hills. Figure 17.14 shows the pattern. When this occurs it is not uncommon for the lee wavelength to decrease during the early evening, with the result that the wave crest is over the valley, and the gliding club's hill soaring ridge is in almost calm air. Thus gliders that are already in the air and shift upwind with the wave can remain airborne, while gliders at the club site are robbed of lift.

Three-dimensional hills

When describing the principal features of lee wave flow it is convenient to refer to the flow across two-dimensional ridges; that is, ridges which can be considered as extremely long prisms placed

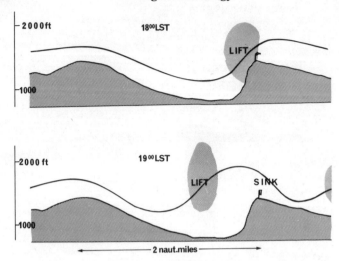

Fig. 17.14 At the gliding site of Camphill, England, it is not uncommon for the lee wavelength to decrease during the evening. At 18.00 hours the lee wave flow triggered off by upstream hills reinforces the hill lift, but as the lee wavelength decreases the zone of wave lift shifts upwind while the Camphill site is in the lee wave downdraught. At this time of the evening pilots in the air who shift upwind with the lee wave lift can remain airborne, while pilots on the ground cannot reach this wave lift because there is now no longer any hill lift.

across the airflow. But most real hills and mountains are of motley shapes. It is practically impossible to observe, calculate or guess the precise effect on airflow of each particular shape. However, it is useful to know that, whereas a long straight ridge can set off a train of lee waves extending some considerable distance downstream, a short ridge produces waves whose amplitudes decrease rather quickly downwind. The longer the ridge the more lee wave clouds there are (provided, of course, that the lee waves are not cancelled out by some out-of-phase downstream ridge). There is no golden rule relating the length of the ridge to the downwind extent of the lee wave train. Even a ridge of only a few miles in length can set off a long train of waves; but it is often difficult to decide whether or not a ridge can be described as long.

A straight ridge lying obliquely across the airflow produces lee waves parallel to itself—not at right angles to the wind direction. But such waves are usually of small amplitude and seldom extend far downstream. A ridge which in plan view presents a concave face to the wind is likely to produce a longer train of lee waves than a ridge that has a convex face to the wind. Airflow passing the convex upwind shape tends to glide around the edge of the ridge instead of over the top especially if the air is very stable.

Compared with long ridges, conical hills are poor generators of lee waves. But single stationary clouds, sometimes saucer shaped, sometimes in the form of a crescent, are occasionally observed in the lee of very large conical mountains, such as Mount Fuji in Japan.

Long mountain ranges, such as the Andes, often block or divert the oncoming air at low levels. But if the air that does flow across such a range has the stability conditions suitable for wave flow, it descends down into the leeward valleys or plains, then up into a wave train. As the air pouring over the mountain crest rushes down to low levels it is warmed by compression and the resultant hot dry flow can be classed as a föhn wind.

Turbulence and eddies

Flight conditions in lee waves are often remarkably smooth; a conspicuous absence of turbulent or eddying motion in the airstream is sometimes the first indication to a pilot that he has flown into a wave flow. But lee wave conditions can also produce some of the most violent turbulence likely to be encountered in the troposphere. The reason for this dichotomous behaviour of a wave flow is that the stable lapse rate usually associated with the wave flow acts to suppress turbulence and eddies, but the wave flow itself creates or intensifies local wind shears that tend to produce turbulence despite the stability. When the locally intensified wind shears (most likely in the crests or troughs of waves) succeed in creating eddies in a stable layer, elements of this stable layer are overturned. These overturned elements are extremely unstable because, during the overturning process, warm air is brought downwards and warmed by adiabatic compression while cold air is carried upwards and cooled by adiabatic expansion. Thus, the stable lapse rate is suddenly transformed into an intensely unstable condition. This local instability adds to the turbulence created by the local wind shear, which in turn transforms elements of the stable layer into intense local instability.

Such turbulence is not always severe; it may amount to no more than shallow patches of ruffled air, sandwiched between layers of smooth wave flow, but in the strong wind shears associated with jet streams even weak waves can trigger off high-level turbulence rough enough to surprise and shake the unwary pilot, and at lower levels, where the wave amplitude often varies considerably with height, turbulence due to wind shear and waves can sometimes be really violent.

The flow in lee of the Sierra Nevada on 18 March 1955 included this type of turbulence. Figure 17.15 illustrates the nature of the flow. In the vicinity of the lee wave cloud the wavelike flow had broken down into a region of chaotic motion. The wave cloud as a whole remained more or less stationary, but it was ragged and

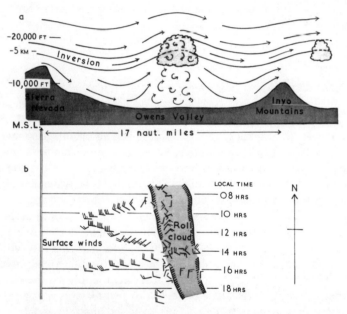

Fig. 17.15   The rotor flow in lee of the Sierra Nevada on 18 March 1955 included a turbulent roll cloud.

Surface winds were recorded throughout the day at several stations in an approximately east-west line across the Owens Valley, and by a mobile observing unit travelling almost along this line. These wind observations are plotted against time in the lower half (*b*) of the figure. Each full feather of the wind arrows represents a speed of 10 knots.

tattered—quite unlike the well-formed lenticulars so characteristic of smoother flow. From a distance this ragged wave cloud looked like a patch of innocuous stratocumulus, but on closer inspection it was possible to observe fragments of the cloud being torn from the trailing edge and to see that the top of the cloud was moving much faster than the base. It was easy to imagine the cloud as a huge stationary roller, and this type of cloud is in fact called *roll cloud*. The type of motion is known as *rotor flow*.

On 25 April 1955 a glider used to explore a Sierra wave was broken up by turbulence in such a cloud. Here is an extract from the report by the pilot Larry Edgar:

'The flight path went into the top of the little cloud puff. It seemed to swell up before the nose in the last moment. I looked at the needle and ball. Suddenly and instantaneously the needle went off centre. I followed with a correction but it swung violently the other way. I was forced sideways in my seat first to the left and then to the right. A fantastic positive G load shoved me down in my seat. Just as I was blacking out it felt like a violent roll to the left with a loud explosion followed by a violent negative G load. I felt my head hit the canopy. I was too stunned to make any attempt to bail out. Just as suddenly as all this violence started it became quiet except for the sound of the wind whistling by. I felt I was falling free of all wreckage except for something* holding both feet.'

Turbulence in a rotor flow is usually at its worst in the roll cloud itself, but it can also be quite formidable in clear regions of rotor flow. Describing a part of his flight from St Yan to St Auban on 11 July 1956 Philip Wills said:

'. . . I broke cloud over the Drome valley, safely south of the mountain I had just left. Suddenly there was a jar and a shock, and my starboard wing fell into nothing. With full opposite aileron I hung and slid into space for what seemed an age. The next ten minutes were unforgettable. Seven pilots eventually completed this flight and all of them confessed that they had never experienced such wild turbulence before.'

* The remnants of the rudder bar.

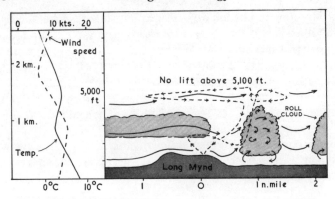

Fig. 17.16   A dotted line marks the wave flight made by Stan Jones from a winch launch on 10 April 1953. The airstream conditions are shown on the left. As in several other diagrams in this chapter the nature of the flow is depicted schematically by streamlines based on the observed effects.

Of course, not all rotor flow is as rough as this. Flying in a wave flow depicted in Figure 17.16, Stan Jones found conditions safe enough even though

> 'very rough air was encountered over the top of the roll cloud and full aileron and rudder control was required to keep the Olympia on an even keel. This turbulence was not of the small-scale type which sometimes gives the pilot the feeling of riding over cobblestones: it was more of the type experienced on rough hill-soaring days.'

Although rotor flow can often be flown through with safety, it should always be treated with caution. The transition between the smooth wave flow and the turbulent zone is usually sharp. The time to tighten safety straps and to secure movable objects such as a camera or a computer, is on the ground or in the deceptively smooth air *before* testing turbulence for strength.

It is wise to look for signs of rotor flow before taking off in wave conditions. One of the danger signals that may be gleaned from meteorological information is a decrease of wind or a sharp change of wind direction through the stable layer likely to be associated with the wave flow. Figure 17.17 shows the type of airstream conditions likely to promote rotor flow. It must not be deduced that no other types of airstream can produce turbulence in wave flow,

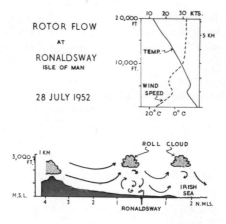

Fig. 17.17 Rotor flow, as evidenced by the roll cloud and variable surface winds at Ronaldsway on 28 July 1952, is often associated with a decrease of wind speed up through a stable layer. The airstream conditions for this occasion are illustrated above.

but a decrease of wind speed or a sharp change of wind direction up through the stable layer should be regarded as warning to explore the waves with special caution.

Often the effect of the turbulence extends to low levels; so another sign of rotor flow is the presence of sudden and erratic wind changes on the ground beneath the rotors. Figure 17.15 illustrates a very marked example of chaotic winds under a strong rotor.

The upwind jump

Wave patterns and wave clouds are not always stationary. The way in which the composite effect of a succession of ridges coupled with a slowly changing wavelength can produce fast and erratic changes in the flow pattern has already been mentioned. But there are movements that cannot be accounted for in this way. Perhaps the presence of eddies on the hill slope and in the valleys changes the effective shape of the high ground; perhaps these eddies form periodically; perhaps they break away from lee slopes and drift downstream at, say, 2–20 min intervals. Such conjectures as these are based on observations, but at present they are little more than plausible ideas. Observations and time-lapse films of clouds have revealed one feature of special interest. Occasionally a wave cloud has been seen to move slowly downwind, travelling between 150 m and $1\frac{1}{2}$ km in 5–10 min before suddenly, in a matter of seconds, jumping (re-forming) upstream back to its original position. This process of a slow downstream drift followed by an *upwind jump* is then repeated over and over again. The reason for such a periodic movement is not yet clear. The phenomenon is most impressive when studied through the medium of time-lapse photography, but it usually requires more than casual observation to be detected from the ground.

To pilots in the air the upstream jump is often all too obvious; at one instant they may be flying just upwind of the wave cloud, but at the next they are in cloud which has suddenly developed round them.

Long waves aloft

Most waves used for soaring are of the type whose amplitude increases from the ground up to a maximum in or near the stable layer likely to be present, and then fades away at higher levels. But some airstreams can undulate on more than one wavelength, and it is not abnormal to find two different wavelengths in operation at once. The shorter wave is usually most pronounced at some low level while the amplitude of the longer wave is at its maximum at a greater height. Furthermore, the long wave pattern includes a nodal surface, usually in the lower half of the troposphere. Because the wave pattern is reversed on passing up through the nodal surface, the most effective part of the longer lee wave flow starts with an ascent immediately to the lee of the hillcrest. Figures 17.18(a), (b) and (c) show how the combination of the two sets of waves can appear to tilt a stack of wave clouds away from the vertical structure characteristic of the simpler type of wave flow. Although these double wave systems complicate the flow pattern they can at least provide occasional opportunities for soaring up through a considerable depth of the atmosphere. The shorter, lower-level waves might well form a stairway to the longer waves aloft.

Wave systems can reach very high into the atmosphere. Powered aircraft have observed wave flow above 18 km; observations of *Mother of Pearl* clouds suggest that wave flow occurs at levels near

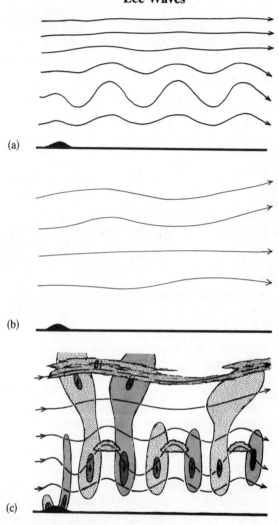

Fig. 17.18 A double wave system comprises:
   (a) a short wave pattern most pronounced at lower levels, and
   (b) a long wave pattern which includes a nodal surface and which is
       most pronounced at high levels.
The combined effect of these two sets of waves can produce the pattern
illustrated in (c). The shaded zones of lift and sink tilt upwind or downwind
as the low-level lift pattern merges with that at high levels. It is not
uncommon for the high-level long wave to be revealed by long arches of
cirrus cloud.

30 km, and more recently radar observation of chaff projected to very high levels revealed signs of waves at 64 km.

Waves and convection

Because one of the requirements for lee waves is a stable layer in the lower atmosphere, lee wave theory is sometimes interpreted incorrectly to mean that convection and lee waves do not exist together. Lee waves and convection clouds are not mutually exclusive. The tops of cumulus cloud in thermal and wave conditions need not be limited to very low levels. Observations show that lee waves can occur when the tops of convective clouds extend upwards as much as three times the height of the mountains. On these occasions it appears that the large cumulus clouds form and persist for long periods over the peaks. In doing so they effectively become an extension of the mountain. The cloud top reaches up to the more stable layer high above the peak and produces undulations in this layer. Wave flow develops in and above this layer. It is somewhat similar to that which produces waves over cumulus cloud streets (as mentioned in Chapter 13).

Thermal waves and shear waves

Thermal waves have already been described in Chapter 13. Unlike lee waves, these thermal waves are not normally stationary; they often move slowly in the direction of, but more slowly than, the wind through them.

Whenever a layer of cold air undercuts a warmer airstream, or a warm airstream flows over cooler air, waves are likely to form in and adjacent to the transition zone between the contrasting warm and cold layers. Most often these waves are weak and scarcely detectable, but when the contrast between the upper and lower airstreams is strong and the transition zone is sharp such waves can be noticeable enough for wave soaring. Because a marked wind shear normally exists through the transition zone, such waves are called *shear waves*. They are somewhat similar to thermal waves in that they do not need any particular high ground feature to set them off, but whereas a thermal wave pattern is normally associated with a distinctive underlying pattern of thermal or cloud streets, shear waves are associated in a less distinctive way with the formation of the transition zone and the wind shear. A cold front can produce classic examples of cold air undercutting a warm airstream, and shear waves are sometimes observed and used for soaring in a cold frontal transition zone. The front need not be active in the sense that it produces abundant rain and cloud. Cold air invading a hot dry land mass can produce the sharp wind and temperature contrasts that produce shear waves without bringing frontal rain. Malcolm Jinks of Waikerie has soared to over 20 000 ft in such waves. Warm fronts can also produce shear waves but warm frontal shear waves are mostly weak, except when a markedly warm airstream penetrates well into a cold land mass. Shear waves associated with frontal transition zones occur mainly at medium cloud levels; they are seldom usable for soaring at low levels.

Katabatic winds, sea-breezes and precipitation downdraughts are also phenomena that cause a cool flow to undercut relatively warm air. They can produce shear waves at the interface between the lower cool and upper warm layers of air. These waves occur at low levels, and they may be visible if there happens to be a source of smoke in the cool air, but they usually have a short wavelength and are too weak for soaring.

Wind shear that frequently exists at the top of thermal layers in subtropical climates can produce usable waves, but these airstreams can also produce thermal or cloud streets, so the waves should be called thermal waves or shear waves according to whether or not their pattern appears to be determined by the underlying pattern of thermal streets.

In general, shear waves are more transitory than thermal waves and the orientation of shear waves is more difficult to predict. This orientation is at right angles to the direction of the wind shear (illustrated in Figure 12.6), but this fact is not much use without a knowledge of the winds above and below the shear.

18

Wave Soaring

Lee waves are much more common than is generally supposed. Although some of the world's best-known waves are associated with mighty mountain ranges, a ridge does not have to be high to trigger off soarable waves. Almost any topography that includes some long, well-marked ridges or lee escarpments across the prevailing wind direction has the potential for promoting soarable waves. If the ridges are not high, say less than 1000 ft (300 m) above the valley floor, they should be reasonably smooth—bare rock, moorland, grassland, or covered with thick snow. Well-wooded or jagged terrain tends to break up the smooth low-level flow, but if the ridges are high the precise nature of the surface will not be quite so important.

The district should also be one which has an appreciable quota of airstreams favourable for lee wave flow. The principal features of airstream conditions that favour lee wave formation have been described in Chapter 17. After studying the upper winds and temperatures, the meteorologist can predict the general likelihood of waves over a region for a period of several hours, but, because lee wave amplitude is determined by the precise details of airstream and high ground structures in an intricate manner, he will seldom be able to predict the precise soarability of the waves at any particular time in a region of generally rugged terrain. He seldom has the means of predicting the speed of vertical lee wave currents, but in some situations he can forecast the height at which these vertical currents will be strongest, and thereby give some indications of the chance of contacting the waves (i.e. climbing up to the soarable zone) from below.

When seeking the forecaster's advice on the chances of wave soaring the relevant questions are:

1 *Will the airstream temperature and wind conditions be suitable for lee wave flow for whatever period and region are being considered?*

Plate 26 WAVE CLOUD NEAR MOUNT COOK
Taken from about 30 000 ft in the vicinity of Mount Cook, New Zealand,
this photograph shows a large bank cloud over the main mountain ranges.
With the wind blowing from right to left in the picture, it is easy to visualize
the air flowing downwards at the edge of the main cloud sheet, then up
again towards the patches of cloud in the first lee wave crest.

2 *What will be the wind direction at low levels?*
3 *Will the airstream change appreciably as a result of:*
   (a) Synoptic changes?
   (b) Diurnal heating or cooling?
4 *At about what height will the wave amplitude be at its max-*
   imum? (Usually in the stable layer or temperature inversion
   likely to be associated with the wave conditions.)

5 *Are the wave crests likely to be marked by wave cloud? If so, at what levels?*

6 *Is turbulence, especially rotor turbulence, likely?* (A marked decrease of wind speed or wind shear up through the stable layer is likely to produce turbulence.)

7 *What will be the lee wavelength* (if it is at all predictable)*?*

8 *Between what levels and of what intensity is icing likely?*

Of course, the forecaster may not be able to answer several of these questions. In normal routine work the forecaster is often more concerned with waves of a different variety; in fact, in his conversational circle waves usually refer to broad-scale horizontal oscillations discernible on the synoptic chart, so when making lee wave inquiries it is wise to ensure that the discussion relates to wave flow which goes up and down vertically, not horizontally.

Local signs

Wave clouds are usually branded with the characteristic lenticular shape and stationary nature, but remember that, when viewed from a distance, many a patch of non-wave cloud has a lenticular outline and appears to be almost stationary, while at close quarters, low-level wave cloud may be recognisable as wave cloud only by observing that it is more or less stationary.

Stationary holes in a cloud layer may be evidence of wave flow, and it is also useful to know that the trailing edge of a wave cloud sometimes breaks into a pattern of thin fingers orientated along the wind direction. These thin fingers or longitudinal rolls may also appear on the upwind side of a wave cloud, but they are more likely to form on the trailing edge.

It is not uncommon to see thin wafers of lenticular cloud adorning the tops of cumulus clouds. As triggers for wave flow convection clouds can indeed be considered as mountains in the sky, but transient mountains whose lenticular crowns (pileus clouds) seldom last for long. When cloud streets form, there is at least a slight chance that thermal waves will be set in motion just above the lines of cumulus clouds.

Other clues to the detection of lee waves aloft may be gleaned from surface winds which tend to be stronger under wave troughs than under the crests, and if rotor flow is present the surface winds will probably be quite erratic under wave crests.

Waves in flight

During flight a lee wave flow can often be detected either by the rotor flow turbulence which may be associated with the waves, or by the uncanny smoothness of flight conditions. On first locating the lift in a wave flow it is usually wise to turn into wind in an attempt to start a climb up through the wave system directly over the spot at which the wave lift was detected. Keeping the egg-shaped pattern of lift (depicted in Figure 17.7) in mind, it is understandable that circling flight or premature horizontal exploration of the wave at low levels may easily lead to the glider dropping out of the soarable zone. But having cautiously climbed up well into the wave system a pilot can then explore the wave in an attempt to find the dimensions of the zone of wave lift. If the wave flow is over rugged terrain it may be impossible and unnecessary to determine the wavelength; wave lift over such terrain is likely to be scattered in variegated bands. Over relatively flat terrain, however, wave flow from an upwind mountain range will be free to undulate regularly up and down, and the lee wavelength may be easy to determine and to use for planning the next stage of the flight.

The dangers

In the smooth luxury of lee wave lift a pilot can soar high, far, and into trouble. Many of the potential hazards are dangerous, not because they are difficult to understand, but because they tend to be overlooked in planning or training to fly in waves. So here is a check-list for the wave soaring pilot to consider.

1 The downdraught down a lee escarpment may be particularly strong.
2 Remember that small gaps between low wave clouds can soon fill up, especially if rain begins to fall from cloud above.
3 With a changing synoptic situation the humps of wave clouds may not keep their positions relative to the mountains below them.

4 Due to cooling by ascent the freezing-level will be lower in wave crests than in wave troughs.

5 An airstream with a shallow freezing-layer below thick, relatively warm cloud can provide the stability conditions for lee waves and conditions for freezing-rain, that is, rain falling from the cloud and freezing in the freezing-layer. Ice accretion in such conditions can be thick and sudden. This type of danger is rare, but when a cold winter spell is about to be broken by the approach of an active warm front, beware of the possibility of freezing-rain.

6 When landing remember that ground-level winds may be very variable beneath the wave crests, especially if rotor flow is present.

7 The transition from smooth wave to turbulent rotor flow is often very sharp.

8 When visiting strange clubs believe the local stories of hair-raising turbulence in rotor flow, no matter how innocuous such flow appears to be at your home site.

9 Waves extending to high levels are often associated with a considerable increase of wind speed with height. Do not rely too much on dead reckoning navigation in such conditions.

10 Strong winds aloft are sometimes associated with double-wave systems; a long wavelength at high levels and short waves below. Such a combination of wind and wavelength changes can also upset navigation.

11 A pilot has been carried up beyond the safety limit of his oxygen equipment. The quickest way to get out of the updraught of a wave is to fly downwind into the descending air.

12 When flying close to the windward side of a wave cloud be prepared for a possible upwind jump of the cloud.

Weather Forecasts

19

Charting the Weather

When consulting a professional meteorologist or listening to his forecast it is helpful to have some knowledge of the organisation on which he depends. The provision of a meteorological service starts with routine observations made at internationally agreed times at a large number of observing stations throughout the world. Because each country has to compromise between economy and meteorological requirements, these observing stations are distributed unevenly throughout the countryside and throughout the world.

Meteorological events over the ocean are just as important as those over land, and it is fortunate that routine observations are made voluntarily on hundreds of ships at sea throughout the world. To supplement these ship reports, special ocean weather-ships maintain stations at a number of selected positions, most of which are chosen with aviation requirements in mind.

Augmenting the land and sea reports are observations made from aircraft on operations ranging from transoceanic flights to specially organised meteorological reconnaissance missions, and although these aircraft observations can seldom be made with the same regularity as those made on land or sea, they play a valuable part in building up a three-dimensional picture of the actual weather systems.

The agreed times for making routine observations from land stations and ships are: 00, 03, 06 . . . 18 and 21 hours GMT daily, but some stations record hourly, or even half-hourly, observations.

The elements observed

The routine observations made at ground-stations and on ships usually include a number, if not all, of the following items:

Surface wind direction ⎱
Surface wind speed
Visibility
Present weather   Of particular interest in
Recent weather   aviation
Cloud amounts
Cloud bases
Cloud types ⎰

Air temperature ⎱ Of particular interest in
Dew point ⎰   fog prediction

Barometric pressure   For compiling pressure
   (MSL)   charts

Barometric change in past 3 hours

All relevant to the
analysis of the
current weather
systems

Amount of rainfall at land stations
   between 09 and 21 hours, or
   between 21 and 09 hours

State of the ground (or sea)
Maximum air temperature between 09 and 21
   hours, or
Minimum air temperature between 21 and 09
   hours
Minimum grass temperature between 21 and 09
   hours
Total amount of sunshine at land stations during
   preceding day

Of interest in making
climatological studies
rather than short-
range forecasting

Radio-sonde observations

An apparatus called a *radio-sonde* is used to measure temperature and humidity air aloft. Carried upwards at about 12 knots
(6 m/s) by a gas-filled balloon, this instrument automatically transmits, in the form of radio signals, pressures, temperatures and
humidities up to about 60 000–80 000 ft and, while the ascent is in
progress, upper winds are determined by tracking the balloon by
radar. At present these radio-sonde ascents are made at set times at
least once a day at selected stations in most well-developed countries and at ocean weather-ships.

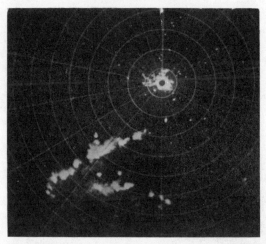

Plate 27   RADAR ECHOES FROM RAINCLOUDS
Bright patches on the lower half of this radar picture are due to echoes
from rainclouds at 15.36 GMT on 18 June 1957. The circles, centred on a
radar station near Dunstable, Bedfordshire, UK, are range markers at 10
mile intervals. The southern section of the echoes were from precipitation
in the stormcloud shown in Plate 22.

Pilot balloons

A cheaper but more restricted method of determining the winds
aloft is to track the ascent of a small gas-filled balloon with the aid of
a theodolite. The height of the balloon at any time is determined
either by filling the balloon to such a size that it rises at a precom-
puted rate, or from measurements of the angular elevation of the
balloon and the apparent length (measured by a scale in the optical
system of the theodolite) of a paper and thread tail suspended from
the balloon itself. Visible through the theodolite as a pinpoint of
reflected sunlight, a *pilot balloon* can be tracked to many thousands
of feet on a fine, clear day, and on clear nights a balloon carrying a
candle lantern or small lightbulb and battery can be detected up to a
few thousand feet. But these balloons cannot, of course, be seen
through clouds and the methods of evaluating their height are
subject to various inaccuracies. So, with' the development of the
more efficient radio-sonde techniques and with the growing interest
in fast, high-level flying the use of pilot balloons has declined in a
number of countries during the last thirty years.

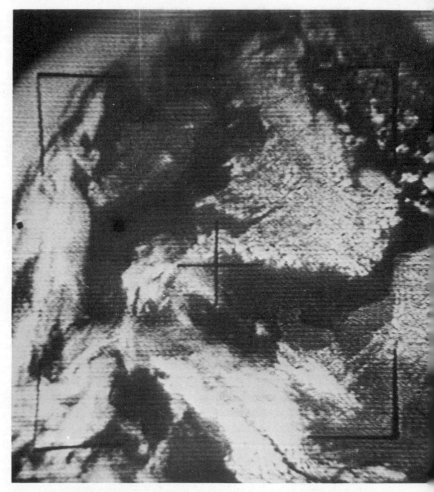

Plate 28 SATELLITE VIEW OF CUMULUS OVER UK
With the heated land surface being sufficient to produce convection cloud,
these convection clouds form a map of much of the underlying terrain.

Atmospherics

A stroke of lightning is an electrical discharge which emits radio
waves in a wide band. Nuisance though they may be when heard as
crackling atmospherics on ordinary radio receivers, these radio

waves enable the lightning to be located by radio direction-finding techniques. A number of countries maintain such direction-finding stations to locate electrical discharges with moderate accuracy up to distances of about 3000 km from a station network. This technique yields hourly reports (known as *SFLOCS*) on the position of thundery outbreaks.

Radar

The ultra-short waves used in radar are reflected by solid objects such as aircraft, but also by agglomerations of raindrops or snowflakes. Areas of rain or snow are seen as bright patches on the radar screen, and by watching the movement of these patches it is sometimes possible to predict with reasonable accuracy the onset or end of precipitation within the next hour or two. Unfortunately, this method of prediction sounds easier to apply than it really is. Radar echoes are not always easy to interpret with confidence; at close range echoes from small clouds are sometimes obscured by local radar reflections; as the range is increased the reduction in the penetrative power of the radar beam impairs the radar view, and, because radar waves usually travel in straight lines, the rain clouds in the troposphere are seldom detected at ranges greater than about 200 km. Some atmospheric conditions, especially low-level inversions, cause the radar beam to become curved and the effective range is therefore increased, but at the same time this refraction of the beam also adds difficulties to interpretation of the echoes.

Light rain or drizzle cannot normally be detected by radar operating on the commonly used 10-cm wavelength, but even when the raindrops are numerous and large enough to produce strong echoes, the forecasting problem remains not only to predict the movement of the rain but also how the area will change in size and shape as it moves.

Communications and codes

Meteorological observations lose much of their value to weather forecasting after they are a few hours old. To minimise delay in collection and dissemination of these observations, meteorological communications are co-ordinated on a world-wide basis.

A speedy exchange of information would be impossible if every observer sent out a detailed report in his own language. So, an international code or shorthand is used. Each report is translated into a few groups of five figures according to a system, which at first sight may appear complicated. However, this international code is an invaluable device for packing copious information into a brief internationally understood message (as evidenced by the example on page 245) and practised meteorologists talk and think in terms of it.

The weather map

At most forecasting offices plotters transpose the incoming coded weather message on to large charts which are usually plotted at three-hourly intervals: 00, 03, 06 ... 21 hours GMT. Naturally the area mapped, the scale of the charts and the frequency with which they are plotted are selected to meet the requirements of each particular office, but the plotting systems are determined by international agreement. As with the codes, the object is to condense a large amount of information into a compact form. The main features of this system used in meteorological practice are illustrated on pages 246 and 247 and typified by Figure 19.1 which shows the

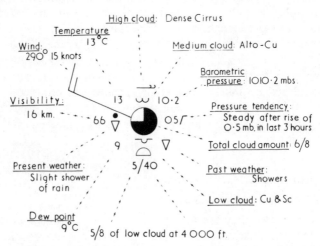

Fig. 19.1   Plotted version of the coded weather observation on page 245.

CODED WEATHER MESSAGE
(WITH MEANING BELOW)

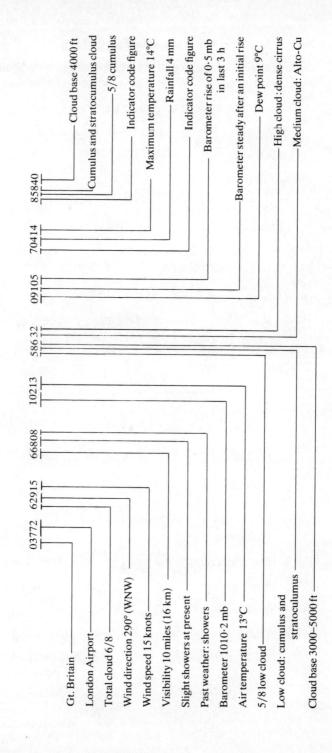

03772	62915	66808	10213	586 32	09105	70414	85840

Gt. Britain
London Airport
Total cloud 6/8
Wind direction 290° (WNW)
Wind speed 15 knots
Visibility 10 miles (16 km)
Slight showers at present
Past weather: showers
Barometer 1010·2 mb
Air temperature 13°C
5/8 low cloud
Low cloud: cumulus and stratoculumulus
Cloud base 3000–5000 ft

Cloud base 4000 ft
Cumulus and stratocumulus cloud
5/8 cumulus
Indicator code figure
Maximum temperature 14°C
Rainfall 4 mm
Indicator code figure
Barometer rise of 0·5 mb in last 3 h
Barometer steady after an initial rise
Dew point 9°C
High cloud: dense cirrus
Medium cloud: Alto-Cu

plotted version of the coded weather message described on page 245.

PRINCIPAL WEATHER SYMBOLS

،	Drizzle		Rain shower
•	Rain	═══	Fog
	Sleet	──	Mist
✳	Snow		Smoke haze
△	Hail shower		Thunderstorm

Subclassifications of precipitation are denoted by arrangements and modifications of the type shown below.

- • Intermittent slight rain
- •• Continuous slight rain
- ⋮ Intermittent moderate rain
- Continuous moderate rain
- ⋮ Intermittent heavy rain
- Continuous heavy rain
- Slight snow shower
- Moderate or heavy rain showers

SELECTION OF CLOUD TYPES

Low cloud

- Small cumulus
- Large CuNim
- St-cu
- Stratus
- CuNim with anvil

Medium cloud

- Thin Alto-St
- Thick Alto-St
- Alto-Cu
- Ac and As
- Turretted or castellated Ac

High cloud

Ci ('mares' tails')

Ci (associated with CuNim)

Ci (in bands)

Ci-St

Ci-cu

Computing aids

Meteorologists were among the first to use high-speed computers in their work. The early usage centred on the forecasting problem and by 1960 it was possible to feed routine synoptic data into a computing system and obtain 24-hour predictions of pressure and wind patterns with about the same accuracy and consistency as that already obtained by the judgement of experienced forecasters. The forecaster supplied with routine computed predictions steadily gained confidence in their reliability, and computer-predicted upper winds were soon in routine use for long-distance flight planning. But pressure and wind prediction is only a first step in weather prediction; such predictions form a framework on which to hang other elements such as temperature, humidity, stability, vertical motion and the consequential local wind, cloud, sunshine, precipitation and visibility which we consider as weather.

The forecaster may recognise a computer-predicted pattern as being favourable for, say, sea-breezes, tornadoes, thunderstorms, etc., but he still has to resort to his judgement or other techniques to forecast whether such phenomena will occur and, if so, how intense they will be.

A lesser-known, but wider use of computers in meteorology is for communication and data processing. Computers are used in many elements of the world-wide meteorological communications network to control telecommunications, edit coded information and store or present it in the form required for forecasters and other users. Maps or graphs can be drawn or presented on television screens by computer-controlled equipment. Even station plots, like that illustrated in Figure 19.1, can be computer produced.

Although the use of computing aids has led to improvements in meteorological services, these improvements have been at the pace of gradual development rather than a sudden step forward.

Weather satellites

In 1960 a new dimension was added to the weather observation by the launching of the first of a series of *TIROS* satellites from Cape Canaveral (now Cape Kennedy), USA. This series of ten satellites was followed by others called *NIMBUS I* in 1964 and *ESSA I* and *ESSA II* in 1966.

Most weather satellites orbit the Earth once every 100 minutes approximately. Each satellite takes a series of photographs of the earth's surface and atmosphere below, and transmits these photographs to ground stations. Most pictures show cloud patterns, but some show patterns of radiation in selected bands of radiation wavelengths. The cloud pictures give a spaceman's view of whole depressions and cloud systems that the forecaster can only deduce imperfectly from earthbound observations. Bands and areas of cloud, cloud streets, wave clouds, convection cloud patterns can be distinguished in many situations. Not all cloud structures are clear because of overlap of cloud layers and miscellaneous technical problems of photographic interpretation, but the weather satellite technology has made such progress that it provides a reliable routine view of cloud patterns.

Most views cover an approximately north–south band about 3000 km (1500 miles) wide during each orbit and the band is shifted approximately 22 degrees westwards on each orbit. This enables any particular locality to be photographed once per day and at about the same time each day. The radiation satellites provide atmospheric data that can be used to derive temperatures in the atmosphere, but at present they are used mainly for research rather than routine forecasting purposes.

Some weather satellite photos can be obtained with radio reception and picture scanning equipment that is not too complicated or expensive for interested amateurs to construct and operate. Pictures received by official meteorological services are sometimes relayed through meteorological communication networks to other stations, but it is more common for forecasters at the main

Plate 29 DISTANT SATELLITE VIEW OF CLOUD PATTERNS
Photographs from distant satellites can cover an entire hemisphere of the
Earth. This picture shows cloud patterns over the Pacific. The Gulf of
California is discernible under clear skies towards the top of the picture.
Geostationary satellites can be set at about 36 000 km over the Equator to
orbit the Earth once per day, thereby holding their set positions over the
Equator.

meteorological office receiving the satellite pictures to sketch their
interpretation of the cloud and meteorological content of each
photograph and transmit these sketches to subsidiary meteorological offices. Such an analysis of cloud distribution and structure is
called a *nephanalysis*. Simple conventional symbols have been
evolved by meteorologists to transmit these nephanalyses over
facsimile networks, so symbolic maps of the satellite pictures are
now used at many meteorological stations, and in some countries
they are shown on television forecasts.

The forecaster's task

While the weather map is being plotted, other assistants are usually at work drawing graphs showing the winds, temperatures and humidities as determined by the radio-sonde ascents, and processing data for the construction of pressure maps at various levels in the atmosphere.

Very briefly, the forecaster's task is to analyse the plotted and processed weather observations into a coherent but continuously changing three-dimensional picture and to predict the subsequent developments. In tackling this formidable task he draws isobars, fronts and very occasionally *isallobars* (isopleths of pressure changes) on the weather maps. He calls these weather maps *synoptic charts* while the instantaneous weather pictures they portray are referred to as *synoptic situations*.

A suitably graduated *geostrophic scale* is often used to measure geostrophic wind speeds at points of special interest on the pressure maps, and the forecaster's routine often includes a study of 'thermal' charts which relate to thermal winds and not to thermals in the gliding sense.

The forecaster's scientific ability is required not to make intricate calculations on a routine basis, but to analyse complex atmospheric processes into elementary and more easily understandable components whose relative significance in any particular circumstances may (with experience) be assessed in the light of current features and trends in the synoptic situation.

One of the principal tasks of the forecasters at the main meteorological offices is to predict the movements and development of the pressure systems at MSL and at several upper levels up to just above the tropopause for 24–36 hours ahead. These forecast pressure charts and the reasoning behind them are used as a framework on which to make forecasts of the weather itself and it is these forecasts that are illustrated on television screens, forecast by radio and presented in diverse forms by the daily press.

For use as background information, descriptions and coded forms of the forecast pressure maps are included in the messages transmitted from central communication centres to regional centres where the forecaster's duties often include the preparation of detailed regional forecasts for about 6–18 hours ahead and aviation forecasts for specified routes. Usually a regional forecast is passed on to local stations to be issued to aviators by forecasters who keep watch on the local weather and the local trend as indicated by current observations within their zone of interest.

Thus, national meteorological organisations are to some extent pyramidal; responsibilities are telescoped along roughly the same channels as the national communications networks—and the national networks themselves are linked within an international global system. The systems, however, are flexible enough to cater for a wide variety of operational requirements. Some large airports, for example, with large forecasting staffs provided with copious information of direct interest to international aviation, can function as independent forecasting units, whereas at some public inquiry offices duty forecasters are so busy answering inquiries that they must rely on a steady flow of forecasts from their parent stations.

20

Temperature-Height Diagrams

A crucial factor in understanding or predicting the development of thermals is the variation of temperature with height. Meteorologists use special diagrams for plotting graphs of temperature with height, but we need not consider these special diagrams until later in this chapter. For our immediate purposes let us consider simple graphs of temperature plotted against height, like that shown in Figure 20.1(a). This figure shows a typical distribution of temperature with height after a cool, cloudless night with little or no wind. Nocturnal cooling by radiation has produced a temperature inversion from 3°C at ground-level to 9°C at 2000 ft (600 m). After sunrise following such a night, heating from the sun will heat the ground, which in turn will warm the air above—and after, say, an hour or two of this heating the temperature-height graph will change to a shape like that in Figure 20.1(b). The lowest part of the graph will acquire a superadiabatic or dry adiabatic lapse rate because the air in this layer will be heated by convection and mixed by turbulence. In most techniques for illustrating or predicting the height to which thermals will rise, the difference between the DALR and superadiabatic lapse rates can be ignored; in Figure 20.1(b) the well-mixed layer is depicted as a dry adiabatic layer from a temperature of 9°C at ground-level to 6°C at 1000 ft. Above this height the temperature-height graph remains unchanged. The low, well-mixed, layer is the dry thermal layer at this stage; it will contain thermals but they will be limited to the layer between ground-level and 1000 ft and they will be mostly weak and short lived. As the day progresses the heating will continue to raise the temperature of the dry thermal layer, so that after another few hours the graph may look like that drawn in figure 20.1(c). Now, the dry thermal layer, in this illustration, has a temperature of 12°C at ground-level and its top is at 1500 ft (500 m). Thermals in this layer will have a little more depth to become organised but they will not go higher than about 1500 ft.

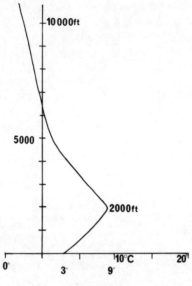

Fig. 20.1(a)

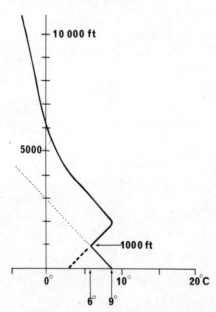

Fig. 20.1 (b), continued on next page

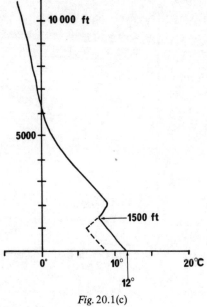

Fig. 20.1(c)

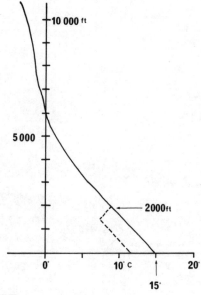

Fig. 20.1(d)

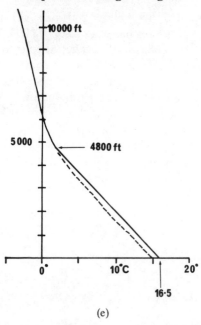

(e)

Fig. 20.1 The continuous curves in this diagram indicate the temperature-height curves referred to in the text. The broken curves are used to indicate changes. For example, the broken line in (b) is a reminder of the lower part of the temperature-height curve in (a). The dotted line in (b) indicates the dry adiabatic lapse.

All the time this is going on the temperature inversion is gradually being eaten away by the low-level heating. By the time the temperature at ground-level gets to 15°C, as sketched in Figure 20.1(d), the inversion will have been completely eliminated—or broken down. In this example, 15°C is the trigger temperature mentioned in Chapter 12. At this stage the dry thermal layer will reach to 2000 ft. Any subsequent heating will be spread, not merely between ground-level and the low-level inversion, but between ground-level and a much greater height which depends on the temperature lapse rate above the original inversion. In this example, if the temperature reaches $16\frac{1}{2}$°C the heating will be spread up to 4800 ft (1600 m), as shown in Figure 20.1(e). In other words, the top of the dry thermal layer will have extended from 2000 ft, at the time the inversion was broken down, up to 4800 ft (1600 m) fairly soon

afterwards. If the sky is fairly clear, there are likely to be moderate
or good thermals up to this height of 4800 ft (1600 m).

So far, in this example, we have taken the air to be too dry for
cumulus cloud to form. Suppose, however, that the thermals rising
from ground-level have a condensation level at 4000 ft. This would
mean that, when the thermal layer extended to 4000 ft and above,
cumulus clouds would form. During their ascent above the condensation level the thermals would be saturated and their temperature
would decrease with height at the saturated adiabatic lapse rate,
which is marked in Figure 20.2. These saturated thermals would be

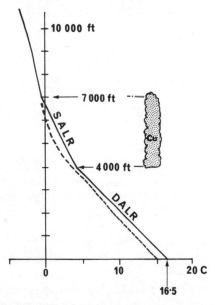

Fig. 20.2   The broken curve denotes the temperature-height curve illustrated in Fig. 20.1(d). The continuous curve denotes the subsequent
changes in this temperature-height curve if heating, in this example, is
sufficient to take the surface air temperature to 16.5°C and if the condensation level is at 4000 ft.

warmer than the surrounding air until they reached 7000 ft in this
example. At this level the temperature of these thermals would be
the same as that of the surrounding air. The thermals would
probably have a little excess buoyancy at this level because of their
excess water vapour over that of the surrounding air, so they may

rise to little more than 7000 ft, but not much more. Therefore, in this example, we would predict that cumulus cloud would form at 4000 ft (1300 m) and cloud tops would be approximately 7000 ft (2300 m).

So, if we know the temperature-height graph early in the day and can predict the rise of temperature during the day and the condensation level, we can predict the all-important height to which thermals will reach on a bright sunny day.

A technique of making such a prediction is described in Chapter 25 of this book, but even if we do not have sufficient information to make a prediction, a familiarity with temperature-height graphs is an almost indispensable aid to understanding thermal development and thermal predictions.

Local Met flights

The best way of knowing how the temperature varies with height is to measure it. At gliding competitions, where the success of a contest day can depend critically on thermal prediction, it is well worth while to use a light aircraft to measure temperatures from ground-level up to about 8000 ft (2500 m). Expensive, sophisticated equipment is not necessary for measuring air temperatures for our purposes. A simple thermometer will be adequate, provided it can be mounted or held in the airflow outside of the aircraft and can be read from inside the aircraft. It should be placed so that it is shaded from direct sunshine, and is not in the flow of heated air from the engine. Air temperature measurements made in such a way are often about $\frac{1}{2}$°C too high (due to effect of airspeed and compression at the thermometer bulb) but, as we shall be more interested in the shape of the temperature-height graph than the absolute accuracy, it is easy to accommodate this error. The rate of climb from ground-level up to about 8000 ft should be about 500 ft/min (150 m/min) or less, so as to avoid excessive errors due to lag in the thermometer readings. When circling the pilot should turn in the best direction for keeping the thermometer in the shade. Readings should be taken at about 500-ft intervals of height, and, if possible, the pilot or observer should try to draw the temperature-height graph during the climb. As the graph is being drawn, the special features of interest, such as base and top of an inversion, will be revealed and will indicate where more readings or more care needs to be taken to determine the temperature profile. Other weather features, such as the local and distant cloud pattern (especially the direction of any medium or high cloud in the distance) and the top of haze or pollution, should be noted. Temperatures can, if necessary, be checked on the descent, but in most situations this is not essential and a more pressing operational requirement is usually that the flight should be made quickly and cheaply.

An indication of the humidity distribution with height can be obtained by measuring both the dry- and wet-bulb temperatures. The wet-bulb temperature can be measured by using another thermometer with its bulb wrapped in a thin piece of muslin kept damp by moisture creeping up through a wick dipped in water. Chapter 4 describes the principle of this wet-bulb thermometer for measuring the moisture content of the air. It is not essential to convert these wet- and dry-bulb temperature readings to relative humidity or actual water vapour content; the simple basic knowledge, that the greater the difference between the dry- and wet-bulb temperatures the lower will be the relative humidity, is adequate for building up experience on the use of wet-bulb temperature readings. These wet-bulb temperatures can be plotted on the same diagram as the temperature-height graph.

The data obtained should be logged not only for immediate use, but for possible future research and development of thermal prediction techniques. An extract of such a log is shown opposite. The wet-bulb temperatures are omitted because they are not relevant to the discussion.

On this particular flight I measured temperatures up to 8500 ft, but only those up to 3000 ft are shown in this extract. The top of the temperature inversion from 500 ft upwards was found to be at 1800 ft where the temperature was 29.8°C, so this reading was noted in addition to those at regular 500 ft intervals. The column headed 'Surface Temp req'd' is for calculated surface temperatures required to produce a dry thermal layer from ground-level up to heights listed in the height column; for example, a surface temperature of 35.5°C would be required to produce a DALR, and therefore dry thermal layer, up to 2500 ft. These required surface temperatures are easily calculated; they are simply the temperature plus 3 times the height in thousands of feet at which it was

MET FLIGHT—RENMARK—07.30–08.05 h—10 JAN 1977
(Local time = LST + 30 min)

Height 1000's ft	Temperatures °C		For DALR to Height of reading				Observations
	Dry	Wet	Surface Temp req'd	Heating increment req'd °Ckft	Total heating req'd °Ckft	Predicted local time	
0.0	25.4		25.4				
0.5	24.2		25.7				Haze top
1.0	26.5		29.5				500 ft
1.5	27.6		32.1				
1.8	29.8		35.2				
2.0	29.4		35.4				
2.5	28.0		35.5				
3.0	26.9		35.9				
—	—	—	—				Bank of thick
—	—	—	—				Cirrus orientated
—	—	—	—				NW–SE far to the
—	—	—	—				SW
—	—	—	—				Patches of
—	—	—	—				Alto-Cu to the
—	—	—	—				N and NE

measured; for example; for a 1500-ft dry thermal layer a surface temperature of $27.6 + 3 \times 1.5 = 32.1°C$ is required.

Use of the other columns, labelled 'Heating Increment req'd', 'Total Heating req'd' and 'Predicted Local Time', will be described in Chapter 25.

Aerological diagrams

The meteorologist uses temperature-height diagrams, but, because he needs to trace atmospheric processes more rigorously, the axes for his temperature-height diagrams are twisted and stretched to allow for easy application of the rules of thermodynamics. Understanding of the special temperature-height charts used by meteorologists is not absolutely essential for the glider pilot, but a familiarity with the diagrams is useful because it can at least improve communication between glider pilots and meteorologists. If a glider pilot wishes to delve more deeply into atmospheric processes, these specially designed diagrams are more

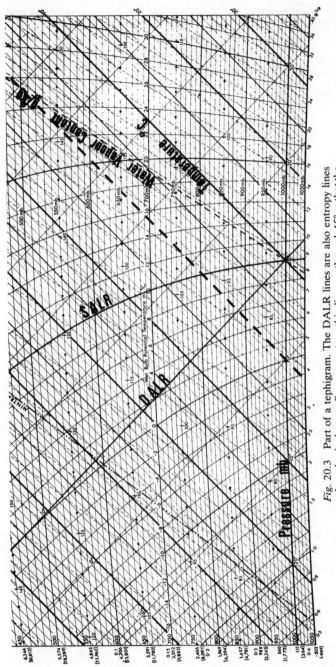

Fig. 20.3   Part of a tephigram. The DALR lines are also entropy lines referred to in the text. Some users turn this diagram through 45° so that the DALR are horizontal and temperature lines vertical. The main feature to remember in acquiring a familiarity with the tephigram is the broad orientation pattern of the lines marked in this diagram.

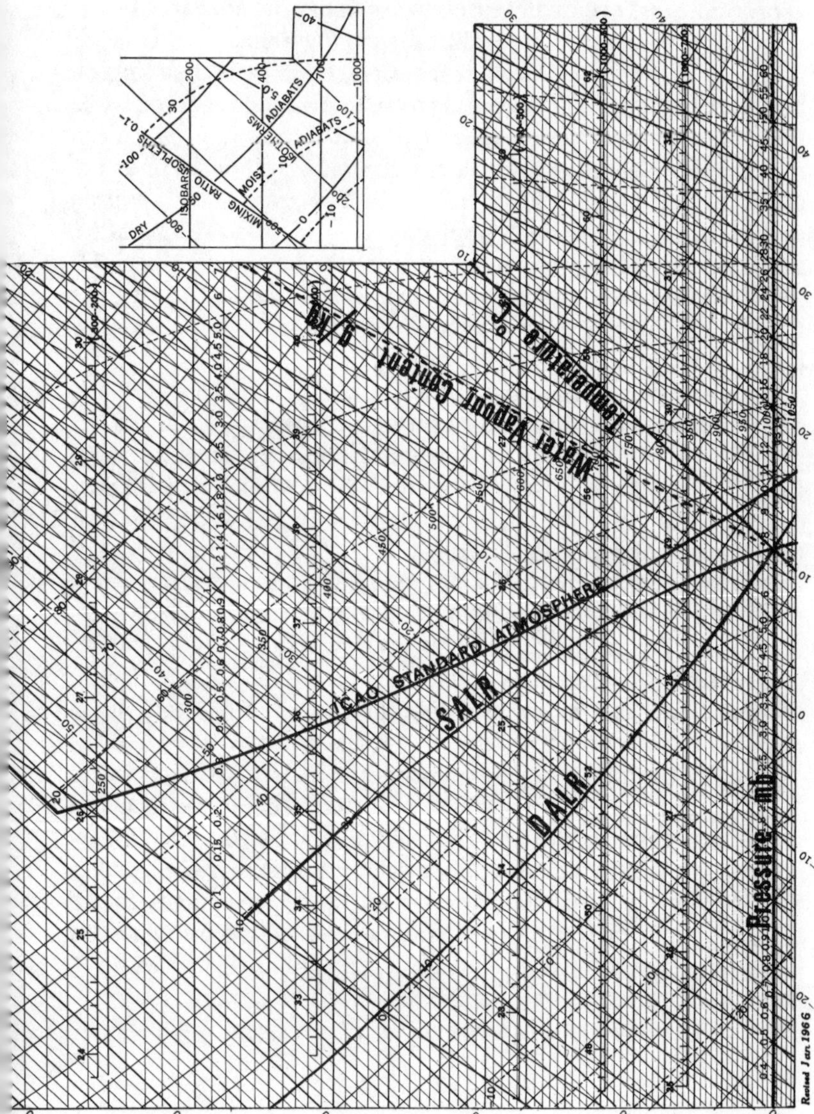

Fig. 20.4 Part of a Skew T-Log P diagram. This diagram is very similar to the tephigram, but the DALR lines are slightly curved. The particular diagram illustrated here also happens to have a heavy line indicating the ICAO standard atmospheric temperatures. More details of this standard atmosphere are oiven in Chanter 23

appropriate and eventually easier to use than what appear to be the more straightforward temperature-height diagrams.

One such diagram is called the *tephigram*. In meteorological literature the letter T is often used to denote air temperature, while the Greek letter ϕ (phi) frequently stands for entropy, which can conveniently though not with strict accuracy be thought of as the potential heat energy of the air. Thus the T–ϕ gram, usually written as tephigram, is a piece of graph paper having the two quantities temperature and entropy as axes. Hence the basic axes of a tephigram include temperature axes (isotherms) marked in degrees Celsius and entropy lines (which are also adiabatic lines), as illustrated in Figure 20.3.

For every pair of values of its temperature and entropy air has a particular pressure which can be calculated once and for all, so it is possible to construct on the diagram lines of equal pressure. Because pressure is closely associated with altitude, these slightly curved isobars stretching across the tephigram give a rough indication of height above MSL. The pressure and temperature of a parcel of air can be represented by a dot marked on the tephigram (for a pressure of 1000 mb and temperature of 19°C, for example, a point T in Figure 26.1 is the representative dot).

Dry adiabatic lapse rates in this diagram are the straight lines at 45 degrees to the isotherms, while the saturated adiabatic lapse rates are the curved lines shown in the diagram.

Another diagram used in a number of meteorological services is the *Skew T-Log P* diagram, which is illustrated in Figure 20.4. The differences between this and the tephigram are slight. One difference is that the dry adiabatic lapse rates are slightly curved rather than straight, but the diagram has the same advantages as the tephigram and there is little to choose between the usefulness of these two thermodynamic diagrams. Tephigrams, Skew T-Log P, and other meteorological diagrams used for similar purposes are all classed as *aerological diagrams*.

21

Gliding Forecasts

For most types of gliding operations, serious thoughts on a day's gliding begin about 12-24 hours ahead; many a pilot casts an anxious eye towards the clouds on an afternoon or evening in contemplation of the flight the next day, and indeed this is about the right time ahead to become acquainted with the current weather situation. For background information there are:

1 *The daily press.* Most newspapers publish weather maps which, though sketchy, may be used to view the general pressure pattern and the frontal situation. Weather maps for morning papers, however, are normally prepared on the previous evening (in time to go to press) and it is advisable to amplify them with more up-to-date information contained in:

2 *Weather bulletins broadcast by radio.* Because most of the bulletins are designed for the general public, careful attention is needed to deduce the synoptic features relevant to gliding. For example, the statement that 'cooler weather will spread from the west' may well refer to the approach of a cold front. A somewhat more direct insight into the broad synoptic situation is obtainable in some regions in special radio bulletins for shipping and flight meteorological services. Observations from selected stations are often included in these bulletins and may be used to prepare sketchy, but nonetheless useful, maps of the synoptic situation. In the United Kingdom, for example, shipping bulletins broadcast on long-wave radio contain enough information to construct up-to-date pressure and frontal maps. A special *METMAP* chart and technique has been designed for this purpose.

Of course, a ready-made view of the flow pattern is sometimes presented in:

3 *Television forecasts.* Unfortunately, the time allocated to television weather bulletins is usually short, and the material

presented is restricted to that likely to appeal to masses of viewers rather than to inform a relatively few glider pilots. However, a number of television weather bulletins include views of satellite cloud pictures, which the glider pilot may otherwise never see.

4 *Weather information by telephone.* The dial-a-forecast type of telephone facility is now available in many cities of the world. These telephone bulletins are not normally geared to gliding requirements, but they at least provide additional background material. In most cities a glider pilot can telephone the local meteorological office to ask for further information. At this stage, however, the forecaster will not normally be able to give more than a rough indication of the soaring prospects for the next day, and no useful purpose is served by trying to press him for superficial details, which he cannot honestly predict. Gliding plans for the next day must be tentatively based on rather elementary interpretations of the forecast pressure and frontal situation.

To add interest and meaning to the weather information obtained by the press, radio, television and telephone, it is instructive to make:

5 *Local observations.* Some of the salient features of the synoptic situation can often be deduced from simple local observations of such elements as the barometric pressure and its tendency, wind direction and speed, cloud structure and movement, and visibility. The keen weather-watcher may even try to deduce the characteristics of the temperature-height curve appropriate to his locality. The object of this observing exercise is not so much to make firm predictions as to build up a logical and objective picture of the current situation and its full potentialities of the next day's gliding.

Short-range forecasts

It is usually at about, or soon after, breakfast time that the decision is made whether or not to attempt a flight, or set a contest task. By this time the official forecasts in the morning press, forecast bulletins and local observations will normally provide sufficient information to narrow down the range of possible operations. The

Plate 30 ALTOCUMULUS CASTELLANUS
Convective instability is sometimes produced within an extensive layer of
slowly rising air. Such instability is often confined to medium levels and is
indicated by the presence of altocumulus castellanus. Because the
updraughts associated with the individual clouds are usually weak and
confined to medium levels, this type of convection is not normally suitable
for thermal soaring. Occasionally altocumulus castellanus tends to form in
straight lines, but in some situations particularly those associated with hot
summer-time depressions, medium-level instability produces convection
clouds over such extensive regions that the cloud mass looks more like
altostratus from below. Sometimes this type of medium-level cloud is
many thousands of feet deep and is then likely to produce prolonged
showers or thunderstorms.

general weather information may indicate that a particular region
or sector is more favourable than others. So, the pilot or organiser is
now in a position to concentrate his thoughts and questions on the
relevant details of weather in the probable operating regions. Now,
if he telephones a meteorological office to obtain a weather forecast,
he can be more specific in his request and he will have the background information as a basis for his understanding of the forecast.

Routine forecasts

Forecasters become better acquainted with gliding requirements when local arrangements can be made with a gliding club or centre for a routine supply of daily or weekend forecasts. The forecaster can then allocate specific time on his schedule to prepare the forecasts. Arrangements for obtaining forecasts may vary according to local circumstances, but usually it is convenient, for communication at least, to itemise routine forecasts under set headings. An example of such headings together with notes on the object of the items is shown below, but before going through the list, it should be noted that a typical forecast itemised in this way is not nearly so lengthy as the note given here.

1 *Area and period for which the forecast applies.* The area and period of time covered by the forecast should be clearly stated so as to avoid misunderstanding.

2 *Brief description of the synoptic situation.* Brief description of pressure and frontal systems, to form the broad scene in which the predicted wind and weather elements will be set.

3 *Surface wind speed and direction.* For take-off and landing direction and hill soaring prospects. Strong winds, severe gustiness, squalls, sharp wind changes and thunderstorm downdraughts can endanger landing approaches and parked aircraft.

4 *Upper wind speeds.* Winds, for flight planning, at three or four levels in the likely soaring height band. Special mention of marked wind shears would be useful to relate to thermal shifts or turbulence, but sufficiently precise wind data is not often available.

5 *Surface temperatures.* Forecast maximum temperature, and temperatures corresponding to development of dry thermal layer to be mentioned in item 8.

6 *Upper air temperatures.* Predicted temperatures at sufficient levels to give an indication of the nature of the temperature structure of the airstream. Special mention of inversions or layers of marked stability.

7 *Weather.* Drizzle, rain, showers, thunder, etc. Special mention if risk of hail is predicted.

8 *Depth of dry thermal activity.* The top of the dry thermal layer. Particular mention of any breakdown of a low level inversion. Prediction of the surface temperatures corresponding to predicted depths of the dry thermal layer for a few times during the day should be mentioned in item 5.

9 *Character and distribution of dry thermals.* There may not be enough information available for the forecaster to say much about this, but thermal strength, frequency, spacing and size, can be included in this item if sufficient data for forecasting is available. Thermal shear, thermal streets, thermal waves, and excessive downdraughts between thermals are also relevent.

10 *Amount, base and top of convection cloud.* Risk of cumulus spreading out, cloud streets, convective storms and line squalls deserve special mention.

11 *Distribution of layer cloud.* Will medium or high cloud spread over the proposed soaring area? If so, from what direction? Is there an easily recognisable pattern in the distribution of this cloud?

12 *Visibility.* Smog, fog, pollution and hill fog predictions.

13 *Sea-breezes and convergence lines.* Are these phenomena likely to develop? If so, where and when?

14 *Lee waves.* Likelihood of lee waves. Height of maximum lee wave amplitude (usually in the stable layer associated with the wave conditions). Risk of turbulence or rotor flow.

15 *Height of $0°C$ isotherm.* Relevant for icing, if cloud flying is contemplated.

16 *Pressure at MSL (or whatever standard reference level is being used for the region).* For altimeter setting on cross-country soaring. Special note if rapid changes expected.

17 *Warnings and remarks.* Any warnings and remarks not already mentioned in other items.

Heights mentioned in aviation forecasts for a large area or route are usually heights above MSL. In forecasts for a particular airfield and its immediate vicinity, or for a generally high-level region, the upper wind levels, cloud base, cloud tops and other heights mentioned are given as heights above the airfield level, or above the reference level used for the high-level region.

When a schedule for a routine supply of forecasts is arranged between a gliding club or centre and a meteorological office, the club or centre should keep as closely as possible to the schedule. A forecaster who prepares scheduled forecasts that are not collected at the scheduled times naturally tends to lose interest in making the forecasts. This interest and expertise in forecasting for gliding can, however, be augmented if both he and his gliding customers work towards, and maintain, a dialogue on their mutual weather interests.

Plate 31   JET STREAM CIRRUS
Occasionally jet streams are indicated by long parallel bands of cirrus along the jet streams. This formation is also associated with long bands of rising air and descending air. The bands of rising air may possibly provide sufficient lift for a very long flight at high levels. Exploration of such a possibility calls more for strategic planning and organisation than the usual tactical detection and use of local lift.

Weather shorthand

A common problem in receiving a weather forecast by telephone
or radio is taking it down. Radio announcers normally speak at
reading speed, and the detail that can be obtained by telephone to a
forecaster can take a long time to write down. But this problem can
be overcome by developing your own weather shorthand. Most
weather bulletins are made up of a few basic concepts wrapped in
conversational phraseology. For example, a forecast that: 'Rain
falling over much of the country this morning will move away during
the morning and be followed by showers later in the day', basically
means: Widespread rain at first; showers later. 'Patches of fog now
affecting some parts of the country will soon clear. But showers will
develop later in the day, and towards evening there will be a
possibility of isolated thunderstorms', could be condensed to: Local
fog at first; then showers; then risk of isolated thunderstorms.
'Fresh southwesterly winds will moderate and veer to north-west
during the day', simply means: Fresh south-west winds at first;
moderate north-west winds later. Thus, most forecasts presented in
a conversational mode can be broken down into references to areas,
durations, weather elements, intensities, distributions, frequencies,
risks, movements, and changes with time, and, if we make do
without some of the precision, shades of meaning and variety that
our language allows us to express, most of the phraseology can be
condensed into a few basic words. The basic words in turn can be
condensed to letters, signs or symbols to form a personal system of
speed writing. Suggestions for such a system are listed below, but
these are intended as examples to illustrate the weather speed-
writing concept. For personal use, it is wiser for each individual to
develop a system that suits himself rather than attempt to conform
rigorously to someone else's speed writing code.

Areas. The easiest method is to sketch a very rough map of the
area expected to be covered, and mark information on the map.
Alternatively, prepare a set of abbreviations for the places most
commonly referred to in the local or regional forecasts.

Wind, weather, visibility, etc. Write down these headings in
readiness for the forecast. Alternatively, use V for visibility; other
main headings will usually be evident from the context.

Pressures and frontal patterns

LO = Low pressure centre
HI = High pressure centre, anticyclone
TR = Trough of low pressure
RI = Ridge of high pressure
TC = Tropical cyclone
CO = Col

WF = Warm front
CF = Cold front, cool change
OC = Occlusion
SB = Sea-breeze front
CL = Convergence line

Weather

F = Fog	D = Drizzle	P = Showers	C = Calm
M = Mist	R = Rain	H = Hail	G = Gale
Z = Haze, smog	X = Snow	T = Thunder	Q = Squall

Cloud amount

CS = Clear sky   BC = Broken   OV = Overcast

Soaring Systems

HI = Hill lift
TH = Thermals
TS = Thermal streets
TW = Thermal waves
CS = Cloud streets

LW = Lee waves
RF = Rotor flow
SB = Sea-breeze front
CL = Convergence line

Intensities

s = slight, light weak, shallow
m = moderate, fresh
h = heavy, strong, intense, deep

p = poor
g = good
q = gusty, squally

Frequencies

o = occasional, at times, sporadic
c = continuous

f = frequent, intermittent

Distributions

i = isolated, here and there, scattered
l = locally, patches

w = widespread, generally
e = especially in, in, especially towards, towards

Risk

r = risk of, chance of, perhaps, possibility of

Movements

a = approaching, moving towards
d = departing from, moving from

k = crossing
n = no movement, stationary

Changes with time

| = becoming, at first then followed by, etc., for example:

   R|P for 'Rain at first, followed by showers'.

   F| for 'Fog at first'.

   |riT for 'Risk of isolated thunderstorms later'.

   Specific times of change can be indicated by writing a time of day
over the vertical stroke, e.g.

   mSW|hS for 'Moderate southwesterly winds at first backing and increasing
to strong southerlies by midday'. (over the stroke: 12)

   pV| for 'Poor visibility until mid-morning'. (over the stroke: 09)

   (Taking mid-morning to be 09.00 hours.)

With a little practice, a speed-writing technique can be used to take down
seemingly lengthy bulletins. The key to speed is not so much memorising the code
letters, as condensing or eliminating stock phrases in the message. Here is an
example:

Bulletin	Speed-written version	Notes on this example
A depression centred over Scotland at midnight is moving east to the North Sea.	LO Scot 00 dE	Scot = Scotland 00 = midnight No need to write 'to the North Sea'.
A cold front extending southwards from the centre of low pressure is expected to clear England by midday.	CF LO-S d Eng| (over stroke: 12)	– = 'to' in LO-S Eng = England 12 = Midday
Strong squally southerly winds will veer and decrease to become moderate westerly behind the front.	hqS|mW	'veer and decrease to become' = becoming No need to write 'behind the front'. This should be apparent from the context.
Intermittent rain will give way to showery conditions with a risk of hail later in the day especially in southern areas.	fR|P|rHeS	'will give way to' = becoming
After the front has passed, visibility will be generally good, but poor in showers.	|Vwg peP	'After the front has passed' condensed to 'becoming'.

International or other signs, symbols and abbreviations can be
used as alternatives to the letters suggested here, but the choice is
best left to each individual for his own personal use. Speed-writing

for taking down forecasts may seem trivial by comparison with the skills needed to predict and use weather for gliding, but the effective value of a forecast is a product not only of the considerable expertise of forecasters backed by a vast organisation but also of the information that filters through the relatively weak communication link between forecaster and pilot.

Forecasts for championships

Weather forecasting at gliding championships is crucial to the success of the event. The problem, however, is not just that of accurate prediction; it also entails adequate communication between the weather forecaster and the pilots or organisers who use his forecasts. During the last decade of weather forecasting for championships, there has been increasing use of signs and symbols in forecasts presented to pilots and organisers. This development was prompted mainly by world championships, in which both brevity and clarity are necessary to minimise the potential for mistranslation and misinterpretation. But international requirements are not the only reasons for using signs and symbols to portray gliding forecasts. Pictorial forecasts can be designed to convey a more comprehensive impression of predicted weather than an itemised verbal or written forecast.

Progress in the development of a pictorial system for gliding forecasts has now reached the stage where a comprehensive system can be recommended for international and general use.

Meteorological briefing display

The pictorial system is best illustrated by examples of meteorological information that should, if possible, be displayed at meteorological briefings for competition gliding. Let us consider what should be presented if sufficient information, time and space are available. The elements recommended for such a display are:

1 *Pressure and frontal maps.* A map to show the general atmospheric pressure and frontal situation is useful to set the general weather scene. The map should be simple, without too much detail. It should indicate the principal systems and their predicted movement. This movement can be indicated by

arrows, but it is better illustrated by showing maps for two times of the day. One map can be a recent actual map, or a predicted map, for early in the day; the other map should be a prediction for later in the day. Figure 21.1 illustrates such a map as it may appear at a gliding championships in Argentina. These maps need not be drawn with great precision in the general meteorological briefing displays; they are intended to illustrate only the main features of the synoptic situation.

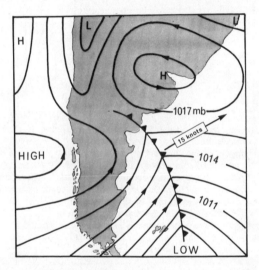

Fig. 21.1   Pressure and frontal situation as it appeared during a day in the 1963 World Gliding Championships in Argentina. Such a map is a useful introduction to meteorological briefing because it provides the framework within which the details relevant to the day's soaring weather can be described.

2 *Temperature-height graph.* A predicted or measured local temperature-height graph should be drawn, like that illustrated in Figure 21.2. Temperature and height axes should be scaled in such a way that the dry adiabatic lapse rates are at approximately 45° to these axes. Predicted changes of the temperature-height curve, together with accompanying surface air temperature predictions, should be shown. Predicted depths of thermal activity and cumulus cloud development should also be shown on this display panel. Special attention

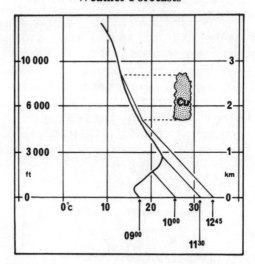

Fig. 21.2 A key feature in many meteorological briefings is a diagram showing the measured or estimated actual temperature-height curve and predicted changes. In this illustration the 09.00 points to the base of the estimated or measured temperature-height curve at 09.00 hours local time. This particular curve shows a shallow dry adiabatic layer capped by a strong inversion up to about 2500 ft. Predicted surface air temperatures and changes in the low-level part of the temperature-height curve are denoted for the times 10.00, 11.30 and 12.45 hours in this example. At 10.00 hours the surface temperature is expected to reach about 25.5°C and the thermal layer (which is also a DALR layer) is expected to extend to almost 2000 ft. At 11.30 hours the temperature is expected to reach 31°C, which is the temperature required to break down the inversion. After this time the depth of the thermal layer is expected to increase rapidly, and by 12.45 hours convection cloud is expected to form at about 5000 ft. The temperature and height scales in this diagram are arranged such that the dry adiabatic lines are at approximately 45° to the horizontal.

should be drawn to the existence and predicted breakdown of a low-level temperature inversion.

3 *Local weather cross-section.* The local weather prediction for the airfield can be depicted in a time/height cross-section, as illustrated in Figure 21.3. The simple, but effective, artistry needed to portray the forecast is not difficult. Notice that the height scale in this cross-section is condensed at high levels, so as to allow ample room for the lower-level details more likely to be used for thermal soaring. Meanings of symbols used in this cross-section are indicated in the figure, but a more com-

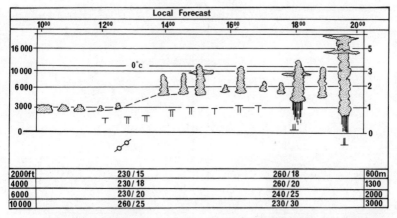

2000ft	230/15	260/18	600m
4000	230/18	260/20	1300
6000	230/20	240/25	2000
10000	260/25	230/30	3000

Fig. 21.3 Schematic cross-section of a local forecast. In this particular example low cloud is expected to break up to form small cumulus by 12.00 hours. It will then burn off as the thermal layer extends to higher levels; then cumulus is expected to form with a risk of occasional spreading out in the early or middle afternoon. Later in the day showers are expected to develop with an occasional cumulonimbus in the early evening. The thermal symbols denote weak thermals at first becoming moderate during the middle of the day. Moderate downdraughts are also indicated in association with the showers. A prediction of thermal streets, orientated SW–NE, is denoted by the thermal street symbol for the early afternoon. Wind directions in degrees true and speeds in knots for a selection of heights are given. If no sharp changes are indicated it should be assumed that the wind changes will be gradual, i.e. at 2000 ft the wind will change gradually from 230/15 to 260/18 during the day.

prehensive key to symbols used in pictorial gliding forecasts can be found at the end of this chapter.

4 *Schematic route forecast.* A plan view of the contest route together with special weather symbols can be used to convey a comprehensive yet uncluttered impression of conditions over the course. To show the predicted change in time during the day, it is advisable to display two such schematic route forecasts: one for early in the expected contest period; the other for later in the day. Figure 21.4 shows such a map.

5 *Pictorial route cross-section.* The plan view shown in the schematic route forecast should be supplemented by a pictorial route cross-section, like that illustrated in Figure 21.5. The style is very similar to the local time cross-section; the main difference being that route cross-section illustrates the pre-

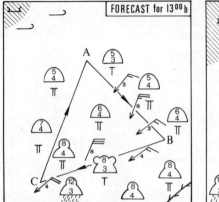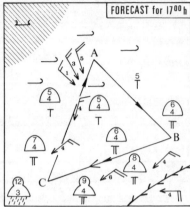

Fig. 21.4   A schematic route forecast illustrated by symbols around a route labelled A B C in this illustration. A key to the symbols is given at the end of this chapter. A sprinkling of predicted upper winds are shown where they are likely to be most needed; for example, in detail for a final glide on the last leg. Unless changes during the day are too slight to be significant for soaring, it is useful to provide two charts to indicate such changes. In this example we see a prediction of cirrostratus spreading from the north-west, while a convergence line is moving in from the south-east.

dicted weather changes as progress is made around the route, while the local cross-section shows predicted changes with time at one place.

6 *Warnings.* A small space should be reserved to indicate any special warnings, such as storms that may hazard parked aircraft not only during the contest period but later in the day or during the coming night.

It is not always necessary to present all of these suggested displays. Often the local time cross-section is so similar to the route cross-section that it can be omitted. When forecasts for two courses (typically one for the Standard Class, the other for the Open Class) have to be presented at a meteorological briefing, the meteorologist usually tries to either combine these forecasts in the displayed maps and cross-sections or illustrate the most useful of the two forecasts and denote what slight differences may be applicable to the other.

Ideally, the briefing meteorologist (and other briefing personnel) should need to say as little as possible during a general

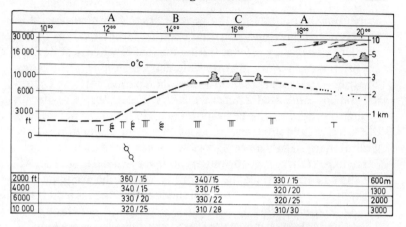

A		B	C	A	

2000 ft		360 / 15	340 / 15	330 / 15	600 m
4000		340 / 15	330 / 15	320 / 20	1300
6000		330 / 20	330 / 22	320 / 25	2000
10 000		320 / 25	310 / 28	310 / 30	3000

Fig. 21.5 A pictorial route cross-section. This particular example illustrates a prediction that thermals will be limited in depth to about 2000 ft until midday. From then on this thermal depth will increase rapidly to about 9000 ft at which level small cumulus clouds will form. By 18.00 hours thermals will be more widely spaced and after about 19.00 hours there will be only weak and isolated thermals. Some dust devils and thermal streets are expected in the early afternoon and thermals are predicted to become strong.

briefing. The objective should be to present the information adequately and in a form that is clearly understood and easy to note. The briefing process itself should be confined to pointing out or highlighting specific features that call for special attention and answering questions that could not be better put as individual queries after the briefing. Pilots, and others especially interested in the general briefing, should be encouraged and assisted to copy down the briefing display information. The best assistance to give them is forms which are of the same pattern and style as the displayed information. It is, of course, essential that the units used in the meteorological services are clearly stated, and that the key to symbols are included in the displayed information or in the material available to pilots.

Task-setting forecasts

Some competition organisations are tempted to arrange task-setting meetings as early as possible, so as to give the organisation ample time to prepare for the general briefing. Meteorologically, however, it is unwise to give a task-setting forecast earlier than is absolutely necessary. Events during the first few hours of daylight are often critical to weather developments for the rest of the day. These few hours span a sensitive transition period between noctur-nal and day-time weather characteristics. The atmospherc literally begins to stir during this early morning period, and the net result of this stirring is seldom clear until about 08.00 hours solar time or even later. If there is early morning fog, how much will it impede the rate of heating? If there is no fog but the air is very humid at sunrise, will the sun's heating reduce the risk of fog, or will the accompanying slight turbulence cause fog to form suddenly? If there is a thin layer of low stratus overhead, how much heating will get through it? These, and other local questions, are very difficult to answer in the first few hours of daylight, and the meteorological forecaster, knowing that the balance between one state of development and another is critical, may not be able to give a confident forecast. However, after this early morning period, the meteorologist's chances of predicting which way events are developing are greatly improved becasuse he has had an opportunity to study the relative significance and trends in these early morning factors.

The content and style of presentation of a forecast for task setting is best left to the individuals themselves at a championship. If a contest appears at all possible, more detailed communication between the meteorologist and the task setter can be enhanced by visualising, or preferably sketching, an envelope of the predicted soaring conditions. Figure 21.6 shows an example of such envelopes. To supplement this meteorological information the task setter should have sufficient glider performance data to calculate the range of probable gliding speeds through the air for the pre-dicted thermal strengths. In modern top-class competitions, most gliders completing a closed-circuit task attain speeds through the air within about 70% of that of the winner on good soaring days, but on poor days the slowest pilots may be slower. Calculated or estimated speeds through the air and the forecast winds should then be used to compute the range of times needed to complete a proposed course. If this range of course completion times, plus whatever is needed for launching and start-time operations, fits into the predicted time boundaries of the soaring envelope, the task should be feasible. It is

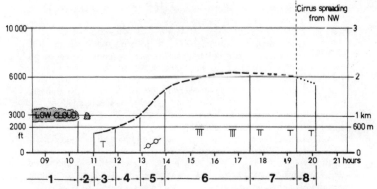

Fig. 21.6 The task setter can use the meteorologist's predictions to construct envelopes containing various phases in the overall soaring conditions. These envelopes are bounded by ground-level, the top of soaring conditions, and times on either side. In this example, the bulk of the diagram is somewhat similar to a pictorial route cross-section. The 2000-ft (600-m) height line is drawn because this is about the minimum height to which thermals or other lift should reach before a serious task could be commenced. Local times, 09 to 21 hours are written below the cross-section. The phases into which a task setter may divide this particular prediction are denoted by the numbers 1 to 8. Characteristics of these phases are:

Phase 1 *Up to 10.20 hours.* No predicted possibility of soaring.
Phase 2 *10.20 to 11.00 hours.* Low cloud expected to break up and disperse but no thermals predicted. No possibility of planning to start a task in this period, but actual weather developments will give an indication of whether the prediction for the day is going according to the forecast.
Phase 3 *11.00 to 12.00 (approx.) hours.* Weak thermals likely to develop but not reaching 2000 ft until almost midday. Not worth launching competing gliders, but a local thermal snifter (reconnaissance) flight would be useful to see whether thermal predictions are developing according to the forecast.
Phase 4 *12.00 to 13.00 (approx.) hours.* Competing aircraft could be launched but a large number of competing aircraft in the air would be confined to a shallow operating layer and could produce an abnormal collision hazard, especially if the visibility is not good. If a long task is envisaged, the congestion would be reduced because pilots would need to start the course as soon as possible. However, if a short task is envisaged it is certain that most pilots would wait for an improvement in the thermal conditions before crossing the start line—thereby increasing the local congestion.
Phase 5 *13.00 to 14.00 hours.* Depth of thermals increasing rapidly. Thermal streets may boost cross-country speeds if they are orientated conveniently for the first leg of the course.

(Fig. 21.6 Caption continued on page 280)

Phase 6   *14.00 to 17.30 hours.* Very good thermal soaring conditions. Fast cross-country speeds likely.

Phase 7   *17.30 to 19.20 hours.* Strength and frequency of thermals decreasing, but still sufficient to provide moderate thermal cross-country soaring conditions. Most aircraft should be on final glides before the thermals become weak.

Phase 8   *19.20 to 20.10 hours.* Cirrus spreading from the north-west. Isolated and weak thermals, not sufficient for fast cross-country soaring but could sustain soaring flight, even though slow.

Thus it will be possible to consider tasks in a range from a very long task using Phases 4 to 8 (with the planned probability that a number of pilots will not complete the course) to a short fast race (which all pilots are likely to complete) in Phase 6 or Phases 5 and 6.

This envelope or phase approach to task setting, coupled with estimated speeds through the air for the range of competitive standards, and flight planning using predicted winds is recommended not only to inject comprehensiveness and objectivity in task setting, but also to provide an objective basis for considering alternatives if and when weather or other conditions differ from predictions.

difficult, if not impossible, to make confident allowance for predicted thermal streets, cloud streets or convergence lines—unless these happen to be well-known habitual features of the locality.

Of course, experienced task setters can often make a good guess at the feasibility of a task without making such detailed calculations as are recommended here, and, because weather predictions can go awry, it could be argued that meticulous calculations are scarcely worth the effort. But the system of dissecting the whole task-setting process into the various meteorological, aircraft performance, and navigation components, makes it easier for task setters to pinpoint and discuss the most critical factors in their estimation of task feasibility. The systematic approach also provides a sounder basis for discussing proposed task changes, if unexpected weather develops.

The task setter should ask the forecaster to indicate roughly the degree of confidence, or percentage of probability, for the predicted items of a forecast, but he should be cautious of making his own allowance for the possible forecast errors. Each day must be considered on its merits. Overestimation of, say, the maximum temperature, thermal strength, or the length of task on one day should not, by itself, be taken as sufficient evidence to underestimate these items on the next day. Previous errors should be examined to discover reasons for the errors, but compensation for such errors should not be applied without reason to all subsequent predictions.

Probably the most nerve-racking experience for the task setter occurs when a sharp change from overcast to soarable weather is confidently forecast for the early afternoon—leaving just enough time for a task to be feasible. As the morning goes by, the task setter finds it harder to suppress his increasing fear that the improvement will not occur, and even though the weather may be developing according to the original forecast, he may well be tempted to cancel the task before the expected soaring conditions arrive.

METEOROLOGICAL SYMBOLS FOR GLIDING FORECASTS

NOTE: *Recommended colours for Meteorological Briefing Boards are green or black for the surface and yellow for the outlines of the background map and forms.*

Fronts: Colours denoted in italics should be used if possible.

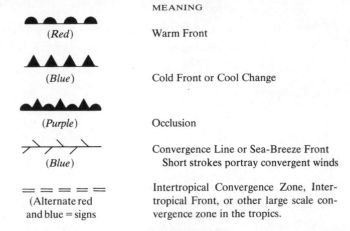

	MEANING
(Red)	Warm Front
(Blue)	Cold Front or Cool Change
(Purple)	Occlusion
(Blue)	Convergence Line or Sea-Breeze Front Short strokes portray convergent winds
(Alternate red and blue = signs	Intertropical Convergence Zone, Intertropical Front, or other large scale convergence zone in the tropics.

Weather: White symbols on black or green background. Black symbols on white background.

• *or* ⠿	Rain
۹ *or* ⠿	Drizzle
▽	Showers
△	Hail

⤴   Lightning

↳⤴   Thunderstorms

Clouds: White symbols on black or green background. Black symbols on white background.

                         MEANING   NOTES

Small Cumulus (*Cu*)

Large Cumulus (*Cu*) T = *Cloud top in thousands of feet. This figure denoting cloud top may often be omitted.*

Cumulonimbus (*Cb*)

Stratocumulus (*Sc*)

Cu spreading out to form Sc B = *Cloud base in thousands of feet.*

Funnel cloud or Tornado

Patches of medium-level cloud (*Ac* and *As*)

Medium-level Altostratus (*As*) cloud layer obscuring the sun

Patches of Cirrus (*Ci*) high-level cloud

Layer of Cirrostratus (*Cs*) high-level cloud

See Wave Lift and Wave Cloud for Lee Wave Cloud Symbols.

Winds: White symbols on black or green background. Black symbols on white background.

	MEANING	NOTES

Wind velocity at height *H* in thousands of feet. Each full feather = 10 knots

A selection of wind arrows should be drawn on the Schematic Route Forecasts. If sufficient evidence is available to predict a particularly sharp wind change with height, this wind shear should be denoted by wind arrows for two heights — one just above and one just below the shear.

(*H*)

Wind less than 15 knots and direction variable or uncertain at height *H* in thousands of feet.

H = 0 *denotes surface wind.*

In forecast cross-sections: VAR = Variable in direction.
LV = Light winds, variable in direction.

Thermal lift: Red symbols.

T

Weak thermals:
1–2 knots
100–200 ft/min
$\frac{1}{2}$–1 m/sec

T

Moderate thermals:
2–6 knots
200–600 ft/min
1–3 m/sec

T = The top of the dry thermal layer in thousands of feet. This figure may be omitted if thermals are expected to extend up into convection cloud.

T

Strong thermals:
more than 6 knots
more than 600 ft/min
more than 3 m/sec

Dust devils
or Willy-Willys

Narrow columns of rising dust rotating rapidly. At low levels they can be rough and narrow but often produce strong lift and develop into layer thermals as they ascend.

See Wave Lift and Wave Cloud for Thermal Wave Symbol.

MEANING	NOTES

—O———O— Thermal or cloud streets

This symbol should be orientated so as to lie along the probable direction of thermal or cloud streets whenever conditions appear to be suitable for street formation. The direction of such streets is usually close to that of the wind direction. Spacing between the symbols does not denote the cross-wind spacing of the streets.

Sink: Blue symbols.

⊥⊥ Moderate downdraughts

⊥⊥⊥ Strong downdraughts

Downdraughts should be denoted only if they are expected to be unusually frequent, widespread or hazardous.

Visibility: Brown symbols.

∞ Haze

☰ Fog

→S→ Sandstorm or duststorm

Wave lift and wave cloud: Purple symbols.

MEANING	NOTES

⟨W⟩ Lee waves

W = Probable height of maximum amplitude, if predictable, in thousands of feet.
W may be omitted if meteorological information is insufficient to predict this height.

Lee waves with rotor flow, implying turbulence.

The direction of the symbol does not denote the orientation of the waves.

Lee waves and wave cloud

Lee waves with rotor
cloud, implying turbulence
which is likely to
be moderate or strong.

 or Thermal waves

Turbulence: Purple symbols

 Moderate turbulence

*Turbulence should be denoted
only if it is expected to
be unusually frequent, widespread or hazardous.*

 Strong turbulence

*Rotor turbulence in lee waves
can also be denoted by the
wave and rotor symbols.*

Special lines on cross-sections

	MEANING	NOTES
___0°C___ (*Blue line*)	0°C isotherm	*Freezing-level.*
_ ___ _ (*Red line with small well-spaced breaks*)	Top of dry thermal layer	*Where thermal convection extends upwards into convection cloud drawn on the cross-section the red line may be omitted.*
_ _ _ _ _ _ _ (*Red broken line*)	Top of dry scattered thermals	
. . . . (*Red dotted line*)	Top of isolated dry thermals	

*Winds in cross-sections should be written as degrees (true)/knots or km/h (the speed
unit used should be clearly indicated).*

EXAMPLES (*using knots*)   MEANING
270/25   270 degrees true, 25 knots.
VAR 10   Variable in direction, 10 knots.

140–180/10–20   Between 140 and 180 degrees,
                         between 10 and 20 knots.

22

Weatherwise

In, say, ten years of gliding some pilots acquire ten years of weather wisdom; others acquire one year's experience ten times. The difference between these two types of experience depends mainly on the care and objectivity with which the pilot interprets the weather he sees and the meteorological information he obtains. He can begin to build up or improve his weather wisdom without necessarily being in the air or even at an airfield. Merely keeping track of day-to-day weather situations as revealed by press, radio and television bulletins and subsequent actual events can add to the pilot's meteorological repertoire. For this type of exercise, however, the pilot should not be content to form overall impressions of the information he receives or the weather he experiences. Overall impressions are far too subjective and often lead to false longer-term impressions. It is wiser to note a few specific features at a time—say, temperature, wind, pressure, visibility, precipitation, or cloud. Write the information down in a notebook; do not rely on memory alone. Of course, unless a pilot is particularly dedicated to meteorological studies, he will not want to go to great lengths in writing down and studying meteorological bulletins and weather observations every day of the year. But he does not need to; the point being made here is that it is better to study the information and observations objectively and meticulously on a few occasions rather than continuously in a vague impressionist way.

Wherever possible, instrumental measurements are preferable to estimation. Estimations of wind speed at ground-level are much less consistent than measurements made with even simple and cheap forms of anemometers. By knowing in advance how far a selection of landmarks are away and seeing which of these landmarks are clearly visible, a far more reliable estimate of visibility can be made than by trying to form a vague impression of the haziness. The direction of movement of medium or high cloud can usually be obtained by watching distinctive features of the clouds as they move past a reference point, such as the corner of a building or the wing-tip of a parked aircraft, but, without a fixed point in the foreground, the movement of medium or high cloud can seldom be readily discerned.

Radio bulletins

As well as being aware that most radio bulletins are designed for the general public, the discerning listener should also note that, although the forecasts are couched in the language of everyday speech rather than technical terms, descriptive words or phrases are used with careful consistency in many countries. Forecasters maintain this consistency by using special definitions of selected common words and phrases; for example, 'sunny periods' may be used to denote variable skies with considerable blue patches and corresponding sunshine, whereas 'bright periods' may mean cloud rather variable in amount with occasionally diffused sunlight at times or even occasionally direct sunshine. The distinction between the two terms when applied to glider pilots is obvious; 'sunny periods' suggests mainly good thermal soaring while 'bright periods' conveys the warning that sunshine is likely to be reduced by cirrus or thin medium cloud, perhaps ahead of a warm front. In countries where such consistency is maintained, pamphlets defining or elaborating the terms used are usually available from the meteorological service. Try to find out what these definitions are for your particular meteorological service and what they mean in terms of gliding weather. A particular word to inquire about is 'fine'. Does this mean cloudless, sunny, dry, or some other combination of weather elements?

Bulletins for the general public often include such phrases as: 'warm for the time of year'. What does 'warm' mean? Does it mean a few degrees or many degrees above normal for the time of year? And what is normal for the time of year? This information is also normally available from the meteorological service supplying the weather bulletins. Get the information, and keep it for future reference.

Casual telephone inquiries

When telephoning a forecaster for advice it is wise to remember that the telephone meteorological service is usually designed for giving general meteorological advice over a wide range of activities rather than a specialist service to any one type of inquirer. The duty forecaster may not be completely familiar with the techniques or the jargon of soaring; he may not have given serious thought to some of the specialist details required; and, if the inquiry is lengthy, his attention may become distracted by the need to serve other inquirers. Therefore, tell the forecaster that you are a glider pilot and make your request for a gliding forecast as specific as possible, for example, 'I am planning a gliding flight from ... towards the region of .... I hope to start at about midday or earlier if conditions are favourable. Can you, please, give me a forecast for the route and some relevant details of wind and convection conditions?' Or 'Could you please tell me the prospects for soaring in lee waves in the region of ... today?' The forecaster's initial reply will usually indicate how prepared he is for this type of gliding inquiry, and it is for the pilot to judge what supplementary questions are necessary.

Vague opening questions such as 'What will the weather be like today?' do not give the forecaster an indication that the inquirer wants anything more specific than a general forecast of the type issued to the public at large. On the other hand, it is unwise to try to help the forecaster by opening with such questions as 'Will this high last?' Or 'When is the front due?' Before answering such questions the forecaster has to ascertain which high or which front is being referred to, and, if he does not seek confirmation on the question, the way is open for considerable misunderstanding between the forecaster and the pilot. Even such an opening question as 'Will there be plenty of convection today?' is charged with potential ambiguity unless properly amplified. A pilot may, in fact, want to know whether or not conditions are favourable for cross-country soaring. He may be elated if the forecaster predicts that there will indeed be plenty of convection. But the elation will turn to despair if the convection is so plentiful that the sky becomes generally cloudy and thermals are only weak at low levels. If, on the other hand, the forecaster predicts only 'limited' convection, it must not be assumed that conditions for cross-country soaring are marginal. Does the word 'limited' mean that convection will be limited to a very short period of the day or does it imply that only small cumulus clouds will form?

'Is it unstable today?' is another inadequate question liable to be drastically misinterpreted. In much meteorological conversation the word unstable is applied to temperature-height curves which presage or explain the development of convection cloud at low or medium levels (regardless of the amount or depth of the cloud), while upper air conditions not conducive to such development are said to be stable—even if they produce dry thermals. Thus, a simple answer to the apparently simple question will be inadequate and possibly misleading when translated into thermal soaring prospects.

More potential sources of ambiguity arise whenever thermals, waves or gradients are mentioned. In general forecasting practice the word 'thermals' is used as an abbreviation for thermal winds, and 'thermal charts' portray the mean temperature (or its equivalent) in some specified layer of the atmosphere. The word 'waves' refers more frequently to kinks on fronts than to soarable waves near mountains. When the word 'gradient' is associated with an airflow it usually refers to the horizontal pressure gradient rather than the 'wind gradient'. So when such phrases as 'thermals are strong', the 'gradient is weak' or 'waves on the front' are mentioned it is wise to ascertain in which sense the terms are being used.

No doubt everyday conversation would lack variety and life without its quota of words used in a loose colloquial sense, but, with suitable preparation and forethought, it is not difficult to seek the forecaster's advice in a colloquial manner designed to give answers to specific questions typified by those already suggested in chapters of this book on thermal soaring prospects and wave soaring.

When listening to a forecast it is sometimes tempting to form a premature overall impression of the prospects for a flight tentatively planned. Such impressions can be misleading; they are apt to be based on casual stresses the forecaster may unwittingly put on items of the forecast and on incidental remarks to which the pilot gives undue thought while the telephone discussion is in progress. Before trying to assess the overall prospects, it is wise to note impartially all the relevant elementary items of the forecast and to treat each situation on its apparent merits.

Sequences of weather can trap the inexperienced pilot into neglecting to study each day on its full merits. For example, several consecutive days with excellent visibility, strong thermals, but adverse winds may instil into a pilot a feeling that, if only the winds would become favourable, he could attempt a particular task. Then comes a day with favourable winds. The pilot thinks, 'At last . . .'—and very humanly fails to give enough thought to convection, which may now be weak, or haziness, which may obscure turning points.

Changing your mind

Casual glances at the sky at odd moments can be misleading. It is very easy to fall into the trap of noticing a sudden change in, say, cloud amount and type, or the wind direction, and to be filled with optimism or despair according to whether the soaring prospects appear brighter or worse than was expected, but unless the change marks an expected or recognisable event, such as the passage of a line squall, it is usually unwise to act on impulsive feelings without waiting at least 10 or preferably 20 minutes to see whether the change was significant or merely a transient fluctuation in the broader pattern of events. Task setters, in particular, should not be swayed subjectively by fluctuations in either local weather or local opinion; they should be sensitive to such fluctuations, but impulsive decisions by task setters can easily create confusion, and hazards, in competition flying.

Long-range forecasting

If a forecaster could predict details of weather situations months or even weeks ahead he would undoubtedly make his fortune, and the apparent dearth of millionaire forecasters is perhaps the most convincing proof that such long-range forecasting is not possible at present. Nor is it likely in the foreseeable future. No doubt more statistical methods of predicting the probability of certain climatic features will be developed. Photographs taken from satellites have literally clarified the meteorologist's view of actual synoptic situations, and the use of high-speed computers has allowed more complication and consistency in some aspects of weather forecasting. But in many synoptic situations only a slight change of detail can make or mar soaring prospects, and it is unlikely that such details can be justifiably predicted for more than a day ahead.

Lack of a detailed long-range forecasting service, however, should not be a deterrent to planning gliding expeditions ahead. It merely means that such planning has to be as flexible as possible. It is wise to consult a meteorologist about the region to be explored; even though he will not normally be able to provide a long-range forecast, he can usually provide climatic data and draw balanced deductions on the probable soaring prospects. Gliding literature naturally highlights successful flights and, without more general climatological data, a reader may inadvertently acquire an unduly optimistic impression of soaring in regions in which he has not had actual flying experience. Some meteorological services are willing, for a small fee, to watch for specified conditions and notify a pilot when these conditions exist or are imminent. The details of this specification are a matter for arrangement between the individual pilot (or club) and the meteorological service.

So—a final thought—weather will be unpredictable for a long time—but it won't become more difficult to understand.

Technical Notes

23

Altimeter Setting

The altimeter in an aircraft measures atmosphere pressure but its scale is marked in feet or metres. The rough-and-ready pressure/altitude relationship we have already used in this book is adequate for general discussion but not accurate enough for precise conversion of millibars to altitude. Pressure surfaces are seldom truly horizontal; they dip down over depressions and bulge upwards over high pressure systems. Changes in temperature can also distort the pattern; heating at low levels pushes the isobaric surfaces upwards, and low-level cooling brings them down. Thus the pressure surfaces move almost incessantly, not by very much and not very fast, but enough to make the pressure/altitude relationship an awkward and international problem. The approach to this problem has been to devise a reasonably simple formula which describes the approximately average state of the atmosphere. Known as the *ICAO* Standard Atmosphere*, the agreed formula is based on the following specifications:

1 Pressure of 1013.25 mb at MSL.
2 A temperature of 15°C (59°F) at MSL.
3 A temperature lapse rate of 6.5°C per km (1.98°C per 1000 ft) up to a height of 11 km (just over 36 000 ft) above MSL.
4 An isothermal atmosphere (−56.5°C) from an altitude of 11 km upwards.

The pressure/altitude relationship derived from these specifications is tabulated at the end of this technical note. It provides an internationally agreed scale for graduating an *aneroid altimeter*, that is, a pressure-measuring instrument which uses the sealed can principle and which is calibrated in units of height instead of pressure.

* International Civil Aviation Organisation.

Of course, a conventionally calibrated altimeter does not always indicate true height above MSL or above ground-level. The pressure at MSL or ground-level is seldom precisely 1013.25 mb. An allowance for variations in the MSL for ground-level pressure is normally made by adjusting the scale of the altimeter so that the zero height corresponds to the pressure at mean sea-level or at the level above which the height is to be measured. This action, known as setting the *pressure subscale*, is equivalent to recalibrating the altimeter by rotating the mechanism to fit some specified reference level. For local soaring it is convenient to set the pressure subscale such that the altimeter is zero at a particular spot on the airfield. With this subscale setting during flight the altimeter will now indicate height above this particular spot on the airfield; the instrument will not indicate height above all points on a sloping airfield. The corrections for non-standard temperatures are usually negligible—about 3.3 ft per 1000 ft (1 m per 300 m) per degree Celsius difference between actual and standard temperatures. However, if the pressure at the airfield rises the altimeter will begin to err on the low side; if the airfield pressure falls then a pilot relying on the instrument will be lower than he thinks he is.

At high-level airfields the pressure at airfield level may be below the range incorporated in the subscale setting mechanism, and at some sites it is often expedient to set the altimeter to read the runway elevation (height above MSL) before take-off and then to use this as a reference level.

During cross-country flying it is usually more useful to set the altimeter to indicate height above MSL* rather than height above any particular piece of ground. This requires a knowledge of the expected change of MSL pressure over the route. On most thermal soaring cross-country flights the MSL pressure changes on route will not amount to very much, but in wave soaring and especially in line squall soaring conditions neglect of the probable MSL pressure changes on route could easily contribute to disaster. In contrast to thermal soaring conditions, both wave situations and line squalls can provide the means for soaring considerable distances across the MSL isobars in conditions in which a pilot can, intentionally or otherwise, lose sight of the ground for long periods. If the flight is

---

* Or some other regionally convenient and specified reference level.

towards a low pressure region and the pressure subscale is left unchanged, every millibar fall of MSL pressure on route brings the pilot another 30 ft (10 m) or so lower than his altimeter reading.

Altimeter settings in controlled airspace

Besides worrying about his own height above ground a glider pilot who is likely to venture close to or into civil airways must also be aware of the systems of vertical separation of aircraft within controlled airspace. Every 'C' class pilot should know the rules governing heights at which he may be allowed to cross or to fly in airways. But the rules would be useless without standard subscale settings for the aircraft altimeter. Each cross-country pilot should find out what rules apply to the region in which he flies. Broadly speaking, at levels at which most thermal cross-country flying is carried out air traffic control authorities use forecast MSL* pressures most appropriate for conveniently sized regions, while at high levels in the realm of high wave soaring or deep convection cloud soaring, a standard setting of 1013 mb is used for vertical separation of aircraft in airways.

To lessen the chances of ambiguity in messages used in international aviation procedures some words relating to altitude are used with limited meanings:

Height is used to denote the vertical distance of an object above the ground immediately below.

Altitude is used to denote height of the aircraft above MSL.

Elevation is used to denote the height of ground (an airfield or runway) above MSL.

The Q code

International procedures also include a system called the Q code which facilitates the exchange of common questions and answers. Code groups relating to altimeter settings are:

	AS A QUESTION	FOR INFORMATION
QFE ...	What is the ground-level pressure at ... ?	Ground-level pressure at ... is ... mb.

* Or some other regionally convenient and specified reference level.

QFF ...   What is the MSL pressure at ... ?   Pressure at MSL at ... is ... mb.

QNH ...   What must my pressure subscale be set to so that my altimeter reads the correct elevation on landing at ... ?   If the pressure subscale is set to ... mb then the altimeter will read the correct elevation on landing at ...

Table 23.1   ICAO STANDARD ATMOSPHERE (DRY AIR)

Pressure	Temperature		Density	Altitude	
mb	°C	°F	g/m³	m	ft
1013.2	15.0	59.0	1225	0	0
1000	14.3	57.7	1212	111	364
950	11.5	52.7	1163	540	1773
900	8.6	47.4	1113	988	3243
850	5.5	41.9	1063	1457	4781
800	2.3	36.2	1012	1949	6394
750	−1.0	30.1	960	2466	8091
700	−4.6	23.8	908	3012	9882
650	−8.3	17.0	855	3591	11 780
600	−12.3	9.8	802	4206	13 801
550	−16.6	2.1	747	4865	15 962
500	−21.2	−6.2	692	5574	18 289
450	−26.2	−15.2	635	6344	20 812
400	−31.7	−25.1	577	7185	23 574
350	−37.7	−36.0	518	8117	26 631
300	−44.5	−48.2	457	9164	30 065
250	−52.3	−62.2	395	10 363	33 999
200	−56.5	−69.7	322	11 784	38 662
150	−56.5	−69.7	241	13 608	44 647
100	−56.5	−69.7	161	16 180	53 083
90	−56.5	−69.7	145	16 848	55 275
80	−56.5	−69.7	128	17 595	57 726
70	−56.5	−69.7	112	18 442	60 504
60	−56.5	−69.7	96	19 419	63 711
50	−56.5	−69.7	80	20 575	67 503

These three Q signals are used so frequently in aviation and meteorological procedures that it is common practice to use them colloquially. 'What is the QFE?' is a common question asked by inquirers at an airfield who wish to know the barometric pressure at the level of the runway in use.

24

Geostrophic Winds

Geostrophic and gradient winds

Because the Earth is spinning about its axis all the objects on the Earth's surface are subjected to a centrifugal force that would, if left to itself, throw us off the Earth. Fortunately, this force is exactly balanced by the Earth's gravitational pull which keeps us where we are. This gravitational force is not precisely vertical at each point on the Earth's surface. It has a component from the Equator towards the Poles. If this poleward component were not present centrifugal force would not throw us off the Earth but it would cause us all to slide towards the Equator. Air on the Earth's surface is subjected to the same centrifugal and gravitational forces. However, when air moves eastwards it rotates about the Earth's axis faster than the Earth's surface over which it flows. Therefore, the centrifugal force acting on the air will be greater than that necessary to balance the poleward component of the gravitational force. If no other forces were present air moving eastwards would turn towards the Equator. But another force that is usually important in airflow situations arises from atmospheric pressure gradients. If the atmospheric pressure decreases from the Equator towards the Poles then the pressure gradient force will be towards the Poles. It is possible, therefore, for this pressure gradient force towards the Poles and the excess centrifugal force towards the Equator to be just balanced—if the speed of the easterly wind is just right to maintain this balance. The wind will then flow along the east–west isobars with what is known as the *geostrophic wind speed*.

The same reasoning leads to the conclusion that air blowing towards the west over the Earth's surface will have a deficit of centrifugal force to balance the poleward gravity and will maintain its westerly course only if it flows along east–west isobars with low pressure towards the Equator.

When air moves towards the Poles it will also move towards the east over the Earth's surface (because the speed at which the Earth's surface moves, due to the Earth's rotation, decreases with latitude) unless there is a pressure gradient force towards the west to balance this easterly drift. Therefore, it is possible for air to maintain a steady flow towards the Poles if there is a pressure gradient force towards the west and the wind speed is just right to maintain the balance. Similarly, the wind can maintain a steady path towards the Equator provided there is a pressure gradient force towards the east and the wind has the geostrophic value.

In all except low latitudes (less than about 15°) the pressure gradient force and the force due to the Earth's rotation (known as the *Coriolis Force*) are the dominant forces controlling air movement, and winds are mostly geostrophic. Piecing together the arguments already used to indicate the relationships between pressure gradients and north, south, east, and west winds we can see that in the northern hemisphere geostrophic winds blow in an anticlockwise direction around low pressure systems, while in the southern hemisphere the direction is clockwise around depressions. Winds around anticyclones blow in the opposite directions.

The geostrophic wind corresponding to an atmospheric pressure gradient at MSL is usually a moderately accurate representation of the wind at about 1500 ft (500 m) above MSL. At lower levels the frictional effect of the ground or sea reduces this wind speed and diverts the flow slightly across the isobars towards low pressure.

The formula for calculating the geostrophic wind speed is:

$$\text{Geostrophic wind speed in knots} = 3832 \times \frac{G \times (273 + T)}{P \times \text{sine } L}$$

where G = horizontal pressure gradient (mb per km)
T = air temperature (°C)
P = pressure (mb)
L = latitude (degrees)

Because the factor $(273 + T)/P$ for MSL varies only slightly with changes of pressure and temperature the meteorologist can apply the formula to his weather map in the following form:

$$\text{Geostrophic wind speed in knots} = \frac{2175}{D \times \text{sine } L}$$

where D = distance in kilometres between consecutive 2 mb isobars on the MSL pressure map.

Although this formula strictly applies to air at a pressure of 1013.2 mb with temperature of 15°C (59°F), it is approximately correct for a wide range of MSL temperatures and pressures and is used to derive the following tables.

GEOSTROPHIC WIND SPEED (KNOTS)

Latitude (deg)	Distances (kilometres) between consecutive 2 mb isobars									
	40	60	80	100	120	160	200	400	600	km
10	315	209	158	125	105	79	63	32	21	
30	109	72	55	44	36	27	22	11	7	
50	71	47	35	29	24	18	14	7	5	knots
70	58	39	29	23	19	15	12	6	4	
90	55	36	27	22	19	14	11	6	4	

Latitude (deg)	Distances (naut. miles) between consecutive 2 mb isobars									
	20	30	40	50	60	80	100	200	300	naut. miles
10	340	226	170	135	113	85	68	34	23	
30	118	78	59	47	39	29	24	12	8	
50	77	51	38	31	26	19	15	8	5	knots
70	63	42	31	25	21	16	13	6	4	
90	59	39	29	24	20	15	12	6	4	

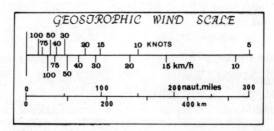

Fig. 24.1(a) Geostrophic wind scale for isobars at 2 mb intervals at latitude 50°. The scale is normally marked on perspex or a similar clear piece of plastic, and used as illustrated in Fig. 24.1(b).

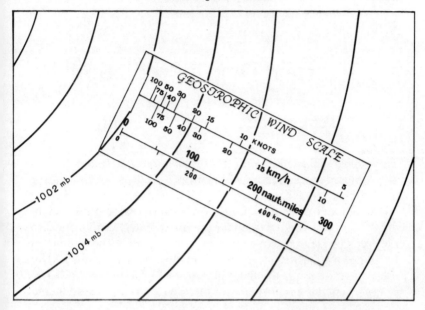

Fig. 24.1(b) When the clear plastic geostrophic wind scale is laid on pressure maps the direct distance between adjacent isobars can be read on the scale as a geostrophic wind speed—which is 20 knots in this illustration.

For any particular latitude a scale can be constructed to measure geostrophic wind speeds directly from a pressure chart; a geostrophic wind scale for isobars at 2 mb intervals at latitude 50° is sketched in Figure 24.1(a), and its use is illustrated in Figure 24.1(b).

Close to the centres of low pressure systems another force comes into play. This is the centrifugal force (called the *cyclostrophic force*) due to air rotating about the centre of low pressure. In general this tends to reduce wind speeds close to the centres of depressions. This force has a very significant effect in tropical cyclones or very deep and intense depressions, but for most of our purposes it can be neglected.

25

Thermal Depth Prediction
using
Temperature–Height Diagrams

The example, used in Chapter 20, of temperature rise and thermal development on a sunny day will be used to illustrate a technique for predicting thermal depth.

The amount of heat required to change a temperature–height graph from one curve to another is approximately proportional to the area between the two curves. In other words, the heat required to change the early morning inversion illustrated in Figure 20.1(a) of Chapter 20, to the dry thermal layer to 4800 ft in Figure 20.1(e) is approximately proportional to the area between the initial and

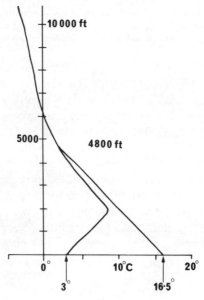

Fig. 25.1   Initial and final temperature-height curves used for the heating example in Chapter 20 and Figs. 21.2(a–e).

final temperature curves, as illustrated in Figure 25.1. Fortunately, sunshine available for such heating on a day of clear sky for any particular time of year is sufficiently constant from year to year to be used for temperature predictions on a potential thermal soaring day. In central England, for example, it has been found that the monthly distribution of heating likely to be available on a day of clear skies is approximately as listed in the table below.

Heating available in central England to change the temperature–height curve between sunrise and the time of maximum temperature on days of clear skies

Month	°C × 1000 ft (°Ckft)
Jan	4.0
Feb	7.3
Mar	10.7
Apr	15.6
May	19.4
Jun	20.1
Jul	19.2
Aug	17.2
Sep	12.7
Oct	8.7
Nov	4.1
Dec	3.0

(*Heating at other latitudes is indicated later in this chapter.*)

The numbers for each month denote areas in terms of degrees Celsius multiplied by height in thousands of feet, i.e. 19.4 for May means that the heating will be sufficient to raise the temperature of a 1000-ft column of air by approximately 19.4°C—or a 2000-ft column by 9.7°C. (In this book this unit of heating, which can be called *thousands of degree feet* or *degree kilofeet*, is denoted °C × 1000 ft or °Ckft; °Ckm means *thousands of degree metres* or *degree kilometres*.) How can we use this information? Let us go back to the heating example and suppose it refers to a day in the month of May. Will the inversion break down? First: What is the area between the temperature–height graph representing the initial inversion and the graph at the time this inversion breaks down?

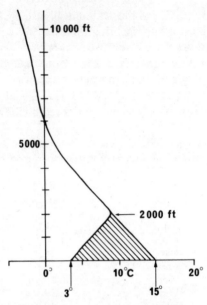

Fig. 25.2   The shaded area between the two temperature-height curves (also shown in Fig. 25.1) is approximately proportional to the heat required to produce this change.

This area is illustrated in Figure 25.2. We can calculate the area as half the increase in surface air temperature multiplied by the height of the top of the inversion, i.e. $\frac{1}{2}(15°C - 3°C) \times 2000\,\text{ft} = 12\,000°\text{Cft} = 12.0°\text{C}$ (3.75°Ckft/km). The heating available shows that 19.4°Ckft should be available on a clear day in May. Therefore, we should predict that the inversion will be broken down. Because this breakdown of the inversion will use up only 12.0 of the 19.4°Ckft of heating available, the remaining 7.4 will be available to raise the temperature and the depth of the thermal layer even more. In the example illustrated in the sequence of diagrams of Figure 20.1, the 7.4°Ckft of heating is used to raise the air temperature approximately $1\frac{1}{2}°$C over a depth of 4800 ft. Figures 20.1(d) and (e) illustrate this final phase of the thermal development.

Predictions of whether or not a temperature inversion will break down and of the ultimate depth of the thermal layer are not sufficient for a keen thermal soaring pilot or the organisers of a contest. They need more detailed predictions of the height to which thermals will reach for various times of the day. Fortunately, more details of the hourly rates of heating available can be obtained. Figure 25.3 shows the heating available in central England for times of the day before sunrise and the time of maximum temperature throughout the year. Using this diagram we can find that, for, say, mid-May, the 12.0°Ckft (3.75°Ckm) that were required to break down the temperature inversion in the example we have been discussing would be available by about 11.15 LST (Local Solar Time). Remember that solar time in this book is taken to be 12.00 h when the sun is at its highest for the locality, i.e. GMT plus (minus) 4 min for every degree of longitude east (west) of the Greenwich meridian. Therefore, the prediction would be that the depth of the thermals would increase to 2000 ft (600 m) by 11.15 h, then increase rapidly to 4800 ft (1600 m) by 14.30 h, which is about the

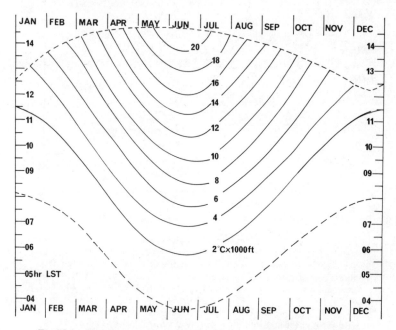

Fig. 25.3   Heating available for changing temperature-height profiles in central England. The curves are labelled in thousands of degree-feet, e.g. 10 means enough heating to produce a 10°C temperature rise through a depth of 1000 ft (or 5°C through 2000 ft, etc.). The lower broken line denotes the approximate time of day when the heating starts.

time the temperature should reach its maximum in May in this part of the world.

Of course, if we know or were to predict that the condensation level in this example would be 4000 ft we would predict that cumulus would form at 4000 ft at midday. If we measure the dry- and wet-bulb temperatures of the surface air, during the late morning we can get an approximate indication of the probable condensation level from Figure 25.4.

In applying this method of predicting temperatures and thermal development, estimation of areas on the temperature–height diagram can be made easier by the following technique. Suppose we wish to know the area involved in changing a temperature–height

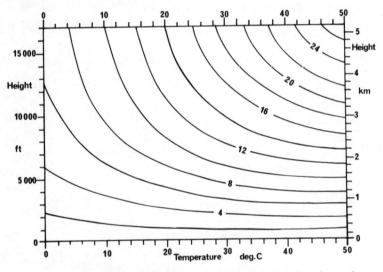

Fig. 25.4   Approximate height of cumulus cloud base for given dry- and wet-bulb temperatures of the surface air. Numbers 4–24 on the curves in the diagram denote differences between the dry- and wet-bulb temperatures. Use of the diagram is best described by an example. Suppose the dry- and wet-bulb temperatures of air in the shade at between 4 and 6 ft (1.25–2 m) above ground-level are 20°C and 12°C. Subtract the 12 from 20 to get 8°C as the difference between these two temperatures. Draw a vertical line through the 20°C on the diagram. Draw a horizontal line through the point where this 20°C line intersects with the 8(°C) temperature difference curve. Read off the approximate height of cumulus cloud base at the end of horizontal line: 6100 ft (1860 m). In practice this approximate cloud height is liable to be an underestimate in dry conditions inland and an overestimate in moist onshore airstreams.

graph from one state to another, like that sketched in Figure 25.2. Draw a horizontal line through the top of the inversion, as illustrated in Figure 25.5. Now draw another straight line parallel to the

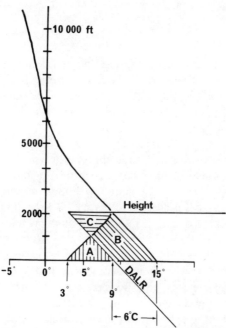

Fig. 25.5   An easy way to estimate areas A + B is to draw a horizontal (height) line through the apex of this area. Then draw a DALR line such that area C looks to be equal to area A. Then area A + B = area C + B, which equals the temperature difference of 6°C (15–9 at the base of area B) multiplied by the height, 2000 ft, i.e. 12 thousands of degree-feet.

DALR such that the areas A and C appear to be approximately equal. This will mean that the area in which we are interested, A plus B, is the same as area B plus C. The area of B plus C is equal to the temperature difference labelled in this illustration multiplied by the height, also labelled in Figure 25.5. Instead of drawing the horizontal height line and dry adiabatic lapse rate line on the temperature–height diagram, it is more convenient to use a small piece of perspex with these two lines marked on them and to slide the perspex across the diagram until the areas in question appear to be equal. It is also useful to make the temperature and height scales of the temperature–height diagram such that the dry adiabatic lapse rates are at approximately 45° to both axes, in other words an interval of 3°C on the temperature axis should correspond to 1000 ft (300 m) on the height axis.

Causes of errors

Like all forecasting techniques the temperature and thermal prediction method just described is a useful but oversimplified picture of events in the real atmosphere. Predictions based on a particular temperature–height graph will not be correct if the airstream changes, or if the airstream itself brings changes in the temperature profile that are unpredictable or ignored.

Over particularly damp soils the energy corresponding to the heating values given is not available for heating the lowest layers of the atmosphere during the first few hours of sunshine. In such localities the values indicated in Figure 25.3 should be reduced by between about 1.0 and 1.5°Ckft, although in midsummer these values may be made up late in the morning. Reduction in the heat available for convection can be particularly noticeable in climates where hot dry weather is interrupted by heavy rainfall; thermal soaring developments can be delayed by several hours over localities recently wetted by convective storms.

Modifications appropriate to hilly districts or sea-breeze effects must be judged according to the situation; for example, temperature may rise relatively quickly on sun-facing slopes while in coastal districts on-shore winds may delay or check the rise of temperature just inland.

The effect of fog or a complete cover of cloud may be assessed using the following factors as a guide:

For thin cloud (about 500 ft (160 m) thick) use 60–95% of the indicated values.

For thick cloud (3000 ft (1000 m) or more thick) use 40–75% of the indicated values.

For shallow fog use 60–70% of the indicated values.

For deep white fog use 40–60% of the indicated values.

For thick fog and pollution, or smog, use 30–50% of the indicated values.

In the example used for illustration in this note we have ignored the fact that the lowest part of the thermal layer is often a superadiabatic layer, not a dry adiabatic layer. The difference is slight for many practical purposes, and it is certainly more convenient to draw DALR lines on the temperature–height diagrams. However, in very hot and dry climates the superadiabatic layer is more pronounced and the temperature–height curve from about mid-morning to early afternoon is more likely to look like that shown in Figure 25.6. Thus the surface air temperature is likely to

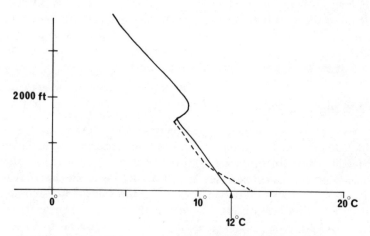

Fig. 25.6   In hot and dry conditions the temperature profile at within a few hundred feet, and occasionally a thousand or so feet, is likely to be superadiabatic, like the lower part of the broken curve in this illustration. The heating is not transferred aloft as quickly as the assumption of the DALR curve implies. Thus this assumption can lead to a slight underestimate in surface air temperature prediction, but it does not make much difference to prediction of the height to which thermals will reach.

be somewhat higher than that predicted by drawing the DALR lines, while the depth to which thermals reach may be slightly lower. But even in these climates precise knowledge of the intensity or depth of the superadiabatic layer is not critical for making thermal height predictions; the dry adiabatic lapse rate assumption is still a very useful guide.

Methods of using surface dry- and wet-bulb temperatures to calculate the condensation level are prone to two particular types of errors. The early morning wet-bulb temperature does not normally attain its value representing the middle of the day convection until late morning, and the mixing of the air in thermals with the air through which the thermals rise causes the water vapour content of thermals to change during ascent. On good soaring days the entrained air is drier than the thermal air, so the condensation level and cloud base become higher than that calculated from dry- and wet-bulb surface temperatures.

The basic premise, that the heat required to change a temperature–height graph from one curve to another is proportional to the area between the two curves, is not strictly accurate, but it is an adequate approximation for our purposes. If greater precision is required, aerological diagrams, such as the tephigram, and Skew T-log P diagrams should be used.

Heating at various latitudes

Solar radiation data and miscellaneous observations and experience suggest that the latitudinal distribution of heating available for changing the temperature–height curve between sunrise and the time of maximum temperature on a clear-sky day is like that shown in Figure 25.7. It should be stressed that the values indicated are tentative; there are considerable gaps in the data and experience so far acquired, and modifications may well be suggested by future research. However, the diagram denotes the main features of the heating available between latitudes 60°N and 60°S and is a useful guide on which to build up regional experience.

Notice that the highest values are not at the Equator. Latitudes between about 20° and 30° get more direct solar radiation and have longer days in the summer. With the length of summer days increasing towards higher latitudes, the decrease of available heating does not decrease with increasing latitudes as much as may be generally supposed. Notice, too, that the southern hemisphere receives slightly more summer heating for convection than the northern hemisphere. This is because the sun is slightly closer to the earth in December than in June.

The convective heating diagram does not show the overall distribution of thermal soaring prospects; it indicates the heating likely on clear days; it does not indicate the likelihood of clear days. It so

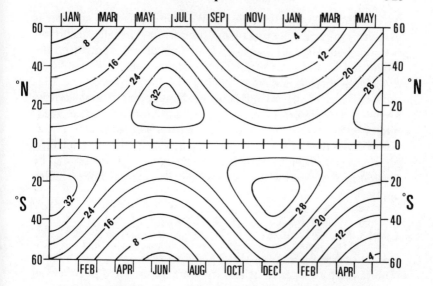

Fig. 25.7   Estimated daily heating available for changing temperature profiles in thousands of degree-feet. In late March, for example, the total heating available at latitude 40°N is about 16°C through 1000 ft (or 4°C through 4000 ft, etc.). It must be stressed that the estimates shown in this diagram are based on forecasting experience and an inadequate (at present) set of data. They should be taken as useful guides to the heating likely to be available, but local research is needed to check or modify the estimates to fit regional climatological and topographic conditions.

happens that the subtropics include the world's major arid regions which have both good heating and abundant clear days.

A guide to the hour-by-hour heating likely to be available at any particular latitude, up to about 50°, can be obtained by assuming that the effective heating will start at about one hour after sunrise and continue steadily to about 14.30 LST.

The assumption of a steady rate of heating is not precisely true, but it is simple, and adequate to form a working basis for further development of the method in any particular locality. A more important factor in any particular place is the heat loss due to typical evaporation in the region. Assessment for this and other local characteristics superposed on the average heating for the latitude of the locality is best estimated from data and experience in the locality.

At latitudes higher than about 50°, where sunrise in summer is very early, effective heating on midsummer days usually starts later than one hour after sunrise; in Finland, for example, sunrise in June is between 02.00 and 03.00 LST, but effective heating does not start until about three hours later.

The risk of errors arising from inadequate data should not be accepted as a deterrent to using thermal depth prediction techniques such as that just described. Errors will inevitably occur, especially in the early days of building up experience for a locality, but these errors can be turned to advantage if their causes can be located and assessed within the framework of the technique being applied.

Using the Met flight log

It is not difficult to use a Met flight log for calculating the heating required before a series of surface temperatures and dry thermal layer depths are reached. The extract from the Met flight log shown in Chapter 20 is reproduced below together with calculations of the heating required and predicted times for dry thermal layers to develop to heights of 0.5, 1.0, 1.5, 1.8, 2.0, 2.5 and 3.0 thousands of feet. The 'Surface Temps req'd' are used in the calculations, (Remember that Surface Temp req'd is the temperature (°C) plus 3 times the height in thousands of feet at which it was measured.)

MET FLIGHT—RENMARK—07.30–08.05 h—10 JAN 1977
(Local time = LST + 30 min)

Height 1000's ft	Temperatures °C		For DALR to Height of reading				Observations
	Dry	Wet	Surface Temp req'd	Heating increment req'd	Total heating req'd	Predicted local time	
0.0	25.4		25.4	—	3.70	07.30	
0.5	24.2		25.7	0.08	3.78	07.30	Haze top to 500 ft
1.0	26.5		29.5	2.85	6.63	08.10	
1.5	27.6		32.1	3.25	9.88	08.55	
1.8	29.8		35.2	5.12	15.00	10.05	
2.0	29.4		35.4	0.38	15.38	10.10	
2.5	28.0		35.5	0.23	15.61	10.10	
3.0	26.9		35.9	1.10	16.71	10.25	

The Heating increment column denotes the heat in °Ckft required to raise the top of the dry thermal layer from one of the listed heights up to the next; for example, the heat required to raise the dry thermal layer from 500 ft to 1000 ft is 0.08°Ckft. These heating increments are calculated by multiplying the difference between the calculated surface temperatures required for two adjacent heights by half the sum of these heights in thousands of feet; for example, the heating increment required to raise the dry thermal layer from 500 ft to 1000 ft is calculated as:

$$(29.5 - 25.7) \times \tfrac{1}{2}(0.5 + 1.0) = 2.85°\text{Ckft}$$

The total heat required is obtained by adding the increments, but before starting the addition the expected heating received between sunrise and the start of the Met flight should be inserted at the zero height level. Meteorological and gliding observations at Renmark (South Australia) indicate that on an early January day this gliding site gets 37°Ckft between 06.40 and 15.00 h local time, and that the rate of receiving this heat is almost steady throughout this period of the day. This means that about 3.70°Ckft should have been received by 07.30 h; so we should start the heating summation with 3.70°Ckft at 7.30 h. The predicted local times (to the nearest 5 minutes) by which the calculated total heating required should be attained are obtained by calculating (or reading from a graph) the proportion of heating from zero at 06.40 h to 37°Ckft at 15.00 h local time.

Computations of heating to one or two decimal places should not be scorned as being over-precise, but they should not beguile the user into forgetting possible causes of over-riding errors in applying the whole technique. On this particular day the rate of development of the dry thermal layer was predicted to develop more slowly than that indicated by the predicted times based on the 07.30 Met flight—the reason being that cooler air was expected to arrive from the southwest during the day. Another Met flight was made at 11.00 h local time to assess the rate of advective cooling and update the thermal predictions.

It is pertinent to inquire whether detailed calculation of heating areas and predicted times are worth making when a paucity of data on advected changes in an airstream can lead to much larger errors. I have found that by attempting to predict in detail the forecaster, or glider pilot, is likely to maintain more consistency and logic in thinking about the various factors that are relevant to his predictions; furthermore, he becomes quicker to notice and diagnose variations from these predictions. When observed temperature changes or thermal depths indicate that a prediction is beginning to go wrong, it is much easier to guess the causes of the errors and make realistic amendments if the original prediction is the result of a systematic technique.

26

Using Aerological Diagrams

For the pilot planning a cross-country flight, a verbal description of the countryside and landmarks around him are inadequate; he needs a map on which can be measured distances and angles according to the rules of navigation. The meteorologist, also finding mere words inadequate, uses a sort of map on which to plan his concepts of certain atmospheric processes, but his map is called an *aerological diagram,* and the lines on it are drawn in accordance with the rules of thermodynamics.

The two most commonly used aerological diagrams, the tephigram and the Skew T-log P diagram, were introduced in Chapter 20. Without being absolutely essential, a familiarity with the use of these diagrams is such a useful aid in tracing and understanding some atmospheric phenomena that it is worth spending a little time getting to know at least one of them. It does not matter which one we become familiar with; they are basically very similar.

The tephigram has a pattern of isobars, isotherms, water vapour content lines, and dry and saturated adiabatic lapse rates like that shown in Figure 26.1. The Skew T-log P diagram has a similar pattern of these lines, but its isobars are straight lines, whereas the isobars on the tephigram are very slightly curved.

Because pressure is closely associated with altitude, the isobars give a rough indication of altitude. We may recall that pressure at mean sea-level is often about 1000 mb; the 10 000-ft (approx. 3000 m) pressure is roughly 700 mb and the 20 000-ft (approx. 6000 m) pressure is about 500 mb. The pressure and temperature of a parcel of air can be represented by a dot marked on the diagram; for a pressure of 1000 mb and temperature of 19°C, for example, the point T in Figure 26.1 is the representative dot. Suppose this parcel of air rises to the 900-mb pressure-level without gaining or losing any of its heat, either by radiation or by mixing with its surroundings. It will expand and cool adiabatically as the pressure decreases, and the representative dot will trace a line on the

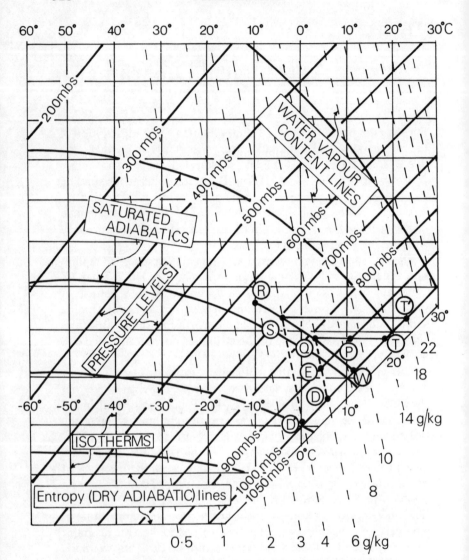

Fig. 26.1 The principal lines of a section of the tephigram are labelled.
Points T, P, Q, etc. in this diagram refer to examples of the tephigram
elaborated in the text.

aerological diagram. It is one of the fundamental laws of thermodynamics that, for unsaturated air, this line will move parallel to the dry adiabatic lapse rate lines on the aerological diagram. (On the tephigram the DALR lines are straight, whereas on the Skew T-log P diagram they are slightly curved.) Thus, as the parcel of air rises to the 900-mb pressure-level the representative dot will trace the dry adiabatic lapse rate line TP in Figure 26.1.

So far, only unsaturated air has been considered, but it is possible for our parcel of air to contain invisible water vapour up to a certain limit, which depends primarily on its temperature. The limit, in this example, is indicated by the value of the sloping water vapour content line running through the point T, the label 14 g/kg meaning that, if the parcel contains 1 kg of dry air then 14 g of water vapour would be required to saturate it. Saturated water vapour content lines for other pressures and temperatures are usually printed as pecked lines, such as those shown in Figure 26.1, and their pattern underlines the statement, made in Chapter 4, that the cooler the air, the lower its capacity to contain water vapour.

If the parcel of air whose temperature is represented by point T contains, say, only 6 g of water vapour per kilogram of dry air the point D at the same pressure-level and on the 6 g/kg water vapour content line can be taken to represent the moisture content of the air. The temperature at D, 6°C, is then the dew point of the air, and the relative humidity of the parcel is:

$$\frac{\text{actual water vapour content}}{\text{saturation water vapour content}} \times 100 = \frac{6}{14} \times 100 = 43\%$$

If this air, together with its 6 g of water vapour, rises again to the 900 mb level, the dot representing the dew point will move from D along the pecked line to E (no water vapour being added to or extracted from the parcel of air in the process) and, since the air remains unsaturated, its temperature will again fall to that denoted by point P.

Now let us see what happens as the parcel of moist air rises higher still. Its temperature will follow a DALR line, but only as far as the point Q on the 6 g/kg water vapour content line. At this level (815 mb or about 5800 ft) saturation is attained, and any subsequent fall of temperature during continued ascent will be at the saturated adiabatic lapse rate, which is indicated by the saturated

adiabatic lines on the diagram. Thus, from Q upwards the condensed excess moisture will be visible in the form of a cloud, and
when the parcel of saturated air reaches the 640 mb level its
temperature will be represented by the point R. The aerological
diagram shows that, at this stage, the parcel can contain only 3 g of
water vapour per kilogram of dry air; the remaining 3 g/kg will
be in some form of liquid or frozen water.

We are now in a position to relate to these basic manoeuvres on
the aerological diagram to actual weather phenomena, and it is an
instructive exercise to use the diagram to study the föhn effect,
wherein air flowing across a mountain range is forced to rise and
form cloud, which precipitates rain or snow on the mountain before
the air descends into the leeward lowland as a comparatively warm
dry wind. The history of the parcel of moist air, already described
with the aid of Figure 26.1, is typical of the first stage of the föhn
effect illustrated by the streamline TPQR in Figure 26.2. During its

Fig. 26.2   In this illustration of the föhn effect the temperatures at points
T, P, Q, etc. are represented by corresponding points marked on the
tephigram in Fig. 26.1, and the whole process is described in the text.

ascent to about 12 000 ft (the 640 mb level) cloud is formed at about
5800 ft and the temperature at the top is indicated by the point R on
the diagram. Now, suppose that 2 g of the water content per
kilogram of dry air falls out in the form of snow (the temperature
being below 0°C). Only 4 g/kg of the water content will be left; so
that, during its descent, the parcel becomes unsaturated on passing
point S, on the 4 g/kg vapour content line. Therefore the subsequent descent will be along the dry adiabatic to the point T'.
Meanwhile the dew point will move along the 4 g/kg pecked line to
D'. Thus, the air will be warmer and drier than it was on the
windward side of the range.

Aerological diagrams are particularly suitable for the technique (described in Chapter 25 on Thermal Depth Prediction) for predicting temperature and thermal depth changes on a sunny day with more precision. The heat required to change a temperature–height curve from one position to another is exactly proportional to the area between the two curves on an aerological diagram—whereas this relationship is only approximate on a simple temperature–height diagram. Aerological diagrams have another advantage in that the angles between the DALR and SALR lines are greater than they are on a temperature–height diagram. So, dry and saturated adiabatic lines are easier to distinguish and follow. On aerological diagrams it is somewhat easier to use pressure levels instead of heights, so heating data of the type given in Chapter 20 is easier to use if it is converted from $°C \times 1000$ ft into $°C \times 100$ mb. This conversion can be made approximately by taking two-sevenths of the heating figures in Chapter 20, but more precise conversions can be calculated.

Aerological diagrams can be used to relate temperature and wet-bulb temperature to dew points, water vapour contents and relative humidity. The relationships between temperature, dew point, water vapour content and relative humidity have already been mentioned in this chapter. Wet-bulb temperature can also be represented on the aerological diagram by a dot, such as that shown by the W in Figure 26.1. The linkage between the temperature, wet-bulb temperature and dew point stems from the fact that the dry adiabatic line through the dry-bulb temperature, the saturated adiabatic line through the wet-bulb temperature and the water vapour content line through the dew point all meet at a point, as shown in Figure 26.1. Therefore, if we remember this construction we can use the aerological diagram to derive any one of these three temperatures from the other two.

Units and Abbreviations
used in this book
(Alternatives in brackets)

Atmospheric pressure	millibars	mb
Wind direction	{ compass points { degrees geographic	
Wind speed	knots (kilometres per hour)	knots (km/h)
Temperature	degrees Celsius (degrees Fahrenheit)	°C (°F)
Visibility	{ metres { kilometres (nautical miles)	m km (naut. miles)
Short distances	metres	m
Long distances	kilometres (nautical miles)	km (naut. miles)
Height	{ feet (metres) { feet (kilometres)	ft (m) ft (km)
Thermal strength and vertical air motion	knots (metres per second)	knots (m/s)
Radiation wavelengths	millimetres	mm
Water vapour	grams per kilogram of dry air	g/kg
Time	(hours { minutes (seconds	h min s

Measure of heating used
  in Chapter 25 for thermal
  prediction technique
	degree feet (degree metres)
	thousands of degree feet
	  (degree kilometres)
		°Cft (°Cm)
		°Ckft (°Ckm)

Alternative values of units in brackets in the text of this book are approximations only.

NUMBERS FORMAT

	Examples	Meaning
Decimal point used to denote tenths	20.5	twenty point five
Commas not used to denote thousands	3500	three thousand five hundred
Space used to denote tens of thousands	15 000	fifteen thousand
Decimal point used in times	10.35 GMT	ten hours and thirty-five minutes GMT

INITIALS

MSL	Mean Sea-Level
DALR	Dry Adiabatic Lapse Rate (1°C/100 m)
SALR	Saturated Adiabatic Lapse Rate (approx. $\frac{1}{2}$°C/100 m at low levels)
ITCZ	Intertropical Convergence Zone
ITF	Intertropical Front
GMT	Greenwich Mean Time
LST	Local Solar Time (Sun highest at 12.00 LST)

Conversion Factors

$$T°F = \tfrac{5}{9}(T-32)°C$$
$$T°C = (32 + \tfrac{9}{5}T)°F$$

Fahrenheit/Celsius conversion table

°C	−40	−30	−20	−10	0	10	20	30	40	50	60
°F	−40	−22	−4	14	32	50	68	86	104	122	140

PRESSURE

Outside of national meteorological services, many barometers are calibrated in inches or millimetres of mercury. Such units are not precise measures of pressure; allowance must be made for variations in temperature and in the force of gravity— which increases towards the Poles. The relationship between millibars and inches or millimetres of mercury at 0°C at latitude 45° N or S is

$$1000\,\text{mb} = 750.1\,\text{mm} = 29.531\,\text{in}$$

DISTANCES

1 mm = 0.03937 in.
1 in. = 25.4 mm

Rainfall is usually measured in
mm or in., but, in some regions,
it is measured in 'points'
1 point = 1 hundredth of an inch.

1 ft = 0.3048 m = $\tfrac{1}{3}$ yd
1 m = 3.2808 ft
1 km = 1000 m = 3280.8 ft = 0.6214 statute mile
 = 0.5396 nautical mile
1 statute mile = 5280 ft = 1609 m = 1.609 km = 0.8684 nautical mile
1 nautical mile = 6080 ft = 1853 m = 1.853 km = 1.1515 statute miles
 = 1 minute of longitude

SPEEDS

	ft/s	*100ft/min*	*m/s*	*km/h*	*mi/h*	*knots*
1 ft/s	1	0.6	0.3048	1.0973	0.6818	0.5921
100 ft/min	1.667	1	0.508	1.829	1.136	0.9868
1 m/s	3.2808	1.968	1	3.6	2.2369	1.9424
1 km/h	0.9113	0.5468	0.2778	1	0.6214	0.5396
1 mi/h	1.4667	0.88	0.447	1.609	1	0.8684
1 knot	1.6889	1.014	0.5148	1.8532	1.1515	1

h = hour, min = minutes, s = seconds, mi = statute miles.

Bibliography

Besselmoulin, J., and Viaut, A., *Manuel de Meteorologie du Vol à Voile*, 3rd edn., Blondel et Rougerie, Paris, 1967.

Lindsay, C. V., and Lacy, S. J., *Soaring Meteorology for Forecasters*, Forecasters Handbook No. 3, National Weather Service, U.S.A., 1972.

Piggott, D., *Gliding: A Handbook on Soaring Flight*, 3rd rev. edn., A. & C. Black, London, 1971.

Reichmann, H., *Strecken-Segelflug*, Motorbuch Verlag, Stuttgart, 1975.

Scorer, R. S., *Environmental Aerodynamics*, Ellis Horwood, Chichester, and John Wiley & Sons, New York, 1977.

Welch, Ann, *Pilots' Weather*, John Murray, London, 1973.

ORGANISATION SCIENTIFIQUE ET TECHNIQUE DU VOL A VOILE PUBLICATIONS:

Forecasters' Manual for Soaring Flight. 1976. Edited by Bradbury, T. A., and Kuettner, J. P.

OSTIV Publications I–XII—scientific, technical and meteorological papers presented at the OSTIV Congresses, 1950–74.

OSTIV Secretariat, Van Halewijnplein 37 Voorburg, Netherlands.

Index

Adelanto Shear Line, 204
Adiabatic lapse rates, 30, 40, 129, 252, 260, 318, 323
Advection fog, 56
Aerological diagrams, 259, 317
Air masses, 86
    pollution, 57, 200
    trajectories, 24
Albedo, 27
Aldrich, John, 202
Altimeter setting, 295
Altocumulus, 48, 51, 65, 69, 77, 265
Altostratus, 48, 52, 64, 67, 69
Amplitude, lee wave, 207, 214
Anabatic wind, 117
Anacold front, 63, 76
Anemometers, 22
Aneroid barometer, 12
Anticyclones, 6, 89, 168
Arctic front, 87
Atmospherics, 242
Azores High, 8, 91

Backing, wind, 20, 75, 76
Bai-u season (Japan), 105
Balloon, pilot, 241
    , radio-sonde, 27, 240
Barograph, 13
Barometer, 4, 12
Barometric pressure, 3
Beaufort wind-scale, 20
Bergeron-Findeison process, 38
Bergwind, 119
Bolster eddies, 113
Breakaway depression, 81
Buran, 104
Buys-Ballot's Law, 16

Camphill, 222
Castellanus, 49, 77, 265
Cellular patterns, thermals, 133
Chart times, 8, 239
Charting, weather, 239
Cirrus cloud, 45, 50, 64, 66, 75, 268
Classification, air masses, 87
    , clouds, 47
    , visibility, 59

, wind speeds, 21
Cloud classification, 47
    , convection 42, 44, 53, 143, 156, 256
    , lee wave, 207, 284
    levels, 49
    , Mother of Pearl, 228
    observations, 52
    , orographic, 42
    , roll, 225
    searchlight, 54
    streets, 150, 178, 284
    symbols, 47, 244, 275, 282
    types, 42
Coalescence process, 37
Codes, weather, 243, 245
Col, 6
Cold anticyclone, 89
    front, 60, 63, 71, 73, 78, 82
    occlusion, 70, 74
Communications, meteorological, 243
Computing, 183, 247
Condensation, 36
    level, 42, 256, 308
Convection cloud, 42, 44, 53, 143, 156, 256
    , medium level, 175
Convergence, intertropical, 95, 103, 106
    , lines, 103, 204
    , orographic, 120
    , sea breeze, 185
Conversion factors, 324
Cool change, 81
Coriolis force, 301
Cross Fell, 213
Cumulonimbus, 43, 48, 66, 98, 159, 205
Cumulus, 43, 48, 53, 64, 69, 77, 98, 143
Cup anemometer, 22
Cyclogenesis, 78
Cyclone, tropical, 99
    , eye of, 99
Cyclostrophic force, 303

Dangers, wave soaring, 225
Degrees kilofeet (km), 305, 322
Depressions, breakaway, 81
    , family, 80

Depressions—*contd.*
, frontal, 78, 80
, lee, 86
, monsoon, 105
, secondary, 81
, thermal, 84
, thundery, 85
, tropical, 99
Dew point, 41, 319
Diurnal variation, lee waves, 213
, pressure, 95
Doctors (cool breezes), 187
Double front, 74
Downdraught, orographic, 235
, precipitation, 165, 179, 231
symbols, 275, 284
Dry Adiabatic Lapse Rate, 30, 129, 252, 260, 318, 323
Dry thermals, 123, 285
Dust devil, 134, 277, 283

Earth's rotation, 3, 300
Easterly wave, 97
Eddies, 113, 114, 223
Edgar, Larry, 225
El Mirage Shear Line, 203
Elsinore Shear Line, 202
Entropy, 262, 318
Equatorial Trough, 95
Esperance Doctor, 187
Evaporation, 39, 131

Family of depressions, 80
Findeisen-Bergeron process, 38
Fog, 55, 59, 284
Föhn wind, 320
Föhngap, 208
Föhnwall, 208
Forecasts, championships, 272
, long range, 290
, routine, 265
, short range, 264
, task-setting, 277
, thermal soaring, 179
, wave soaring, 232
Freezing point, 36
nuclei, 37
levels, 37, 39, 64, 67, 69, 236, 285
Fremantle Doctor, 187
Front, anacold, 63, 76
, Arctic, 87

Front, cold, 60, 64, 71, 73, 76, 78, 82
, double, 74
, intertropical, 95
, katacold, 63, 67, 71
, Mediterranean, 87
, occluded, 74
, pseudo-, 74
, sea-breeze, 198
, smog, 200, 203
, subsiding, 65, 69
, trowal, 74
, upper, 74
, warm, 61, 67, 72, 75, 78, 82
Frontal cross sections, 63, 69
troughs, 70
Frontogenesis, 78
Funnel cloud, 172

Gale, wind speed, 21
Geostrophic scale, 250, 302
wind, 16, 300
Glaciation, 39
Glacier wind, 117
Gloom, anticyclonic, 92
Gradient wind, 116, 289, 300
Ground fog, 56
Group structure, thermals, 153
Gustiness, 116

Haboob, 173
Hail, 39, 164
Halo, 47, 50, 68, 75
Hangabwinde, 119
Hangaufwinde, 119
Haze, 59, 246, 284
Heat low, 84
Heating available for thermals, 305, 307, 313
Helm Bar, 213
High pressure systems, 6, 8, 89, 91, 168
Hill fog, 56
Hill lift, 111
Humidity, 40, 319
Hurricane, 83, 99
Hygrometer, wet- and dry-bulb, 40

ICAO Standard Atmosphere, 261, 295, 298
Ice accretion, 158, 236

crystals, 38, 45
Insolation, 26, 130, 252
Intertropical Front, 95
Convergence Zone, 95, 103, 106
Inversion, temperature, 30, 55, 57, 98, 252
Isallobars, 250
Isobars, 6
Isothermal layer, 31

Jet stream, 19, 72, 268
Jinks, Malcolm, 231
Jones, Stan, 226

Katabatic wind, 117, 119
Katacold front, 63, 65, 66, 71, 77

Lapse rate, average, 30
, ICAO, 295
, isothermal, 30
, superadiabatic, 32, 128, 177
Lasham, 189, 197
Late thermal sources, 133
Latent heat, 39
Layer clouds, 44
Lee depression, 86
Lee wave, amplitude, 207, 214
, clouds, 207, 284
, conditions, 209
, diurnal variation, 213
, forecasts, 232
, long waves aloft, 228
, rotor flow, 216, 225, 284
, upwind jump, 227, 236
, wavelength, 206
Lenticular clouds, 49
Lightning, 160
Lindsay, Charles, 182
Line squall, 72, 77, 163, 168
Low pressure systems, 6, 71, 78, 82, 84

Mackenzie, J. K., 189
Mammatus cloud, 162, 168
Measurements, cloud height, 52
, humidity, 40
, pressure, 4, 12, 295
, temperature, 34
, visibility, 58
, wind, 20
Mediterranean front, 87
Met flight, local, 257, 314

METMAP, 263
Millibar, 5
Moisture, 36, 130
Monsoon, 102, 105
Mother of Pearl clouds, 228
Mountain and valley winds, 119

Nephanalysis, 249
Night cooling, 34
Nimbostratus, 48, 64, 67
Nocturnal radiation, 34
Nodal surface, 228
Northers, (U.S.A.), 104

Observations, cloud, 52
, lee waves, 234
, visibility, 58
, weather, 239
, wind, 20
Occlusions, 63, 70, 74, 80
Oktas (cloud amount), 52
Orographic cloud and rain, 42
Ortner, R., 167
Overclouding, 148, 178

Pause, thermal, 134
Photochemical smog, 58
Pilot balloons, 241
Plotting weather reports, 244
Polar front, 87
low, 84
Pollution, 57, 130, 178, 200
Precipitation, 37, 84
downdraught, 165, 179, 231
processes, 37, 42
Pressure, 3
decrease with height, 11
, diurnal change, 95
gradient, 15
map, 5
subscale, 296
systems, 6
tendency, 14
-tube anemometer, 22
Pseudo front, 74
sea-breeze front, 198

Q code, 297

Radar, 154, 163, 175, 241, 243
Radiation, 26, 34, 131
fog, 55

Radio-sonde, 27, 240
Rainfall processes, 37
, frontal, 64, 75
, orographic, 42
Recurve, of cyclone track, 102
Recycling, 148
Reisch, Hanna, 171
Relative humidity, 40, 319
Renner, Ingo, 153
Residual thermal sources, 134
Ridge of high pressure, 6, 94
Roll cloud, 225
Rotor flow, 216, 225, 284

St Elmo's fire, 161
San Fernando Convergence Zone, 202
Satellite observations, 54, 83, 151, 242, 248
Saturated Adiabatic Lapse Rate, 30, 40, 256, 260, 318, 323
Scale for geostrophic winds, 250, 302
Scorer, R. S., 209
Sea fog, 56
smoke, 56
Sea-breeze, 185
, case histories, 193
, conditions, 191
, effects of mountains, 201
, front, 188, 198
, pseudo, 198
Secondary depressions, 81
sea-breeze front, 198
Sensors, thermal, 183
SFLOCS, 243
Shear lines, 202
, wave, 230
, wind, 135, 149, 167, 177, 283
Showers, 64, 246, 281
Shurin season (Japan), 105
Siberian anticyclone, 91
Sierra Nevada wave studies, 224
Skew T-log P diagram, 261, 317
Smog, 58, 200
front, 200, 203
Snow, 39, 84
Spreading out of cumulus, 148, 178
Squall line, 72, 77, 163, 168
Stability, 32
Stable layer, 32, 209

Standard Atmosphere, ICAO, 261, 295, 298
Station circle, 6, 244
Steam fog, 56
Stevenson screen, 35
Storm, convective, 156
, tropical, 99
, wind speed, 21
Stratocumulus, 48, 64, 67, 69
Stratosphere, 27
Stratus, 45, 48, 51, 66, 69
Streams, cloud, 150
, thermal, 137
Streets, cloud, 150, 178, 284
, thermal, 137, 178, 284
Subcloud layer, 147, 178
Subsidence, 65
, anticyclonic, 82, 92, 178
Superadiabatic layer, 128, 177
Supercooling, 37, 68
Supersaturation, 36
Swifts, radar echoes, 154, 163
Symbols, cloud, 47, 244, 275, 282
, downdraught, 275, 284
, frontal, 61, 71, 281
, lee wave, 284
, thermal, 275, 277, 279, 283
, thermal streets, 275, 279, 284
, visibility, 59, 284
, weather, 244, 246, 281
Synoptic charts, 250

Task-setting forecasts, 277
Tehachapi Roll, 121
Shear Line, 122
Temperature, 26
, dry-bulb, 40
, -height diagrams, 252, 273, 304
, measurements, 34
, surface, 35, 127
, trigger, 127, 255
, wet-bulb, 40
Tephigram, 260, 262, 317
Terrestrial radiation, 26
Thermal, 43, 93, 123, 285
, cloudy, 143
depressions, 84
, group structure, 153
layer, 126, 177, 252, 285
pause, 134

sensors, 183
shift, 136
soaring forecasts, 179, 279
sources, 130, 133
streams, 137
streets, 137, 178, 284
strength, 182
structure, 123
symbols, 275, 277, 279, 283
waves, 152, 178, 230, 285
wind, 180, 289
Thermograph, 35
Thunder, 65, 77, 104, 160, 265
Thunderbolts, 163
Thunderstorm high, 168
Thundery depression, 85
Tornadoes, 173
Tracks of depressions, 9, 11, 84
Trade winds, 96
Trajectories, air, 24
Transverse wave, 97
Trigger temperature, 127, 255
Tropical cyclone, 99
  depression, 99
  storm, 99
  weather, 95
Tropopause, 27
Troposphere, 27
Trough, Equatorial, 95
  of low pressure, 6, 76
Trowal, 74
Turbulence, 223, 285
  cloud, 45
  symbols, 285
  , wave flow, 216, 225, 284
Twister, 174
Typhoon, 99

Units, 305, 322
Unstable katacold front, 63, 65, 71
Unstable layer, 32
Upper front, 74
  winds, 72
Upslope fog, 56
Upwind jump of lee wave, 227, 236

Valley fog, 55
Vapour, water, 36

Veering, wind, 20, 75
Visibility, classification, 59
  , observation, 58
  , symbols, 59, 284
Vortex ring, 125

Warm anticyclone, 89
  front, 61, 67, 72, 75, 78, 82
  front wave, 81
  occlusion, 70
  sector, 62, 78
Water droplets, 37
  -spouts, 175
  vapour content, 36, 40, 261, 318
Wave, Easterly, 97
  cloud, 207
  conditions, 209
  disturbance, 97
  forecasts, 232
  , lee, 206, 284
  , shear, 230
  , symbols, 284
  , thermal, 152, 178, 230, 285
  , transverse, 97
Weather, charting, 244
  observations, 239
  satellites, 54, 83, 151, 242, 248
  symbols, 244, 246, 281
Weatherwise, 286
Wet- and dry-bulb hygrometer, 40
Wills, Philip, 225
Willy Willy, 135
Wind, 15, 100, 283, 285
  , anabatic, 117
  , backing, 20, 75
  directions, 21
  , geostrophic, 16, 300
  , glacier, 117
  , gradient, 116, 289, 300
  , katabatic, 117, 119
  measurements, 20, 22
  , mountain and valley, 119
  shadow, 132
  shear, 135, 149, 167, 177, 283
  speed classification, 21
  , surface, 17
  , thermal, 180, 289
  , upper, 72
  , veering, 20, 75